CELL
MESSENGERS
AT
FERTILIZATION

COVER ILLUSTRATION

Djungarian hamster spermatozoa (left) stained to show the acrosome (green) on a background of neutral red staining (yellow) and (right) the initiation of the fertilization calcium wave (yellow) in a sea-urchin egg, with area of lower calcium shown blue. Photographs by courtesy of Harry Moore and Michael Whitaker.

JOURNAL OF REPRODUCTION AND FERTILITY

The *Journal* publishes original papers, reviews and bibliographies on the morphology, physiology, biochemistry and pathology of reproduction in man and other animals, and on the biological, medical and veterinary problems of fertility and lactation. Clinical subjects are welcome. The *Journal* is the official organ of the Society for the Study of Fertility.

The *Journal* also publishes Supplements which are distinct from the regular issues, are not associated with any particular volume and are known by their serial number and date. Proceedings of symposia and other similar meetings may also be published as Symposium Reports.

The *Journal of Reproduction and Fertility* is published every two months, two issues forming one volume. The subscription rate for 1990 is £130.00 (U.K. and overseas, by surface mail), $250.00 (U.S.A., Canada and Mexico, by air freight), £148.00 (Japan only, by ASP), per annum.

Published by the *Journals of Reproduction and Fertility Ltd,* 22 Newmarket Road, Cambridge CB5 8DT, U.K.

JOURNAL OF REPRODUCTION AND FERTILITY

SUPPLEMENT No 42

CELL
MESSENGERS
AT
FERTILIZATION

Proceedings of a Symposium

of the

British Society for Developmental Biology

and the

Society for the Study of Fertility

held at the

University of Warwick

December 1989

EDITED BY

Michael Whitaker, Lynn R. Fraser and Barbara J. Weir

Journal of Reproduction & Fertility

1990

First published 1990

ISSN 0449-3087
ISBN 0 906545 20 X

Published by **The Journals of Reproduction and Fertility Ltd.**

Agents for distribution: **The Biochemical Society Book Depot, P.O. Box 32, Commerce Way, Whitehall Industrial Estate, Colchester, CO2 8HP, Essex, U.K.**

Printed in Great Britain by
Henry Ling Ltd., at
The Dorset Press, Dorchester, Dorset

CONTENTS

J. Reprod. Fert., Suppl. **42** (1990), vii

Preface

We have learned a lot about cell signalling in gametes over the past 10 years. This volume is a compilation of reviews that outline the contributions cell messengers make at fertilization. We are very pleased that so many of the people who were among the first to look at cellular signals in gametes have written an article that summarizes their work over the past few years. We hope that the book will provide a reasonably comprehensive account of the interaction of eggs and spermatozoa at fertilization.

There is only one acceptable justification for this sort of review volume: that it will educate postgraduate students into the field in a straightforward way and be a useful source for others to dip into for facts and references. We should like to thank the authors for having created a book that we think meets this criterion.

We particularly thank Martin Johnson who, as Chairman of the BSDB, not only invited us to convene the Conference that led to the publication of this volume, but also solicited the help of our sponsors, to whom we are most grateful.

Lynn Fraser
Michael Whitaker

Sponsors

Bridge Fertility Centre, London Bridge Hospital, London
Department of Obstetrics & Gynaecology, Birmingham Maternity Hospital, Birmingham
Department of Obstetrics & Gynaecology, Bristol Maternity Hospital, Bristol
Department of Obstetrics & Gynaecology, Hammersmith Hospital, London
Department of Obstetrics & Gynaecology, King's College Hospital, London
Department of Obstetrics & Gynaecology, University Hospital of South Manchester, Manchester
University Department of Obstetrics & Gynaecology, Jessop Hospital for Women, Sheffield
Embryo & Gamete Research Group, The Rosie Maternity Hospital, Cambridge
Fertility & IVF Unit, Humana Hospital, Wellington, London
Hallam Medical Centre, London
Infertility Advisory Centre, London Independent Hospital, London
IVF Programme, Cromwell Hospital, London
In Vitro Fertilisation Unit, Lister Hospital, London
Journals of Reproduction & Fertility Ltd., 22 Newmarket Road, Cambridge
Manchester Fertility Services, BUPA Hospital, Manchester
Parke Hospital, Nottingham
The Royal Society of London

SPERM ACTIVATION AND THE ACROSOME REACTION

Chairman
R. Jones

J. Reprod. Fert., Suppl. **42** (1990), 3–8

Molecular mechanisms of sea-urchin sperm activation before fertilization

B. M. Shapiro, S. Cook, A. F. G. Quest, J. Oberdorf and D. Wothe

Department of Biochemistry SJ-70, University of Washington, Seattle, WA 98195, USA

Summary. Several mechanisms are used to control the behaviour of sea urchin spermatozoa while fertilizing eggs. These include discrete regulatory steps that modulate the sperm activation sequence from spawning to gamete membrane fusion. After release from the testis, sperm motility is instantaneously activated, by using intracellular pH as a throttle mechanism to control the rate of the dynein motor that catalyses axonemal bending. To support motility, energy is transported from the mitochondrion to the tail, by using a shuttle mechanism involving phosphocreatine diffusion. This shuttle employs a novel, endotriplicated, creatine kinase of M_r 140 000 in the flagellar axoneme as its terminus. The steering mechanism that determines where the spermatozoon swims is unknown, but may involve an egg peptide-induced guanylate cyclase activation, mediated by a cGMP-dependent Ca^{2+} channel, and attenuated by a plasma membrane cGMP phosphodiesterase. Upon arriving at the egg, which is identified by virtue of its proteoglycan coat (egg jelly), the spermatozoon undergoes a univesicular secretion that prepares it to fuse with the egg. This acrosome reaction involves several altered ionic fluxes in its mechanism, terminating in a massive Ca^{2+} uptake. If the spermatozoon is fortunate enough to fuse with an egg, a new member of the species is generated; if the acrosome reaction occurs without gamete fusion, the spermatozoon rapidly dies. All of these activation processes involve changes in the intracellular ionic milieu that are co-ordinated with altered enzyme activities, often in a causal fashion. Even with our current imperfect understanding of the process, a few of the steps in sperm activation may be defined by biochemical pathways that include specific modulatory control points.

Keywords: fertilization; ionic fluxes; creatine kinase; cell activation; cGMP; motility

Introduction

The regulation of sperm behaviour before fertilization can provide insights into general control mechanisms in cell biology, because sperm behaviour is carefully regulated as part of the existential decision to abandon the haploid state and fuse with an egg. The regulatory phenomena that determine this process involve a series of ionic fluxes coupled to internal metabolic changes, each of which is specifically triggered. This control is best seen in the activation of sea urchin spermatozoa, for which many features of the mechanisms have been elucidated. However, it is clear that many mechanisms are shared with spermatozoa from other species, as well as with somatic cells. Sea urchin spermatozoa provide a classic model system for understanding the relationship of the cellular excitability manifested by ionic fluxes to behavioural changes. While using components of other excitable cells, such as the ion channels and pumps employed by nerve and muscle, the spermatozoon has expanded its response repertoire to include changes in motility, secretion, and spatial orientation in the effector pathway. This brief review will consider several aspects of the molecular controls on sperm behaviour, focussing primarily upon results in the past few years from our laboratory and others. Several recent articles deal with the background discoveries in a more comprehensive fashion (Trimmer & Vacquier, 1986; Shapiro, 1987; Garbers, 1989).

In pursuing the path from testis to egg plasma membrane, sea urchin spermatozoa exhibit discrete responses based upon their interpretation of local conditions. These behavioural decisions are taken rapidly and absolutely, with quantal changes in cellular activities. For example, the spermatozoa may be stored in sea urchin testes for months as immotile, barely respiring cells. However, upon being ejaculated into the ocean they immediately (within 1 sec) initiate motility and respiration at a maximal rate: indeed, the respiratory rate of motile spermatozoa is 50-fold higher than that of immotile spermatozoa (Christen *et al.*, 1982). While swimming in the ocean, the spermatozoa react to diffusional gradients of peptides released from eggs of the same species (reviewed by Garbers, 1989). These peptides dramatically change sperm metabolism, and, in at least one case, act as chemoattractants to lure spermatozoa toward the egg (Ward *et al.*, 1985). After arriving at the egg, the spermatozoa acquire a property rarely encountered in biology, i.e. the capacity to fuse with another cell. To do this, they undergo the acrosome reaction, involving exocytosis from an apical vesicle and extension of an actin filament-containing process that serves as the contact point with the egg and the site of gamete membrane fusion (see Shapiro *et al.*, 1981). That juxtaposition of the gametes is effected with high efficiency is ensured by removal of surface coat material by a protease released from the acrosomal vesicle, as well as by a species-specific binding protein (bindin) that glues the spermatozoon to its partner (Vacquier & Moy, 1977; Trimmer & Vacquier, 1986; Vacquier, 1986). Thus, in preparing to fertilize eggs, spermatozoa undergo three specific behavioural transitions: (1) they initiate motility when placed into sea water; (2) they respond to eggs with chemotaxis towards diffusible peptides: (3) they undergo the acrosome reaction in response to the egg glycocalyx. We consider below some data and hypotheses about the molecular events that lead to these behavioural transitions.

Induction of the acrosome reaction

Within seconds of contacting egg jelly, spermatozoa undergo the acrosome reaction. During this process, spermatozoa take up Ca^{2+} and Na^+ and release H^+ and K^+ (Schackmann & Shapiro, 1981; Christen *et al.*, 1983a), with an associated increase in intracellular pH (pH_i; Schackmann *et al.*, 1981). Along with these ionic changes, there is a rapid, transient plasma membrane hyperpolarization (Gonzalez-Martinez & Darszon, 1987) and then a sustained depolarization of 30 mV (Schackmann *et al.*, 1984). All aspects of the acrosome reaction are inhibited by dihydropyridine and phenylalkalamine Ca^{2+} channel antagonists (Schackmann *et al.*, 1978; Kazazoglou *et al.*, 1985). These organic antagonists bind specifically to sperm plasma membranes, in both the head and tail regions, with relatively high affinities ($K_d = 10^{-7}$ M) and inhibit the acrosome reaction over the same concentration range. The antagonist binding sites are sensitive to the ionic composition of the medium (Toowicharanont & Shapiro, 1988), with a significant decrease in the number of binding sites in the presence of Na^+ or primary amines. These data suggest that regulated Ca^{2+} channels may be an important component of the induction mechanism, but this has been difficult to prove with direct experiments, although specific Ca^{2+} channels have been found in sperm membranes incorporated into lipid bilayers (Lievano *et al.*, 1989). Guerrero & Darszon (1989) provide evidence for two different sperm Ca^{2+} channels that are activated by egg jelly: a rapidly (1 sec) opening channel that is sensitive to the dihydropyridine nisoldipine, and a slower (5 sec) one that requires increased pH_i to open. The specific controls of these Ca^{2+} channels, such as whether they respond to GTP-binding regulatory proteins (Casey & Gilman, 1988) or membrane potential, are still unresolved issues, as is the pathway of induction. The target of the egg jelly that induces the reaction is thought to include a glycoprotein of the sperm plasma membrane of M_r 210 000, since antibodies directed against that protein cause transient increases in Ca^{2+} influx (Trimmer *et al.*, 1986). Although the relationship of this protein to the several Ca^{2+} channels has not yet been defined, this is a subject of great current interest.

Response to egg peptides

Spermatozoa of the sea urchin *Arbacia* swim towards peptides released from *Arbacia* eggs (Ward *et al.*, 1985). This is the only directly demonstrated chemoattractant effect of such peptides, but the release of peptides by sea urchin eggs is a general phenomenon, as is the fact that these peptides induce transient elevations in cGMP in spermatozoa of the same species along with other metabolic effects (Shimomura & Garbers, 1986). Whether the most extensively studied egg peptide, speract from *Strongylocentrotus purpuratus*, causes an alteration in sperm swimming is not clear, but several phenomena are consistent with this being a chemotactic effector. Speract causes transient elevations in cGMP (Hansbrough & Garbers, 1981), as well as in Ca^{2+} (Schackmann & Chock, 1986). Inhibition of a specific, flagellar membrane cGMP phosphodiesterase (Toowicharanont & Shapiro, 1988) by isobutylmethylxanthine leads to prolongation of the elevated Ca^{2+} (Schackmann & Chock, 1986), suggesting that Ca^{2+} uptake is linked to the elevation of cGMP. Moreover, Ca^{2+} affects the wave form of sea urchin flagella and even leads to an unusual form of flagellar arrest when added to permeable, beating flagellar preparations (Brokaw & Nagayama, 1985).

The above data lend themselves to a hypothetical chemotaxis pathway, as illustrated below, which we are using as a point of departure for evaluating the role of cGMP in spermatozoa.

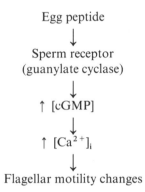

The different parts of this hypothetical pathway have been analysed separately. Whether they act in a causal fashion as implied above is still not clear. The fact that the cGMP phosphodiesterase is essentially completely located in the sperm tail plasma membrane (Toowicharanont & Shapiro, 1988) where it exists at very high activity is consistent with a role in signal attenuation. The flagella of *S. purpuratus* spermatozoa have several cGMP-binding proteins, one of which is the cGMP phosphodiesterase (S. Cook, unpublished data) and another a protein of M_r 60 000, exhibiting Mg^{2+}-dependent cGMP binding (J. Oberdorf, unpublished data). The protein of M_r 60 000 may be an effector of cGMP signalling; of interest is that it is the same size as a cGMP-gated ion channel of retinal rods (Cook *et al.*, 1987). In collaboration with Alberto Darszon, we identified a cGMP-dependent calcium conductance in sperm plasma membranes (unpublished data). Such a channel could serve as a linkage between the elevation of cGMP induced by activation of guanylate cyclase and the transient elevation in Ca^{2+}_i, to fill in one of the steps in the hypothetical pathway portrayed above.

When peptides bind to the receptor–guanylate cyclase, the enzyme is activated and rapidly inactivated, the latter being associated with dephosphorylation (Bentley *et al.*, 1986). Thus, a transient increase in [cGMP] could be effected by the action of cGMP phosphodiesterase, as well as by inactivation of the guanylate cyclase after peptide stimulation. This could produce a transient increase in Ca^{2+}_i upon sensing a change in egg peptide concentration, and this might lead to an alteration in flagellar motility and directional change of the spermatozoon. The ability to attenuate the cGMP signal, as noted above, would allow the system to remain responsive. Although this scenario is speculative, we are continuing to look for a cGMP-dependent channel, now by concentrating on the cGMP-binding protein of M_r 60 000. The regulatory controls on the cGMP-specific phosphodiesterase activity of the flagellar plasma membrane are of interest, since they could be a mechanism for signal attenuation in the above pathway.

Activation of sperm motility and respiration

The absolute linkage between sperm motility and respiration is due to a direct effect of intracellular pH on the flagellar dynein ATPase activity (Christen *et al.*, 1982). This is an exquisitely sensitive phenomenon: spermatozoa increase their respiratory rates 50-fold with a 0·5 unit increase in pH_i. Activation of mitochondrial respiration is secondary to flagellar activation (Christen *et al.*, 1982, 1983b) and caused by stimulation of coupled respiration by the ADP made available by ATP hydrolysis. Motile spermatozoa are unusual in expending virtually all of their energy in flagellar bending while producing energy primarily from mitochondrial respiration via fatty acid oxidation (Mohri, 1957; Mita & Yasumasu, 1983). This accounts for the tight coupling between motility and respiration in sea urchin spermatozoa.

The transport of energy from the mitochondrion to the end of the tail is not by diffusion of ATP, but of phosphocreatine, a guanido compound belonging to a class of high energy phosphate donors called phosphagens. Phosphagen kinases, like creatine kinase, use phosphagens, like phosphocreatine, to generate ATP in a reversible reaction. Sea urchins have two types of phosphagen kinase: spermatozoa contain only creatine kinase, eggs contain only arginine kinase, and somatic tissues have both forms. A primordial phosphagen kinase may have given rise to these two enzyme forms, probably as a result of gene duplication during the course of evolution (Watts, 1971); the fact that echinoderms contain both forms may indicate their role as a transitional organism in this process.

That sea urchin spermatozoa use a phosphocreatine transport system to move energy from the mitochondria to the tail was shown by inducing a creatine kinase deficiency in spermatozoa and measuring the effects on metabolism and motility (Tombes & Shapiro, 1985; Tombes *et al.*, 1987). Such a phosphocreatine shuttle mechanism has been proposed for muscle and other cells (for example, see Wallimann *et al.*, 1989), based upon the localized placement of creatine kinase isoenzymes and certain kinetic considerations. Sea urchin spermatozoa have provided some of the clearest evidence for such a mechanism. They have two isoenzymes of creatine kinase, one in the mitochondrion and the other along the flagellum (Tombes & Shapiro, 1987). This creatine kinase system is required for provision of energy to the distal tail, because when a chemical phenocopy of a creatine kinase deficiency is introduced, a paralysis of the distal tail ensues (Tombes *et al.*, 1987). This distal tail paralysis can be reversed by making the plasma membrane permeable and providing ATP (but not phosphocreatine), whereupon the flagellum beats normally. The other lesion that occurs with a creatine kinase deficiency is a decrease in coupled, but not uncoupled, respiration (Tombes & Shapiro, 1985). This is exactly as expected for metabolic compartmentation introduced by a phosphocreatine shuttle; in normal spermatozoa mitochondrial creatine kinase produces ADP to allow maximal respiration, whereas when the shuttle is interfered with, the ATP concentration at the mitochondrion would be high, ADP low, and respiration would decrease.

In sea urchin spermatozoa, the concentration of creatine kinases at both mitochondrial and tail regions is very high. It is interesting that other spermatozoa of primitive morphology (e.g. those of the sand dollar, starfish, salmon), in which the mitochondrion is small and located at a site distant from an elongated tail, also have relatively high levels of creatine kinase. On the other hand, modified spermatozoa (e.g. those of bull, mouse, man), which have a mitochondrion that extends down an elongated midpiece region, have lower concentrations of creatine kinase (Tombes & Shapiro, 1989). These results are compatible with highly polarized cells, like primitive spermatozoa, needing such a phosphocreatine shuttle in order to transport energy a relatively great distance. Modified spermatozoa, which use glycolysis as well as respiration to make ATP, and in which the mitochondria extend along the tail, have less need for such a shuttling mechanism.

The flagellar creatine kinase is a component of the axoneme. Indeed, when extracted from the axoneme, flagellar creatine kinase partly, but specifically, reassociates with it (Tombes *et al.*, 1988). Moreover, a significant fraction of the flagellar creatine kinase exists in a complex with tubulin and microtubule-associated proteins (A. F. G. Quest, unpublished data). The flagellar creatine kinase is an unusual isoenzyme, in being a monomer of M_r 145 000. Other known cytosolic creatine kinases are active as dimers (Eppenberger *et al.*, 1967) of monomers of M_r 40 000–45 000, and mitochondrial creatine kinases are oligomeric (probably octamers) of similar size (Schlegel *et al.*, 1988). Because of the unusual length of the flagellar creatine kinase, and to study aspects of its structure that might be responsible for its insertion into the flagellum, we have cloned this enzyme and obtained its complete sequence (D. Wothe, unpublished). The flagellar creatine kinase is an endotriplicated variant, containing 3 essentially complete domains that are homologous to one another as well as to mammalian creatine kinases. At the amino terminus, the carboxy terminus, and between each of the creatine kinase domains there are substantial non-homologous regions of sequence. The active site cysteine and surrounding region is highly conserved and similar to other creatine kinases. In fact, each repeated domain of the sea urchin flagellar creatine kinase has about 67% identity to the other two repeats, and this identity is approximately the same as that seen for creatine kinases from chicken muscle, chicken brain, chicken mitochondria, and *Torpedo* electric organ (Babbitt *et al.*, 1986).

These results indicate that the flagellar creatine kinase was created by a gene triplication around the time of the chordate–echinoderm divergence, after which all these creatine kinase forms evolved independently. Whether such a triplication provided a mechanism for a primitive phosphagen kinase to evolve into the several phosphagen kinase types found in invertebrates is unclear; perhaps echinoderms were the agent of introduction of multiple genes for a phosphagen kinase, which later changed into creatine kinase, arginine kinase, etc. Such speculation is unsupported, but might be justified after comparison of sequences from the different enzyme forms. We are currently exploring whether the additional, non-homologous sequence in the flagellar creatine kinase (or the creatine kinase sequences themselves) is responsible for integration of that enzyme into the axoneme. We are also investigating whether all 3 domains of this endotriplicated protein are catalytically competent. We view this specifically localized creatine kinase as a useful tool for exploring the biochemistry of assembly of a complex organelle like the flagellar axoneme.

References

Babbitt, P.C., Kenyon, G.L., Kuntz, I.D., Cohen, F.E., Baxter, J.D., Benfield, B.A., Buskin, J.D., Gilbert, W.A., Hauschka, S.D., Hossle, J.P., Ordahl, C.P., Person, M.L., Perriard, J.-C., Pickering, L.A., Putney, S.D., West, B.L. & Ziven, R.A. (1986) Comparison of creatine kinase primary structures. *Prot. Chem.* **5**, 1–14.

Bentley, J.K., Tubb, D.J. & Garbers, D.L. (1986) Receptor-mediated activation of spermatozoan guanylate cyclase. *J. biol. Chem.* **261**, 14859–14862.

Brokaw, C.J. & Nagayama, S.M. (1985) Modulation of the asymmetry of sea urchin sperm flagellar bending by calmodulin. *J. Cell Biol.* **100**, 1875–1883.

Casey, P.J. & Gilman, A.G. (1988) G protein involvement in receptor-effector coupling. *J. biol. Chem.* **263**, 2577–2580.

Christen, R., Schackmann, R.W. & Shapiro, B.M. (1982) Elevation of the intracellular pH activates respiration and motility of sperm of the sea urchin *Strongylocentrotus purpuratus*. *J. biol. Chem.* **257**, 14881–14890.

Christen, R., Schackmann, R.W. & Shapiro, B.M. (1983a) Interactions between sperm and sea urchin egg jelly. *Devl Biol.* **98**, 1–14.

Christen, R., Schackmann, R.W. & Shapiro, B.M. (1983b) Metabolism of the sea urchin sperm. Interrelationships between the intracellular pH, ATPase activity and mitochondrial respiration. *J. biol. Chem.* **258**, 5392–5399.

Cook, J.N., Hanke, W. & Kaupp, V.B. (1987) Identification, purification and functional reconstitution of the cyclic GMP-dependent channel from rod photoreceptors. *Proc. natn. Acad. Sci. USA* **84**, 585–589.

Eppenberger, H.M., Dawson, D.H. & Kaplan, N.D. (1967) The cooperative enzymology of creatine kinase. I. Isolation. *J. biol. Chem.* **242**, 204–209.

Garbers, D.L. (1989) Molecular basis of fertilization. *Ann. Rev. Biochem.* **58**, 719–742.

Gonzales-Martinez, M. & Darszon, A. (1987) A fast transient hyperpolarization occurs during the sea urchin sperm acrosome reaction induced by egg jelly. *FEBS Lett.* **218**, 247–250.

Guerrero, A. & Darszon, A. (1989) Evidence for the activation of two difference Ca^{2+} channels during the egg jelly induced acrosome reaction of sea urchin sperm. *J. biol. Chem.* **264**, 19593–19599.

Hansbrough, J.R. & Garbers, D.L. (1981) Sodium dependent activation of sea urchin spermatozoa by speract and monensin. *J. biol. Chem.* **256**, 2235–2241.

Kazazoglou, T., Schackmann, R.W., Fossett, M. & Shapiro, B.M. (1985) Calcium channel antagonists inhibit the acrosome reaction and bind to plasma membranes of sea urchin sperm. *Proc. natn. Acad. Sci. USA* **82**, 1460–1464.

Lievano, A., Vega-Saenz de Miera, E.C. & Darszon, A. (1990) Ca^{2+} channels from the sea urchin sperm plasma membrane. *J. gen. Physiol.* **95**, 273–296.

Mita, M. & Yasumasu, I. (1983) Metabolism of lipid and carbohydrate in sea urchin spermatozoa. *Gamete Res.* **7**, 133–144.

Mohri, H. (1957) Endogenous substrates of respiration in sea urchin spermatozoa. *J. Fac. Sci. Univ. Tokyo Sec. IV* **8**, 51–63.

Schackmann, R.W. & Chock, P.B. (1986) Alteration of intracellular $[Ca^{2+}]$ in sea urchin sperm by the egg peptide speract. *J. biol. Chem.* **261**, 8719–8728.

Schackmann, R.W. & Shapiro, B.M. (1981) A partial sequence of ionic changes associated with the acrosome reaction of *Strongylocentrotus purpuratus*. *Devl Biol.* **81**, 145–154.

Schackmann, R.W., Eddy, E.M. & Shapiro, B.M. (1978) The acrosome reaction and activation of *Strongylocentrotus purpuratus* sperm: ion requirements and movements. *Devl Biol.* **65**, 483–495.

Schackmann, R.W., Christen, R. & Shapiro, B.M. (1981) Membrane potential depolarization and increased intracellular pH accompany the acrosome reaction of sperm. *Proc. natn. Acad. Sci. USA* **78**, 6066–6070.

Schackmann, R.W., Christen, R. & Shapiro, B.M. (1984) Measurement of plasma membrane and mitochondrial membrane potentials in sea urchin sperm. *J. biol. Chem.* **259**, 13914–13922.

Schlegel, J., Zurbriggen, B., Wegmann, G., Wyss, M., Eppenberger, H.M. & Wallimann, T. (1988) Native mitochondrial creatine kinase forms octameric structures. I. Isolation of two interconvertible mitochondrial creatine kinase forms, dimeric and octameric mitochondrial creatine kinase: characterization, localization and structure–function relationships. *J. biol. Chem.* **263**, 16942–16953.

Shapiro, B.M. (1987) The existential decision of a sperm. *Cell* **49**, 293–294.

Shapiro, B.M., Schackmann, R.W. & Gabel, C.A. (1981) Molecular approaches to the study of fertilization. *Ann. Rev. Biochem.* **50**, 815–842.

Shimomura, H. & Garbers, D.L. (1986) Differential effects of resact analogues on sperm respiration rates and cyclic nucleotide concentrations. *Biochemistry, NY* **25**, 3405–3410.

Tombes, R. & Shapiro, B.M. (1985) Metabolite channeling: a phosphorylcreatine shuttle mediates high energy phosphate transport between sperm mitochondrion and tail. *Cell* **41**, 325–334.

Tombes, R. & Shapiro, B.M. (1987) Enzyme termini of a phosphorylcreatine shuttle: purification and characterization of two creatine kinase isozymes from sea urchin sperm. *J. biol. Chem.* **262**, 16011–16019.

Tombes, R. & Shapiro, B.M. (1989) Energy transport and cell polarity: relationship of phosphagen kinase activity to sperm function. *J. exp. Zool.* **251**, 82–90.

Tombes, R.M., Brokaw, C.J. & Shapiro, B.M. (1987) Creatine kinase dependent energy transport in sea urchin spermatozoa: flagellar wave attenuation and theoretical analysis of high energy phosphate diffusion. *Biophys. J.* **52**, 75–86.

Tombes, R.M., Farr, A. & Shapiro, B.M. (1988) Sea urchin sperm creatine kinase: the flagellar isozyme is a microtubule associated protein. *Expl Cell Res.* **178**, 307–317.

Toowicharanont, P. & Shapiro, B.M. (1988) Regional differentiation of the sea urchin sperm plasma membrane. *J. biol. Chem.* **263**, 6877–6883.

Trimmer, J.S. & Vacquier, V.D. (1986) Activation of sea urchin gametes. *Ann. Rev. Biochem.* **58**, 719–742.

Trimmer, J.S., Ebina, Y., Schackmann, R.W., Meinhof, C.-G. & Vacquier, V.D. (1986) Characterization of a monoclonal antibody that induces the acrosome reaction of sea urchin sperm. *J. Cell Biol.* **105**, 1121–1128.

Vacquier, V.D. (1986) Activation of sea urchin spermatozoa during fertilization. *Trends in Biochem. Sci.* **11**, 77–81.

Vacquier, V.D. & Moy, G.W. (1977) Isolation of the protein responsible for adhesion of sperm to sea urchin eggs. *Proc. natn. Acad. Sci. USA* **74**, 2456–2460.

Wallimann, T., Schnyder, T., Schlegel, J., Wyss, M., Wegmann, G., Ross, A.M., Hemmer, W., Eppenberger, H.M. & Quest, A.F.G. (1989) Subcellular compartmentation of creatine kinase isozymes, regulation of CK and octameric structure of mitochondrial CK: important aspects of the phosphoryl-creatine circuit. In *Muscle Energetics*, pp. 159–176. Eds R. J. Paul, G. Elzinga & K. Yamada. A. R. Liss, New York.

Ward, G.E., Brokaw, C.J., Garbers, D.L. & Vacquier, V.D. (1985) Chemotaxis of *Arbacia punctulata* spermatozoa to resact, a peptide from the egg jelly layer. *J. Cell Biol.* **101**, 2324–2329.

Watts, D.C. (1971) Evolution of phosphagen kinases. In *Molecular Evolution*, Vol. 2, pp. 150–173. Ed. E. Schofferiels. New Holland Pub. Company, Amsterdam.

J. Reprod. Fert., Suppl. **42** (1990), 9–21

Cyclic nucleotides and mammalian sperm capacitation

Lynn R. Fraser and Nicola J. Monks†

Anatomy and Human Biology, Biomedical Sciences Division, King's College London, Strand, London WC2R 2LS, UK; and †Sheffield Fertility Centre, 26 Glen Road, Sheffield S7 1RA, UK

Keywords: capacitation; acrosome reaction; hyperactivated motility; cAMP; adenylate cyclase; adenosine; calcium; phosphodiesterase

Introduction

It has long been recognized that when mammalian spermatozoa leave the male reproductive tract they are not immediately capable of fertilizing oocytes, despite being morphologically complete and capable of independent motility. The requirement for a period of time during which spermatozoa become fertile was reported by Austin (1951) and Chang (1951). This acquisition of the capacity to penetrate the zona pellucida and then to fuse with the oocyte plasma membrane is termed capacitation (Austin, 1952). While normally occurring in the female reproductive tract, capacitation can be achieved under in-vitro culture conditions. This has made it possible to evaluate the specific changes that result in a fertilizing gamete.

A difficulty which has yet to be overcome in the study of capacitation is that, while it clearly requires a species-specific length of time for completion (Bedford, 1970), there are no obvious characteristics that can be evaluated to allow measurement of degree of transition towards the fully capacitated state. No gross morphological changes, which might be monitored easily, occur (e.g. Bedford, 1970; Yanagimachi, 1988) and at present no biochemical parameters have been defined that could give such information. There are, however, two terminal, pre-fertilization events which do give some indication of fertilizing potential: the acrosome reaction and hyperactivated motility. Considerable evidence indicates that the acrosome reaction is obligatory both for penetration of the zona pellucida and for fusion with the oocyte plasma membrane (discussed by Yanagimachi, 1981, 1988) and that hyperactivated motility is obligatory for zona penetration although it may not be required for the fusion process *per se* (Fraser, 1981). Because evidence indicates that capacitation is a reversible process (Bedford & Chang, 1962; Oliphant *et al.*, 1985) while the acrosome reaction is clearly irreversible, capacitation is taken to encompass events up to, but not including, the acrosome reaction. Events involved may be studied using culture conditions shown to support capacitation, with the best assessment being the ability of spermatozoa to penetrate oocytes. To achieve synchronous populations, environments which allow suspensions to undergo capacitation but block them just before the acrosome reaction may be used. A change to permissive conditions will trigger the acrosome reaction in these capacitated cells in a synchronous fashion and will permit immediate interaction with oocytes to effect fertilization.

Over the past two decades evidence has been accumulating that cyclic nucleotides may play a role in mammalian sperm capacitation, acrosome reaction and motility (reviewed by Garbers & Kopf, 1980; Tash & Means, 1983; Fraser, 1984; Fraser & Ahuja, 1988). In general, the introduction of either cyclic nucleotides/analogues or putative cyclic nucleotide phosphodiesterase inhibitors (to inhibit cyclic nucleotide breakdown) has been shown to stimulate motility and to enhance fertilization of oocytes *in vitro*. The possible mechanisms involved in these responses will be considered below.

Cyclic nucleotide metabolism

Before considering roles for cyclic nucleotides in capacitation and fertilization in detail, it is important to review, albeit briefly, the pathways involved in their metabolism. Since relatively little attention has been paid to cyclic GMP (cGMP), the focus will be on cyclic AMP (cAMP). cAMP is produced from ATP by adenylate cyclase and is metabolized to 5'-AMP by cyclic nucleotide phosphodiesterase. 5'-AMP can be metabolized to adenosine by 5'-nucleotidase and adenosine to inosine by adenosine deaminase. This pathway is shown in Fig. 1. Several studies have demonstrated that mammalian spermatozoa possess these enzymes (e.g. Garbers & Kopf, 1980; Stein & Fraser, 1984). Modulation of these enzymes to alter the availability of cyclic nucleotides may be important during capacitation.

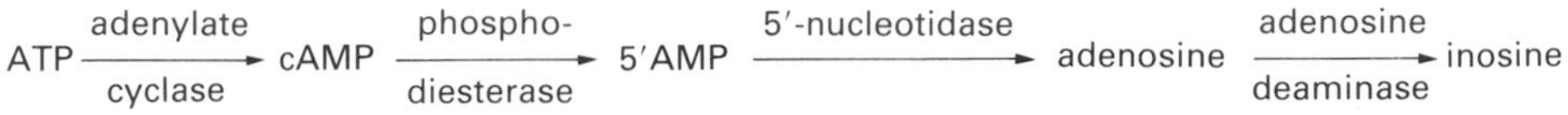

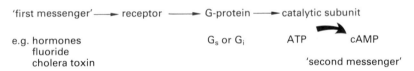

Fig. 1. Enzymes involved in the production and metabolic degradation of cAMP.

Sperm adenylate cyclase

The somatic cell adenylate cyclase system consists of at least three components: (1) hormonal receptors for recognition of the 'first messenger' ligand cyclase activity; (2) coupling guanine nucleotide-binding (G) proteins, either stimulatory (G_s) or inhibitory (G_i), each being a heterotrimer (α,β,γ subunits) and acting as substrate for ADP-ribosylation by cholera toxin ($G_s\alpha$) or pertussis toxin ($G_i\alpha$); (3) a catalytic subunit which catalyses the conversion of ATP to cAMP, the intracellular 'second messenger' (Gilman, 1984; Fig. 2).

'first messenger' ⟶ receptor ⟶ G-protein ⟶ catalytic subunit

e.g. hormones G_s or G_i ATP ⟶ cAMP
     fluoride
     cholera toxin   'second messenger'

Fig. 2. Components of the somatic cell adenylate cyclase system.

Spermatozoa appear to have a unique adenylate cyclase which differs significantly from its somatic cell counterpart. It is insensitive to most hormones, fluoride and cholera toxin (Hoskins & Casillas, 1975; Cheng & Boettcher, 1982; Stengel *et al.*, 1982) and has been reported to lack the guanine nucleotide regulatory components (Cheng & Boettcher, 1982; Hildebrandt *et al.*, 1985). Despite this, several studies have reported that GTP and/or its analogue 5'-guanylylimidodiphosphate [Gpp(NH)p] can stimulate adenylate cyclase activity in bull (Casillas *et al.*, 1980), human (Cheng & Boettcher, 1979; Hyne & Lopata, 1982) and mouse spermatozoa (Monks *et al.*, 1986; Stein *et al.*, 1986). The mechanisms involved in this stimulation have yet to be defined. A guanine nucleotide-binding protein has been demonstrated in invertebrate and mammalian spermatozoa (Bentley *et al.*, 1986; Kopf *et al.*, 1986), but whether it interacts with the catalytic subunit has yet to be ascertained.

Sperm adenylate cyclase activity is markedly higher in the presence of Mn^{2+} than Mg^{2+}, a characteristic also exhibited by the isolated catalytic component of somatic cell adenylate cyclase (Hildebrandt *et al.*, 1985). The enzyme substrate is ATP complexed with a divalent cation and there is also a distinct metal ion regulatory site (Brown & Casillas, 1982). Experimental evidence indicates that Ca^{2+} can stimulate adenylate cyclase activity (bull: Braun, 1975; guinea-pig: Garbers *et al.*, 1982; human: Hyne & Lopata, 1982; mouse: Monks *et al.*, 1986; ram: Goh & White, 1988). In some cases Ca^{2+} appears able to stimulate the enzyme directly, possibly via an allosteric divalent cation binding site (Gordeladze & Hansson, 1980). Another possibility is mediation of Ca^{2+} effects via calmodulin which is present in spermatozoa, both in the head and the tail (Jones *et al.*, 1980;

Feinberg *et al.*, 1981). Initial attempts to demonstrate calmodulin modulation of adenylate cyclase activity were equivocal (Hyne & Garbers, 1979b; Gordeladze *et al.*, 1982), but more definitive evidence for such an interaction has been obtained with equine spermatozoa (Gross *et al.*, 1987). Stimulation of cAMP levels in guinea-pig spermatozoa by Ca^{2+} required bicarbonate but did not appear to involve adenylate cyclase directly (Garbers *et al.*, 1982), although bicarbonate was reported to have a stimulatory effect on adenylate cyclase activity in boar spermatozoa (Okamura *et al.*, 1985). Calcium effects may also be mediated via protein kinase C, as indicated by recent indirect evidence with hamster spermatozoa (Visconti & Tezon, 1989).

Another possible modulator of adenylate cyclase is adenosine. The observation that exposure of brain slices to exogenous adenosine altered cAMP content (Sattin & Rall, 1970) led to the discovery of externally directed adenosine receptors which can either inhibit (A_1) or stimulate (A_2) adenylate cyclase (Van Calker *et al.*, 1979), at least in somatic cells (Londos *et al.*, 1983). Expression of these effects usually requires GTP (Fain & Malbon, 1979; Londos *et al.*, 1983). Indirect evidence for A_1 and A_2 receptors on mouse spermatozoa has been reported by Stein *et al.* (1986), the stimulatory A_2 receptors being expressed in uncapacitated cells and the inhibitory A_1 receptors in capacitated cells. Evidence for a third site, the intracellular GTP-independent P-site, has been reported for bull (Brown & Casillas, 1984), human (Hyne & Lopata, 1982), mouse (Stein *et al.*, 1986) and ram (Henry *et al.*, 1986) spermatozoa.

Sperm cyclic nucleotide phosphodiesterase

Somatic cells appear to contain multiple forms of cyclic nucleotide phosphodiesterase (for brevity, subsequently referred to as phosphodiesterase) with differing kinetics and substrate specificities, e.g. cAMP vs cGMP (Wells & Hardman, 1977); at least one form may be regulated by calmodulin.

Mammalian spermatozoa also appear to contain multiple forms with differing substrate specificities (Tash & Means, 1983) and complex kinetics which may be explained by the presence of several isoenzymes or by single forms which express negative co-operativity (Stephens *et al.*, 1979; Monks & Fraser, 1987). There is evidence for the presence of a calmodulin-dependent phosphodiesterase in epididymal rat spermatozoa (Wasco & Orr, 1984) and in male mouse germ cells (D'Agostino *et al.*, 1983; Geremia *et al.*, 1984).

Other enzymes

Mammalian spermatozoa have a 5'-nucleotidase with kinetics similar to that of somatic cells and, at least in mouse spermatozoa, it appears to be present as an ecto-enzyme (Monks & Fraser, 1988a). Considerable levels of enzyme activity are found additionally in epididymal (Jones, 1978; Monks & Fraser, 1988a) and seminal (Levin & Bodansky, 1966) fluids.

Adenosine deaminase is an ubiquitous enzyme in somatic cells, its absence being associated with pathological conditions (Parkman *et al.*, 1975). Although spermatozoa have some capacity to metabolize adenosine to inosine, current evidence regarding adenosine deaminase is somewhat limited. The detection of measurable quantities of inosine in bull spermatozoa suggests the presence of intracellular adenosine deaminase (Goh & Hoskins, 1985), but mouse spermatozoa appear to have a very limited capacity to metabolize adenosine (Monks & Fraser, 1987, 1988a). Much higher enzyme activity has been reported in mouse epididymal fluids (Monks & Fraser, 1988a).

Cyclic nucleotides, the acrosome reaction and hyperactivated motility

Hyne & Garbers (1979a) observed a correlation between increasing intracellular cAMP levels and incidence of the acrosome reaction in guinea-pig spermatozoa and White & Aitken (1989) noted an increase in intracellular cAMP preceding the onset of hyperactivated motility in hamster spermatozoa. These observations suggest that capacitation is associated with elevated cAMP. Furthermore, exogenously supplied cyclic nucleotides or putative phosphodiesterase inhibitors, treatments which would raise intracellular cAMP, promote fertilization *in vitro* in many mammalian species (e.g. man: Aitken *et al.*, 1983; monkey: Chan *et al.*, 1981; Boatman & Bavister, 1984; mouse: Fraser, 1979, 1981; rabbit: Rosado *et al.*, 1974; rat: Toyoda & Chang, 1974).

Specific evidence for involvement in the acrosome reaction has been obtained for the hamster (Mrsny & Meizel, 1980), guinea-pig (using dibutyryl cGMP rather than dibutyryl cAMP [dbcAMP]: Santos-Sacchi & Gordon, 1982) and mouse (Fraser, 1981). In the last of these, acrosome loss occurred in medium containing dbcAMP but lacking glucose; in the absence of dbcAMP, such a composition inhibits the acrosome reaction (Fraser & Quinn, 1981).

Considerable evidence has accumulated to indicate that cyclic nucleotides, particularly cAMP, can stimulate mammalian sperm motility (reviewed by Garbers & Kopf, 1980; Tash & Means, 1983). Some studies have used cAMP or its analogues, others putative phosphodiesterase inhibitors such as caffeine, theophylline and isobutylmethylxanthine. Indeed, experiments with these inhibitors were the first to suggest that cAMP plays a role in regulating sperm motility (e.g. Garbers *et al.*, 1971), although evidence suggests that caffeine may not necessarily stimulate motility by affecting the cAMP system (Schoff & Lardy, 1987).

While results from a variety of species, both mammalian and non-mammalian, suggest that cAMP may play a primary role in the onset of progressive motility associated both with epididymal maturation and release from the male tract (discussed in detail by Garbers & Kopf, 1980; Tash & Means, 1983), motile spermatozoa are not necessarily fertile. Evidence clearly indicates that, unless mammalian spermatozoa express hyperactivated motility, they are unable to penetrate the zona pellucida even if they are able to undergo an acrosome reaction (Fraser, 1981). Numerous studies have indicated that cAMP analogues and/or phosphodiesterase inhibitors promote development of hyperactivated motility (e.g. Boatman & Bavister, 1984), in some instances precociously (hamster: Mrsny & Meizel, 1980; mouse: Fraser, 1979, 1981). It has also been noted that this expression requires an appropriate metabolic substrate. For example, mouse spermatozoa require a glycolysable compound in order to exhibit hyperactivated motility: precocious expression of this motility pattern in the presence of dbcAMP was only observed when glucose was also present (Fraser, 1981).

Because cAMP/phosphodiesterase inhibitor treatment of sperm suspensions can improve motility and fertilizing ability, there is considerable interest in its possible application to human in-vitro fertilization, if sperm quality is poor, and to donor insemination for which the motility of the frozen–thawed semen samples is frequently reduced. Reports that caffeine-treated spermatozoa showed morphological abnormalities (Harrison *et al.*, 1980) caused concern. However, Barkay *et al.* (1984) failed to confirm such damage and demonstrated an apparent increase in pregnancies obtained after insemination with frozen–thawed semen when caffeine was added at the time of insemination. Improved penetration rates into zona-free hamster oocytes after caffeine treatment of poor quality sperm samples have been reported (e.g. Aitken *et al.*, 1983; Cai & Marik, 1989; Rogers, 1981).

Capacitation-related changes in enzyme activity

The observation that intracellular cAMP levels increase during capacitation suggests changes in activity of the enzymes involved in its metabolism. Evidence that adenylate cyclase activity increases during this time has been obtained for several species, e.g. in guinea-pig spermatozoa capacitated *in vitro* (Morton & Albagli, 1973). A rise in activity was reported for boar spermatozoa incubated for 2 h *in vivo* in the gilt uterus (Berger & Clegg, 1983), but whether these conditions support capacitation is not known.

We have investigated changes in sperm enzyme activity using a well-characterized mouse in-vitro capacitation and fertilization system (e.g. Fraser, 1981, 1982, 1983, 1987) in which conditions capable of stimulating or inhibiting capacitation have been identified by evaluating hyperactivated motility, the acrosome reaction and penetration of homologous eggs. Using such conditions we (Stein & Fraser, 1984; Monks *et al.*, 1986) have shown a significant increase in adenylate cyclase activity when mouse sperm suspensions were sampled first early during capacitation *in vitro* (30 min incubation) and then at the end of capacitation (120 min incubation) when cells would be highly fertile (Fraser, 1983). In similarly-incubated suspensions, phosphodiesterase activity was shown to decrease significantly during capacitation (Stein & Fraser, 1984; Monks & Fraser, 1987). Together, this potential for increasing formation of cAMP and decreasing breakdown of cAMP to 5′-AMP suggests increasing availability of cAMP. Although Stein & Fraser (1984) were unable to demonstrate significant capacitation-related alterations in cAMP itself, significant elevations have been measured in hamster spermatozoa (White & Aitken, 1989).

Following the original observations of capacitation-related changes in adenylate cyclase and phosphodiesterase activities during capacitation in the presence of calcium, we extended our studies to calcium-deficient conditions which inhibit capacitation. When mouse sperm suspensions are incubated in calcium-deficient medium for 2 h, receive the standard $1 \cdot 80$ mM Ca^{2+} and are assessed immediately, they are poorly fertile. However, if these suspensions are incubated for an additional hour in the presence of calcium, they become highly fertile and functionally equivalent to counterparts incubated in calcium-containing medium for 2 h (Fraser, 1982, 1987). Thus only partial capacitation is achieved under calcium-deficient conditions; complete capacitation requires the presence of calcium during the final hour of incubation. Modification by exclusion of glucose permits capacitation if calcium is present but inhibits the acrosome reaction (Fraser & Quinn, 1981).

Adenylate cyclase activity was measured, at 30 and 120 min as before, in mouse sperm suspensions incubated for a total of 2 h in calcium-containing and calcium-deficient media (both lacking glucose). Glucose was excluded because we reasoned that membrane changes accompanying the acrosome reaction might alter the measurable adenylate cyclase activity; most sperm adenylate cyclase is membrane-bound (Stengel *et al.*, 1982). Under these conditions, the relative increase in enzyme activity with time was similar when calcium-containing and calcium-deficient media were compared, but the absolute activity was significantly higher in the calcium-incubated suspensions (Fig. 3a; Monks *et al.*, 1986). Thus cAMP production in mouse spermatozoa could be higher throughout incubation under fully capacitating conditions than under the restrictive conditions of calcium deficiency. Consistent with this, White & Aitken (1989) have reported significantly higher levels of cAMP in hamster spermatozoa incubated in the presence of calcium than in its absence.

Evidence from other studies has suggested that intracellular calcium increases as capacitation proceeds (e.g. Singh *et al.*, 1978; White & Aitken, 1989) and, as discussed earlier, adenylate cyclase can be stimulated by interaction with calcium either directly or indirectly via calmodulin. The capacitation-related increases in adenylate cyclase activity in our study (Monks *et al.*, 1986) and in cAMP (White & Aitken, 1989) in calcium-incubated spermatozoa could therefore represent responses to rising intracellular calcium.

Phosphodiesterase was investigated using the same variations in medium composition (Monks & Fraser, 1987). The magnitude of the decrease in activity as sperm incubation lengthened, originally noted by Stein & Fraser (1984), was greater in suspensions incubated in the presence of calcium (i.e. fully capacitated) than in those incubated under calcium-deficient conditions (Fig. 3b). Furthermore, incubation in glucose-containing medium promoted a larger decline in phosphodiesterase activity than glucose-free medium. Both hyperactivated motility and the acrosome reaction are supported when glucose is present in the medium, suggesting that the potentially increased availability of cAMP due to decreased phosphodiesterase could contribute to these events.

Again using these same media, we have also investigated possible capacitation-related changes in the other sperm-intrinsic enzyme, 5′-nucleotidase, which converts 5′-AMP to adenosine. There was a small but significant decrease with time within any one set of conditions and the activity was

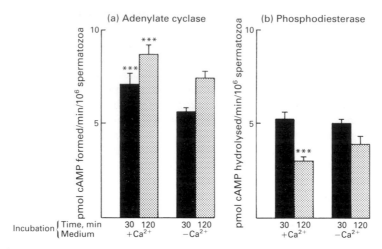

Fig. 3. Adenylate cyclase and phosphodiesterase activities in mouse sperm suspensions incubated with and without calcium for 120 min; assays were done at 30 min (uncapacitated) and 120 min (capacitated if in $+Ca^{2+}$ medium). Adenylate cyclase activity was significantly higher at both times in the $+Ca^{2+}$ than in the $-Ca^{2+}$ suspensions (data from Monks *et al.*, 1986); phosphodiesterase activity was similar in both groups at 30 min but significantly lower in the $+Ca^{2+}$ suspensions at 120 min (data from Monks & Fraser, 1987). Data are presented as mean $\pm$ s.e.m. for 3 replicates in each experimental series. *** $P < 0.001$ compared with $-Ca^{2+}$ counterparts.

significantly higher at both times of sampling (30 and 120 min) in calcium-deficient medium. This suggests a decreased production of adenosine with time, but overall higher levels in the absence of added calcium (Monks & Fraser, 1988a).

Adenosine modulation of sperm adenylate cyclase

The mechanisms controlling sperm cAMP production are poorly understood, although clearly differing from those in somatic cells as reflected by the insensitivity of the sperm enzyme system to many regulatory molecules which act via classical receptor/G-protein interactions with adenylate cyclase. As mentioned earlier, one possible modulator could be adenosine, acting via externally directed inhibitory (A_1) or stimulatory (A_2) receptors. We have obtained indirect evidence that adenosine can modulate mouse sperm adenylate cyclase under our standard capacitating conditions (Stein *et al.*, 1986). When adenosine deaminase was included in the assay to deplete endogenous adenosine, enzyme activity decreased significantly in suspensions sampled at 30 min (poorly fertile) but increased in samples taken from the same suspensions at 120 min (highly fertile). This suggests that endogenous adenosine had a stimulatory effect on adenylate cyclase in partially capacitated spermatozoa, possibly via A_2 receptors, and an inhibitory one in capacitated cells, possibly via A_1 receptors. The observed response was modified by the inclusion of the GTP analogue Gpp(NH)p, consistent with an effect on adenosine receptors (Fain & Malbon, 1979). In response to exogenous adenosine there was a detectable but non-significant rise in adenylate cyclase activity in the high nanomolar–low micromolar range of adenosine concentration and a significant inhibition at $> 100 \, \mu M$-adenosine. The latter is consistent with action at the intracellular inhibitory P-site which requires higher adenosine than the A_1 and A_2 sites (Londos & Wolff, 1977; Londos *et al.*, 1983). The lack of significant effects at low concentrations of adenosine may reflect the presence of endogenous adenosine deaminase of epididymal fluid origin in the suspensions (Monks & Fraser, 1988a).

Adenosine-related effects on sperm function

The above results, coupled with the demonstration that mouse sperm suspensions possess the enzymes required to produce endogenous adenosine, led us to look for evidence that available adenosine might modulate capacitation and hence fertilization in our in-vitro system. Initially, compounds previously shown to inhibit adenosine-metabolizing enzymes in mouse sperm suspensions (Monks & Fraser, 1988a) were used. The specific inhibitor of membrane 5′-nucleotidase, α,β-methylene adenosine diphosphate (AMPCP), was used to reduce production of endogenous adenosine, while the adenosine deaminase inhibitor coformycin was used to reduce breakdown of endogenous adenosine. AMPCP caused a concentration-dependent, significant inhibition of fertilization achieved with partially capacitated (30 min preincubation; Fig. 4) suspensions but had no effect on capacitated (120 min preincubation) suspensions. In contrast, inclusion of coformycin significantly increased fertilizing ability in the majority of suspensions tested after 30 min preincubation (Fig. 5). The addition of coformycin to fully capacitated suspensions caused a significant decrease in fertilization (Monks & Fraser, 1988b).

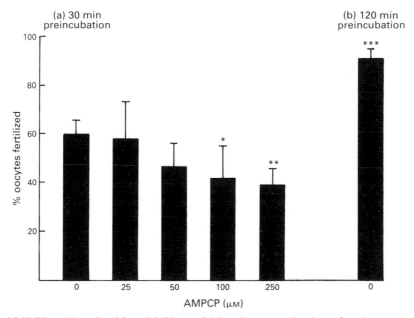

Fig. 4. AMPCP, a 5′-nucleotidase inhibitor which reduces production of endogenous adenosine, significantly inhibits mouse sperm fertilizing ability *in vitro* (data from Monks & Fraser, 1988b). Data are presented as mean ± s.e.m. for 9 replicates. * $P < 0.05$, ** $P < 0.025$, *** $P < 0.01$ compared with 30 min 0 AMPCP suspensions.

These results suggest that adenosine is produced during incubation and that it can stimulate the early stages of capacitation. However, the sensitivity to adenosine appears to change as capacitation proceeds, an observation consistent with our earlier data showing capacitation state-dependent changes in adenylate cyclase activity when adenosine deaminase was added (Stein *et al.*, 1986).

More recently we have demonstrated that the introduction of exogenous adenosine can stimulate fertilizing ability of suspensions in the early stages of capacitation in a concentration-dependent manner (Fraser, 1990). A significant response to adenosine at 10 and 100 μM was observed, both in the absence and presence of the adenosine uptake inhibitor dipyridamole (Cass *et al.*, 1987), suggesting

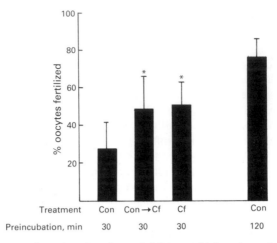

Fig. 5. Coformycin, an adenosine deaminase inhibitor which reduces breakdown of endogenous adenosine, significantly stimulates mouse sperm fertilizing ability *in vitro* (data from Monks & Fraser, 1988b). Con, control suspensions; Con → Cf, control suspensions diluted into coformycin-containing medium; Cf, coformycin-incubated suspensions. Data are presented as mean ± s.e.m. for 4 replicates. * $P < 0.05$ compared with 30-min control.

adenosine action at an external site (Fig. 6). This would be consistent with the reported inability of bull spermatozoa to take up adenosine (Brown & Casillas, 1984; Vijayaraghavan & Hoskins, 1986). Of the adenosine analogues evaluated, 2'-deoxyadenosine was no more potent than adenosine but 2-chloroadenosine, 5'-N-ethylcarboxamidoadenosine (NECA) and (R)-N^6-phenylisopropyl adenosine (R-PIA) were consistently and significantly stimulatory at concentrations lower than adenosine, i.e. down to 0·1 μM, with NECA stimulatory at 0·01 μM (Fig. 7). In the presence of effective concentrations of adenosine or analogues, subjective evaluation indicated that more cells exhibited hyperactivated motility than in the untreated controls. Assessment of capacitation state using chlortetracycline fluorescence patterns (Ward & Story, 1984) indicated significantly fewer cells expressing the uncapacitated F pattern and significantly more with the capacitated AR pattern, compared with controls.

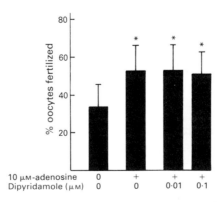

Fig. 6. Dipyridamole, an adenosine uptake inhibitor, does not reduce adenosine stimulation of mouse sperm fertilizing ability *in vitro*; this suggests that adenosine is acting at an external site (from Fraser, 1990). Data are presented as mean ± s.e.m. for 6 replicates. * $P < 0.05$ compared with 0 adenosine.

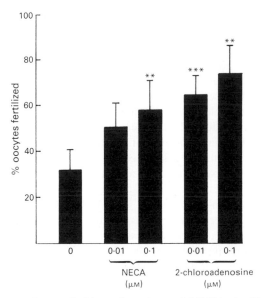

Fig. 7. The adenosine analogues 2-chloroadenosine and NECA significantly stimulate mouse sperm fertilizing ability, NECA being effective at concentrations as low as 0·01 μM (data from Fraser, 1990). Data are presented as mean ± s.e.m. for 5 replicates except for 0·1 μM-NECA where $n = 4$. ** $P < 0.025$, *** $P < 0.01$ compared with 0 drug.

The above data provide the most direct evidence to date that adenosine can significantly stimulate the expression of capacitation- and fertilization-related characteristics, namely hyperactivated motility and the acrosome reaction, correlating well with the demonstrable increase in proportion of oocytes fertilized. The greater sensitivity to NECA, 2-chloroadenosine and R-PIA, relative to adenosine and 2′-deoxyadenosine, is consistent with interaction at stimulatory A_2 receptors (Daly *et al.*, 1987). Other studies using mammalian spermatozoa have only indicated an ability of adenosine and/or analogues to increase the number of motile cells in a suspension. Vijayaraghavan & Hoskins (1986) found that while micromolar concentrations of adenosine stimulated bull sperm motility, 2′-deoxyadenosine was even more effective. Aitken *et al.* (1986) observed motility stimulation in cryopreserved human sperm suspensions by 2′-deoxyadenosine, but only at millimolar concentrations. In the studies of Vijayaraghavan & Hoskins (1986) and Aitken *et al.* (1986), cAMP levels were higher in treated suspensions although the mechanism of production was unclear.

While there is evidence that adenosine receptors may affect other systems, e.g. calcium fluxes, in addition to adenylate cyclase-cAMP (Daly *et al.*, 1987), our earlier observation that introduction of adenosine deaminase produced significant alterations in adenylate cyclase activity (Stein *et al.*, 1986) suggests that the adenosine/analogue-induced functional responses in mouse spermatozoa were elicited via stimulation of adenylate cyclase.

Finally, adenosine modulation of sperm function *in vivo* is a distinct possibility: 5′-nucleotidase, is an ecto-enzyme, allowing extracellular production of adenosine by the cells themselves, and adenosine is present in micromolar concentrations in female reproductive tract fluids (Eppig *et al.*, 1985; Samuelson *et al.*, 1985).

cAMP functions in spermatozoa

Responses to cAMP are mediated via activation of cAMP-dependent protein kinase (Flockhart & Corbin, 1982), with the subsequent phosphorylation events promoting alterations in cell function. Mammalian spermatozoa contain significant amounts of cAMP-dependent protein kinases (Paupard *et al.*, 1988). However, identification of specific phosphoproteins and, more importantly, their functions is minimal to date. Evidence from sea urchin (Brokaw, 1984), bull (Brandt & Hoskins, 1980) and dog (Tash *et al.*, 1984) spermatozoa indicates that a soluble phosphoprotein, termed axokinin by Tash *et al.* (1984), of $M_r \sim 56\,000$ plays a pivotal role in initiation cAMP-dependent motility. At present some confusion exists since Paupard *et al.* (1988) have provided evidence that the major soluble cAMP-dependent phosphoprotein of $M_r \sim 56\,000$ is the regulatory subunit of a type II cAMP-dependent protein kinase (R II). Whether the motility-initiating protein in bull spermatozoa is a minor component, relative to R II in bull spermatozoa, has yet to be determined. However, these events are associated with the onset of motility; there is no evidence that a phosphoprotein such as axokinin plays a specific role in expression of hyperactivated motility.

Using our well-characterized in-vitro system, we have begun to look for capacitation-related changes in phosphorylation patterns. Sperm suspensions incubated for 2 h in the continuous presence of glucose are fully capacitated, expressing hyperactivated motility and being highly fertile. In contrast, suspensions incubated in the absence of glucose are capacitated but non-fertilizing with sluggish motility. Addition of glucose to the latter suspensions rapidly stimulates motility, hyperactivation being observed within minutes, and fertility is indistinguishable from counterparts incubated continuously in glucose (Fraser & Quinn, 1981). Comparison of phosphorylation patterns among glucose-free suspensions after different incubation times and after the introduction of glucose indicated little change in the array of detectable phosphoproteins but considerable alterations in the level of protein phosphorylation (Duncan & Fraser, 1990). Given the pronounced effects of substrate availability on the qualitative and quantitative expression of motility, the majority of phosphoproteins detected may be concerned with motility. The exception was a protein of $M_r \sim 95\,000$ observed in capacitated but not uncapacitated suspensions, suggesting that the appearance of this phosphoprotein may be related to a capacitation event. In general, however, our data suggest that a change in the overall level of protein phosphorylation may be important in the acquisition of fertilizing ability.

Conclusions

Mammalian sperm capacitation can be influenced by alteration of cAMP metabolism, suggesting a central role for cAMP in these events. The capacity for cAMP accumulation increases during capacitation *in vitro*, with increased adenylate cyclase and decreased phosphodiesterase activities. However, the intrinsic mechanisms which control both cAMP production and the subsequent biochemical events remain unclear. Although not affected by hormones capable of regulating activity of the somatic cell enzyme, evidence suggests that sperm adenylate cyclase may be controlled by intracellular calcium and extracellular adenosine. Calcium could affect the enzyme directly or act via calmodulin. Adenosine availability has been shown to modulate sperm adenylate cyclase, with responses to alterations indicating stimulation by adenosine in uncapacitated spermatozoa and inhibition in capacitated cells. Spermatozoa are able to generate adenosine on their extracellular surface and this production promotes fertilizing ability in early stages of capacitation *in vitro*. Similar stimulation obtained with exogenous adenosine and its analogues is consistent with an effect at stimulatory A_2 adenosine receptors. Together these observations provide the most complete evidence to date for concurrent regulation of both sperm adenylate cyclase and the events of capacitation. The capacitation-related decline in phosphodiesterase activity would also influence the availability of cAMP to act as a second messenger. However, assuming that cAMP effects are mediated via cAMP-dependent protein kinases, the substrates for phosphorylation which ultimately promote the changes in sperm function remain to be elucidated. Thus although we are beginning to identify mechanisms controlling production of this intracellular messenger, we know relatively little about mechanisms whereby the message is processed to prepare spermatozoa for the events of fertilization.

We thank Andrew Osborne for the artwork. Our studies discussed here were supported by the Agricultural and Food Research Council and the Medical Research Council.

References

Aitken, R.J., Best, F., Richardson, D.W., Schato, R. & Simm, G. (1983) Influence of caffeine on movement characteristics, fertilizing capacity and ability to penetrate cervical mucus of human spermatozoa. *J. Reprod. Fert.* **75**, 19–27.

Aitken, R.J., Matki, A. & Irvine, S. (1986) Paradoxical stimulation of human sperm motility by 2-deoxyadenosine. *J. Reprod. Fert.* **78**, 515–527.

Austin, C.R. (1951) Observations on the penetration of the sperm into the mammalian egg. *Aust. J. sci. Res. B* **4**, 581–596.

Austin, C.R. (1952) The 'capacitation' of the mammalian sperm. *Nature, Lond.* **170**, 326.

Barkay, J., Bartoov, B., Bcn-Ezra, S., Langsam, J., Feldman, E., Gordon, S. & Zuckerman, H. (1984) Influence of in vitro caffeine treatment on human sperm morphology and fertilizing capacity. *Fert. Steril.* **41**, 913–918.

Bedford, J.M. (1970) Sperm capacitation and fertilization in mammals. *Biol. Reprod.*, Suppl. **2**, 128–158.

Bedford, J.M. & Chang, M.C. (1962) Removal of decapacitation factor from seminal plasma by high speed centrifugation. *Am. J. Physiol.* **202**, 179–181.

Bentley, J.K., Garbers, D.L., Domino, S.E., Noland, T.D. & Van Dop, C. (1986) Spermatozoa contain a guanine nucleotide-binding protein ADP-ribosylated by Pertussis toxin. *Biochem. Biophys. Res. Commun.* **138**, 728–734.

Berger, T. & Clegg, E.D. (1983) Adenylate cyclase activity in porcine sperm in response to female tract secretions. *Gamete Res.* **7**, 169–177.

Boatman, D.E. & Bavister, B.D. (1984) Stimulation of rhesus monkey sperm capacitation by cyclic nucleotide mediators. *J. Reprod. Fert.* **71**, 357–366.

Brandt, H. & Hoskins, D.D. (1980) A cAMP-dependent phosphorylated motility protein in bovine epididymal sperm. *J. biol. Chem.* **255**, 982–987.

Braun, T. (1975) The effect of divalent cations on bovine spermatozoal adenylate cyclase activity. *J. cyc. Nucleotide Res.* **1**, 271–281.

Brokaw, C.J. (1984) Cyclic AMP-dependent activation of sea urchin and tunicate sperm motility. *Ann. N.Y. Acad. Sci.* **438**, 132–141.

Brown, M.A. & Casillas, E.R. (1982) Evidence for a divalent cation regulatory site in bovine sperm adenylate cyclase. *Fedn Proc. Fedn Am. Socs exp. Biol.* **41**, 1406.

Brown, M.A. & Casillas, E.R. (1984) Bovine sperm adenylate cyclase: inhibition by adenosine and adenosine analogs. *J. Androl.* **5**, 361–368.

Cai, X. & Marik, J.J. (1989) Improving penetration capacity of spermatozoa with poor motility by addition of caffeine at coincubation with zona-free hamster ova. *Fert. Steril.* **51**, 719–721.

Casillas, E.R., Elder, C.M. & Hoskins, D.D. (1980) Adenylate cyclase activity of bovine spermatozoa during maturation in the epididymis and the activation of sperm particulate adenylate cyclase by GTP and polyamines. *J. Reprod. Fert.* **59**, 297–302.

Cass, C.E., Belt, J.A. & Paterson, A.R.P. (1987) Adenosine transport in cultured cells and erythrocytes. In *Cardiac Electrophysiology and Pharmacology of Adenosine and ATP: Basic and Clinical Aspects* (Progress in Clinical and Biological Research, Vol. 230), pp. 13–40. Alan R. Liss, New York.

Chan, P.J., Asakawa, T. & Dukelow, W.R. (1981) Cyclic nucleotide involvement in capacitation and the acrosome reaction as assessed in a primate *in vitro* fertilization system. *Biol. Reprod.* **24**, Suppl. 1, 38A., abstr.

Chang, M.C. (1951) Fertilizing capacity of spermatozoa deposited into Fallopian tubes. *Nature, Lond.* **168**, 697–698.

Cheng, C.Y. & Boettcher, B. (1979) Effects of cholera toxin and 5-guanylylimidodiphosphate on human spermatozoal adenylate cyclase activity. *Biochem. Biophys. Res. Commun.* **91**, 1–9.

Cheng, C.Y. & Boettcher, B. (1982) Partial characterization of human spermatozoal phosphodiesterase and adenylate cyclase and the effect of steroids on their activities. *Int. J. Androl.* **5**, 253–266.

D'Agostino, A., Monaco, L., Conti, M. & Geremia, R. (1983) Calmodulin in mouse male germ cells: a qualitative and quantitative study. *Cell Differ.* **13**, 35–40.

Daly, J.W., Jacobson, K.A. & Ukena, D. (1987) Adenosine receptors: development of selective agonists and antagonists. In *Cardiac Electrophysiology and Pharmacology of Adenosine and ATP. Basic and Clinical Aspects* (Progress in Clinical and Biological Research, vol. 230), pp. 41–63. Alan R. Liss, New York.

Duncan, A.E. & Fraser, L.R. (1990) Patterns of endogenous protein phosphorylation during the in vitro capacitation of epididymal mouse sperm. *J. Reprod. Fert., Abstr. Ser.* **4**, in press.

Eppig, J.J., Ward-Bailey, P.F. & Coleman, D.L. (1985) Hypoxanthine and adenosine in murine ovarian follicular fluid: concentrations and activity in maintaining oocyte meiotic arrest. *Biol. Reprod.* **33**, 1041–1049.

Fain, J.N. & Malbon, C.C. (1979) Regulation of adenylate cyclase by adenosine. *Molec. cell Pharmacol.* **25**, 143–169.

Feinberg, J., Weinmann, J., Weinmann, S., Walsh, M.P., Harricane, M.C., Gabrion, J. & Demaille, J.G. (1981) Immunocytochemical and biochemical evidence for the presence of calmodulin in bull sperm flagellum. *Biochim. biophys. Acta* **673**, 303–311.

Flockhart, D.A. & Corbin, J.D. (1982) Regulatory mechanisms in the control of protein kinases. *CRC Crit. Rev. Biochem.* **12**, 133–186.

Fraser, L.R. (1979) Accelerated mouse sperm penetration *in vitro* in the presence of caffeine. *J. Reprod. Fert.* **57**, 377–384.

Fraser, L.R. (1981) Dibutyryl cyclic AMP decreases capacitation time *in vitro* in mouse spermatozoa. *J. Reprod. Fert.* **62**, 63–72.

Fraser, L.R. (1982) Ca^{2+} is required for mouse sperm capacitation and fertilization in vitro. *J. Androl.* **3**, 412–419.

Fraser, L.R. (1983) Mouse sperm capacitation assessed by kinetics and morphology of fertilization *in vitro*. *J. Reprod. Fert.* **69**, 419–428.

Fraser, L.R. (1984) Mechanisms controlling mammalian fertilization. In *Oxford Reviews of Reproductive Biology*, vol. 6, pp. 174–225. Ed. J. R. Clarke. Oxford University Press.

Fraser, L.R. (1987) Minimum and maximum extracellular Ca^{2+} requirements during mouse sperm capacitation and fertilization *in vitro*. *J. Reprod. Fert.* **81**, 77–89.

Fraser, L.R. (1990) Adenosine and its analogues, possibly acting at A_2 receptors, stimulate mouse sperm fertilizing ability during early stages of capacitation. *J. Reprod. Fert.* **89**, 467–476.

Fraser, L.R. & Ahuja, K.K. (1988) Metabolic and surface events in fertilization. *Gamete Res.* **20**, 491–519.

Fraser, L.R. & Quinn, P.J. (1981) A glycolytic product is obligatory for initiation of the sperm acrosome reaction and whiplash motility required for fertilization in the mouse. *J. Reprod. Fert.* **61**, 25–35.

Garbers, D.L. & Kopf, G.S. (1980) The regulation of spermatozoa by calcium and cyclic nucleotides. *Adv. Cyclic Nucl. Res.* **13**, 251–306.

Garbers, D.L., Lust, W.D., First, N.L. & Lardy, H.A. (1971) Effects of phosphodiesterase inhibitors and cyclic nucleotides on sperm respiration and motility. *Biochemistry, NY* **10**, 1825–1831.

Garbers, D.L., Tubb, D.J. & Hyne, R.V. (1982) A requirement of bicarbonate for Ca^{2+}-induced elevation of cyclic AMP in guinea pig spermatozoa. *J. biol. Chem.* **257**, 8980–8984.

Geremia, R., Rossi, P., Mocini, D., Pezzotti, R. & Conti, M. (1984) Characterization of a calmodulin-dependent high-affinity cyclic AMP and cyclic GMP phosphodiesterase from male mouse germ cells. *Biochem. J.* **217**, 693–700.

Gilman, A.G. (1984) G proteins and dual control of adenylate cyclase. *Cell* **36**, 577–579.

Goh, P. & Hoskins, D.D. (1985) The involvement of methyl transfer reactions and S-adenosylhomocysteine in the regulation of bovine sperm motility. *Gamete Res.* **12**, 399–409.

Goh, P.P. & White, I.G. (1988) Control of ram sperm adenylate cyclase by divalent cations. *Aust. J. biol. Sci.* **41**, 377–385.

Gordeladze, J.O. & Hansson, V. (1980) Mn^{2+}-dependent adenylate cyclase (AC) in rat testis: kinetic properties and optimalization of assay conditions. *Int. J. Androl.* **3**, 539–552.

Gordeladze, J.O., Conti, M., Purvis, K. & Hansson, V. (1982) The effect of calmodulin, trifluoperazine and other psychoactive drugs on the activity of the Mn^{2+}-dependent adenylate cyclase (AC) in testicular germ cells. *Int. J. Androl.* **5**, 103–112.

Gross, M.K., Toscano, D.G. & Toscano, W.A. (1987) Calmodulin-mediated adenylate cyclase from mammalian sperm. *J. biol. Chem.* **262**, 8672–8676.

Harrison, R.F., Shepherd, R.L. & Kaliszer, M. (1980) Observations on the motility, ultrastructure and elemental composition of human spermatozoa incubated with caffeine. *Andrologia* **12**, 34–38.

Henry, D., Ferino, F., Tomova, S., Ferry, N., Stengel, D. & Hanoune, J. (1986) Inhibition of the catalytic subunit of ram sperm adenylate cyclase by adenosine. *Biochem. Biophys. Res. Commun.* **137**, 970–977.

Hildebrandt, J.D., Codina, J., Tash, J.S., Kirchick, H.J., Lipschultz, L., Sekura, R.D. & Birnbaumer, L. (1985) The membrane-bound spermatozoal adenylyl cyclase system does not share coupling characteristics with somatic cell adenylyl cyclase. *Endocrinology* **116**, 1357–1366.

Hoskins, D.D. & Casillas, E.R. (1975) Hormones, second messengers and the mammalian spermatozoa. In *Advances in Sex Hormone Research*, vol. 1, *Molecular Mechanisms of Gonadal Hormone Action*, pp. 283–324. Eds R. L. Singhal & J. A. Thomas. University Park Press, Baltimore.

Hyne, R.V. & Garbers, D.L. (1979a) Calcium-dependent increase in adenosine 3′,5′-monophosphate and induction of the acrosome reaction in guinea pig spermatozoa. *Proc. natn. Acad. Sci. USA* **76**, 5699–5703.

Hyne, R.V. & Garbers, D.L. (1979b) Regulation of guinea pig sperm adenylate cyclase by calcium. *Biol. Reprod.* **21**, 1135–1142.

Hyne, R.V. & Lopata, A. (1982) Calcium and adenosine affect human sperm adenylate cyclase activity. *Gamete Res.* **6**, 81–89.

Jones, H.P., Lenz, R.W., Palevitz, B.A. & Cormier, M.J. (1980) Calmodulin localization in mammalian spermatozoa. *Proc. natn. Acad. Sci. USA* **77**, 2772–2776.

Jones, R. (1978) Comparative biochemistry of mammalian epididymal plasma. *Comp. Biochem. Physiol.* **61B**, 365–370.

Kopf, G.S., Woolkalis, M.J. & Gerton, G.L. (1986) Evidence for a guanine nucleotide-binding regulatory protein in invertebrate and mammalian sperm. *J. biol. Chem.* **261**, 7327–7331.

Levin, S.J. & Bodansky, B. (1966) The double pH optimum of 5′-nucleotidase of seminal plasma. *J. biol. Chem.* **241**, 51–76.

Londos, C. & Wolff, J. (1977) Two distinct adenosine-sensitive sites on adenylate cyclase. *Proc. natn. Acad. Sci. USA* **74**, 5482–5486.

Londos, C., Wolff, J. & Cooper, D.M.F. (1983) Adenosine receptors and adenylate cyclase interactions. In *Regulatory Function of Adenosine*, pp. 17–32. Eds R. M. Byrne, T. W. Race & R. Rubio. Martinus Nijhoff, The Hague.

Monks, N.J. & Fraser, L.R. (1987) Phosphodiesterase activity of mouse sperm incubated under conditions that modulate fertilization potential in vitro. *Gamete Res.* **18**, 85–96.

Monks, N.J. & Fraser, L.R. (1988a) Enzymes of adenosine metabolism in mouse sperm suspensions. *J. Reprod. Fert.* **83**, 389–399.

Monks, N.J. & Fraser, L.R. (1988b) Inhibition of adenosine-metabolizing enzymes modulates mouse sperm fertilizing ability: a changing role for endogenously generated adenosine during capacitation. *Gamete Res.* **21**, 267–276.

Monks, N.J., Stein, D.M. & Fraser, L.R. (1986) Adenylate cyclase activity of mouse sperm during capacitation in vitro: effect of calcium and a GTP analogue. *Int. J. Androl.* **9**, 67–76.

Morton, B. & Albagli, L. (1973) Modification of hamster sperm adenyl cyclase by capacitation in vitro. *Biochem. Biophys. Res. Commun.* **50**, 697–703.

Mrsny, R.J. & Meizel, R. (1980) Evidence suggesting a role for cyclic nucleotides in acrosome reactions of hamster sperm *in vitro. J. exp. Zool.* **211**, 153–157.

Okamura, N., Tajima, Y., Soejima, A., Masuda, H. & Sugita, Y. (1985) Sodium bicarbonate in seminal plasma stimulates the motility of mammalian spermatozoa through direct activation of adenylate cyclase. *J. biol. Chem.* **260**, 9699–9705.

Oliphant, G., Reynolds, A.B. & Thomas, T.S. (1985) Sperm surface components involved in the control of the acrosome reaction. *Am. J. Anat.* **174**, 269–283.

Parkman, R., Gelfland, E.W., Rosen, F.S., Sanderson, A. & Hirschhorn, R. (1975) Severe combined immunodeficiency and adenosine deaminase deficiency. *N. Eng. J. Med.* **292**, 714–719.

Paupard, M.C., Macleod, J., Wasco, W. & Orr, G.A. (1988) Major 56 000-dalton soluble phosphoprotein present in bovine sperm is the regulatory subunit of a type II cAMP-dependent protein kinase. *J. Cell Biochem.* **37**, 161–175.

Rogers, B.J. (1981) Factors affecting mammalian *in vitro* fertilization. In *Bioregulators of Reproduction*, pp. 459–486. Eds G. Jagiello & H. J. Vogel. Academic Press, New York.

Rosado, A., Hicks, J.J., Reyes, A. & Blanco, I. (1974) Capacitation *in vitro* of rabbit spermatozoa with cyclic adenosine monophosphate and human follicular fluid. *Fert. Steril.* **25**, 821–824.

Samuelson, U.E., Wilund, N.P. & Gustafsson, L.E. (1985) Dual effects of adenosine and adenosine analogues on motor activity of the human fallopian tube. *Acta physiol. Scand.* **125**, 369–376.

Santos-Sacchi, J. & Gordon, M. (1982) The effect of ATP depletion upon the acrosome reaction in guinea pig sperm. *J. Androl.* **3**, 108–112.

Sattin, A. & Rall, T.W. (1970) The effect of adenosine and adenine nucleotides on the cyclic adenosine 3′,5′ phosphate content of guinea pig cerebral cortex slices. *Molec. Pharmacol.* **6**, 13–23.

Schoff, P.K. & Lardy, H.A. (1987) Effects of fluoride and caffeine on the metabolism and motility of ejaculated bovine spermatozoa. *Biol. Reprod.* **37**, 1037–1046.

Singh, J.P., Babcock, D.F. & Lardy, H.A. (1978) Increased calcium flux is a component of capacitation of spermatozoa. *Biochem. J.* **172**, 519–556.

Stein, D.M. & Fraser, L.R. (1984) Cyclic nucleotide metabolism in mouse epididymal spermatozoa during capacitation in vitro. *Gamete Res.* **10**, 283–299.

Stein, D.M., Fraser, L.R. & Monks, N.J. (1986) Adenosine and Gpp(NH)p modulate mouse sperm adenylate cyclase. *Gamete Res.* **13**, 157–158.

Stengel, D., Guenet, L. & Hanoune, J. (1982) Proteolytic solubilization of adenylate cyclase from membranes deficient in regulatory component. *J. biol. Chem.* **257**, 10818–10826.

Stephens, D.T., Wang, J.L. & Hoskins, D.D. (1979) The cyclic AMP phosphodiesterase of bovine spermatozoa: multiple forms, kinetic properties and changes during development. *Biol. Reprod.* **20**, 483–491.

Tash, J.S. & Means, A.R. (1983) Cyclic adenosine 3′,5′ monophosphate, calcium and protein phosphorylation in flagellar motility. *Biol. Reprod.* **28**, 75–104.

Tash, J.S., Kakar, S.S. & Means, A.R. (1984) Flagellar motility requires the cAMP-dependent phosphorylation of heat-stable NP-40-soluble 56 kD protein, axokinin. *Cell* **38**, 551–559.

Toyoda, Y. & Chang, M.C. (1974) Capacitation of epididymal spermatozoa with high K/Na ratio and cyclic AMP for the fertilization of rat eggs *in vitro. J. Reprod. Fert.* **36**, 125–134.

Van Calker, D., Muller, M. & Hamprecht, B. (1979) Adenosine regulates via two different types of receptors, the accumulation of cAMP in cultured brain cells. *J. Neurochem.* **33**, 999–1005.

Vijayaraghavan, S. & Hoskins, D.D. (1986) Regulation of bovine sperm motility and cyclic adenosine 3′,5′-monophosphate by adenosine and its analogues. *Biol. Reprod.* **34**, 468–477.

Visconti, P.E. & Tezon, J.G. (1989) Phorbol esters stimulate cyclic adenosine 3′,5′ monophosphate accumulation in hamster spermatozoa during in vitro capacitation. *Biol. Reprod.* **40**, 223–231.

Ward, C.R. & Storey, B.T. (1984) Determination of the time course of capacitation in mouse spermatozoa using a chlortetracycline fluorescence assay. *Devl Biol.* **104**, 287–296.

Wasco, W.M. & Orr, G.A. (1984) Function of calmodulin in mammalian sperm: Presence of a calmodulin-dependent cyclic nucleotide phosphodiesterase associated with demembranated rat caudal epididymal sperm. *Biochem. Biophys. Res. Commun.* **118**, 636–642.

Wells, J.W. & Hardman, J.G. (1977) Cyclic nucleotide phosphodiesterases. *Adv. cyclic Nucleotide Res.* **8**, 119–143.

White, D.R. & Aitken, R.J. (1989) Relationship between calcium, cyclic AMP, ATP and intracellular pH and the capacity of hamster spermatozoa to express hyperactivated motility. *Gamet Res.* **22**, 163–177.

Yanagimachi, R. (1981) Mechanisms of fertilization in mammals. In *Fertilization and Embryonic Development in Vitro*, pp. 81–182. Eds L. Mastroianni & J. D. Biggers. Plenum Publishing, New York.

Yanagimachi, R. (1988) Mammalian fertilization. In *The Physiology of Reproduction*, vol. 1, pp. 135–185. Eds E. Knobil, J. Neill, L. L. Ewing, C. L. Markert, G. S. Greenwald & D. W. Pfaff. Raven Press, New York.

J. Reprod. Fert., Suppl. **42** (1990), 23–31

Egg signals for triggering the acrosome reaction in starfish spermatozoa

M. Hoshi, T. Amano*, Y. Okita†, T. Okinaga and T. Matsui‡

Department of Life Science, Tokyo Institute of Technology, Meguro-ku, Tokyo 152, Japan

Summary. Upon encountering the jelly coat of an egg, starfish spermatozoa undergo the acrosome reaction. To induce the acrosome reaction, 3 jelly components act in concert on the spermatozoa: a sulphated glycoprotein named acrosome reaction-inducing substance (ARIS), a group of steroidal saponins named Co-ARIS, and an oligopeptide presumably having an ability to increase the intracellular pH of the spermatozoon. All three are required to mimic the full ability of jelly coat to induce the acrosome reaction instantaneously. A combination of ARIS and Co-ARIS is enough for induction in normal sea water, although its action is almost 2 min slower than the jelly. ARIS can induce the acrosome reaction by itself in high Ca^{2+} or high pH sea water. When spermatozoa meet the jelly coat, the acrosome reaction is eventually induced because ARIS and Co-ARIS co-operatively increase the intracellular Ca^{2+} by stimulating verapamil- and maitotoxin-sensitive Ca^{2+} channels and the oligopeptide increases the intracellular pH by stimulating Na^+/H^+ exchange systems.

Keywords: egg jelly; acrosome reaction; glycoprotein, steroid saponin; sperm activating peptide; ARIS/Co-ARIS system

Introduction

Animal eggs are generally encased in one or a few layers of coats in contrast with naked spermatozoa. For example, spawned echinoderm eggs have two acellular coats, the jelly coat and the vitelline coat. These coats serve not merely as an armour to protect the egg but more importantly as signals for spermatozoa to undergo spatio-temporally matched changes which are essential for successful fertilization.

The acrosome reaction is one such change, the most central one probably. It is basically an event of exocytosis by which spermatozoa expose their devices essential for penetration through the egg coats and for fusion with the egg plasma membrane, and it is therefore indispensable for fertilization in various animals. In echinoderms and some other marine invertebrates, exocytosis of acrosomal vesicles is accompanied by the formation of an acrosomal process at the tip by polymerizing stored actin molecules or by extruding a pre-formed actin fibre. Although solutions of the egg jelly are known to induce the acrosome reaction in many marine invertebrates and much information is available on morphological, physiological and biochemical changes accompanying the acrosome reaction (for reviews see Dan, 1967; Tilney, 1985), where the fertilizing spermatozoa undergo the acrosome reaction and what triggers it still remain open questions for most animals including sea urchins. In the starfish, however, there is conclusive evidence that spermatozoa undergo the acrosome reaction upon encountering the jelly coat (Dale *et al.*, 1981; Ikadai & Hoshi,

*Present address: Department of Pharmacology, Tokyo Metropolitan Institute of Gerontology, Itabashi-ku, Tokyo 173, Japan.
†Present address: Suntory Pharmatech Center, Chiyoda-machi, Gunma 370-05, Japan.
‡Present address: Institute for Comprehensive Medical Science, Fujita-Gakuen Health University School of Medicine, Aichi 480-11, Japan.

1981a). We therefore attempted to isolate and identify an egg-jelly component(s) responsible for triggering the acrosome reaction in the starfishes, *Asterias amurensis* and *Asterina pectinifera*.

While searching for such a molecule, we found that the histones of jelly-treated spermatozoa start to degrade (T. Amano & M. Hoshi, unpublished data). This observation led to the hypothesis that the jelly also triggers a key reaction that leads eventually to decondensation of the sperm nucleus. We have found that the acrosome reaction and histone degradation are independent events triggered by the same jelly components.

This paper summarizes our recent findings on the physiological signals for the acrosome reaction in starfish.

Egg jelly

The jelly coat of starfish eggs is a transparent and gelatinous layer consisting of three groups of organic molecules as indicated below.

(1) Glycoproteins
   High mannose glycoprotein
   Sulphated glycoprotein [ARIS]
(2) Sulphated steroid saponins
   Co-ARIS substances
   Sperm agglutinins
   Others
(3) Oligopeptides
   Sperm activating peptides
   Others

Glycoproteins

Two glycoproteins are found in the jelly: a high mannose glycoprotein of molecular weight $\sim 80\,000$ and a highly sulphated, fucose-rich glycoprotein of an extremely high molecular weight. Although the high mannose glycoprotein has unique saccharide structures (Endo *et al.*, 1987), it does not seem to be directly related to the acrosome reaction. Instead, the highly sulphated glycoprotein does serve as a key molecule for inducing the acrosome reaction and is named acrosome reaction-inducing substance (ARIS). Although ARIS, but no other jelly components, can induce the acrosome reaction by itself in high Ca^{2+} or high pH sea water, it requires a diffusible jelly component named Co-ARIS for induction of the acrosome reaction in normal sea water (Ikadai & Hoshi, 1981a, b; Matsui *et al.* 1986a).

The activities of ARIS are species specific, resistant to pronase digestion and mainly ascribed to the saccharide and sulphate moieties (Matsui *et al.*, 1986a, b). This allows us to substitute a pronase digest of ARIS (P-ARIS) for intact ARIS. ARIS contains fucose, galactose, xylose and *N*-acetylgalactosamine as the sugar constituents (T. Okinaga & M. Hoshi, unpublished data). Sugar compositions are significantly different in the two species of starfish.

Sulphated saponins

Starfish jelly contains sulphated saponins, some of which are known to agglutinate spermatozoa in *Asterias* (Uno & Hoshi, 1978). Some others are found to serve as a Co-ARIS. Three principal Co-ARIS substances in *Asterias* are identified as shown in Fig. 1 (Nishiyama *et al.*, 1987a; Fujimoto *et al.*, 1987). Mixtures of the three are more effective in terms of specific activity than the individuals, suggesting that they act synergistically on spermatozoa in natural circumstances (Fig. 2). The total quantity of Co-ARIS substances in the jelly coat is roughly estimated to be about the optimum for the induction of acrosome reaction (Nishiyama *et al.*, 1987b). The action of Co-ARIS is not very species-specific. Whereas the sulphate moiety and the side chain of the steroid are important for the activity, the saccharide chain seems unnecessary to be strictly specific (Nishiyama *et al.*, 1987b). Saponins are rare in animals, but asteroids are rich in steroid saponins (asterosaponins) and holothurians are rich in triterpenoid saponins (holothurins). It will be interesting to test whether holothurins serve as Co-ARIS in sea cucumbers.

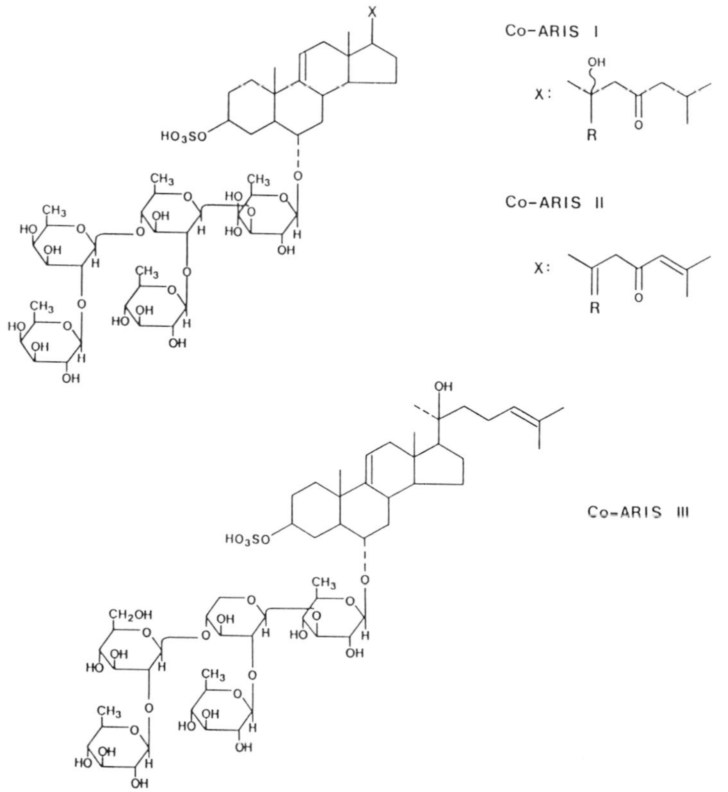

Fig. 1. Structures of Co-ARIS I, II and III. Co-ARIS I and II are expressed in the hydrated form at 6-deoxy-*xylo*-hexos-4-ulose. (From Fujimoto *et al.*, 1987.)

Oligopeptides

It is well established that the jelly coat contains sperm-activating peptides in the echinoderms (for a review, see Suzuki, 1989). Although such peptides have not been isolated from starfish, the following results suggest that a sperm-activating peptide also participates in the physiological induction of the acrosome reaction. The amounts of Co-ARIS and ARIS required for inducing the acrosome reaction are much lower if a crude preparation of Co-ARIS named Fraction M_8 is used instead of mixtures of or each of the purified ones. Fraction M_8, but none of the purified Co-ARIS substances, increases the intracellular pH (pH_i) of spermatozoa, and thus it activates their motility and respiration. When Fraction M_8 is digested with pronase to which Co-ARIS is resistant, the apparent activity of Co-ARIS in the fraction is much reduced with a concomitant loss of sperm activating capacity (Hoshi *et al.*, 1986, 1988; Matsui *et al.*, 1986b, c; Nishiyama *et al.*, 1987a, b).

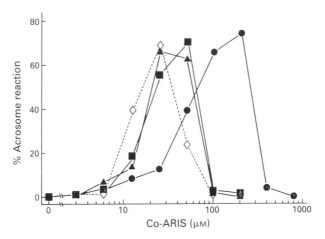

Fig. 2. Dose-dependent effect of Co-ARIS on the acrosome reaction. A sperm suspension was added to a mixture of 25 µg P-ARIS/ml and Co-ARIS as indicated. Values are means for at least 3 different experiments. ●, Co-ARIS I; ▲, Co-ARIS II; ■, Co-ARIS III; ◇, mixture of Co-ARISs I, II and III in a molar ratio of 2:1:1. (From Nishiyama *et al.*, 1987b.)

Acrosome reaction

Induction by jelly

The acrosome reaction, which is generally inducible by calcium ionophores, is quickly, species-specifically and dose-dependently induced by the egg jelly in starfish. As found in sea urchins and other animals, the jelly-induced acrosome reaction is very dependent upon external cations, especially Ca^{2+} and H^+, susceptible to Ca^{2+}-channel antagonists (verapamil and diltiazem), facilitated by an increase in pH_i. It is accompanied by an abrupt uptake of external Ca^{2+}, a Na^+-dependent transient increase in pH_i and a remarkable but transient increase in cAMP (Matsui *et al.*, 1986a, c). It is generally accepted, therefore, that the egg jelly induces the acrosome reaction by stimulating Ca^{2+} channels and Na^+/H^+ exchangers in the sperm plasma membrane (Schackmann & Shapiro, 1981; Tilney, 1985; Hoshi *et al.*, 1986, 1988).

Induction by ARIS and Co-ARIS

Combinations of ARIS (or P-ARIS) and Co-ARIS trigger Ca^{2+} uptake, cAMP increase and the acrosome reaction in normal sea water, but individually they are not able to trigger any of these changes (Ikadai & Hoshi, 1981a, b; Matsui *et al.*, 1986a). They induce the acrosome reaction by stimulating a verapamil- and diltiazem-sensitive Ca^{2+} channel to an extent similar to, but significantly slower than, that induced by the jelly (Fig. 3). Accordingly, Ca^{2+} uptake and cAMP increase proceed more slowly in the spermatozoa treated with combinations of P-ARIS plus Co-ARIS (Hoshi *et al.*, 1986, 1988).

It should be stressed here that a sodium-dependent transient pH_i increase, that is always observed in the jelly-induced acrosome reaction, has never been detected in one induced by ARIS/Co-ARIS by using 9-aminoacridine as a fluorogenic probe (Fig. 4). Similarly, in 50 mM-Ca^{2+} sea water, P-ARIS can induce the acrosome reaction without increasing the pH_i. Conversely, Fraction M_8, but none of the Co-ARIS substances, in normal sea water or the jelly in Ca^{2+}-deficient sea water increases the pH_i without inducing the acrosome reaction (Matsui *et al.*, 1986c). It is concluded that the pH_i increase is not sufficient nor obligatory for triggering the acrosome reaction, at least in starfish spermatozoa (Hoshi *et al.*, 1988). Nevertheless, we think that a sperm-activating

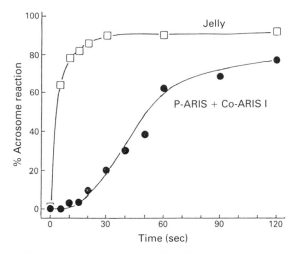

Fig. 3. Reaction rates of the acrosome reaction. Jelly, 40 µg sugar/ml; P-ARIS, 30 µg sugar/ml and Co-ARIS I, 150 µM. (From Hoshi *et al.*, 1988.)

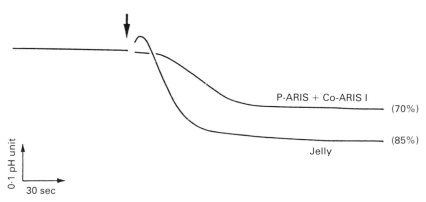

Fig. 4. Changes in sperm pH_i on the acrosome reaction. The arrow indicates the addition of the egg jelly or its components. Figures in parentheses show the percentage of acrosome-reacted spermatozoa. Jelly, 50 µg sugar/ml; P-ARIS, 25 µg sugar/ml and Co-ARIS I, 200 µM. (From Hoshi *et al.*, 1986.)

peptide(s) is significantly involved in the induction of the acrosome reaction under natural conditions as discussed below.

Both ARIS and Co-ARIS act on spermatozoa dose-dependently: the incidence of the acrosome reaction increases sigmoidally as the concentration of ARIS increases. When the concentration of Co-ARIS exceeds the optimum, the activity drops remarkably and reaches zero at concentrations only a few-fold above the optimum (Fig. 2). As the activity drops to zero, Co-ARIS inhibits both the sperm motility and jelly-induced acrosome reaction. At much higher concentrations, it causes the sperm heads to swell and finally destroys them (Nishiyama *et al.*, 1987b), suggesting that, at high concentrations, Co-ARIS is cytolytic for the spermatozoa. The plasma membrane of starfish cells is rather resistant to the cytolytic action of saponins because it contains Δ^7-sterols instead of Δ^5-sterols and an appreciable amount of cholesteryl sulphate (Burnell & ApSimon, 1983). Plant saponins, holothurins, asterosaponins having very different structures from Co-ARIS, deoxycholate and Triton X-100 do not act as a Co-ARIS so far as we have tested (I. Nishiyama & M. Hoshi,

M. Hoshi et al.

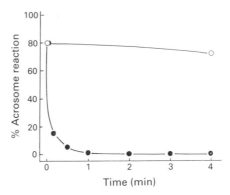

Fig. 5. Effects of the jelly in Ca^{2+}-deficient sea water on the acrosome reaction. Spermatozoa were treated with jelly of 50 μg sugar/ml in Ca^{2+}-deficient sea water for a given period and then Ca^{2+} was added to give a normal concentration of 10 mM (—●—), or the spermatozoa were treated first with Ca^{2+}-deficient sea water, and then sufficient jelly and Ca^{2+} were added to give a concentration of 50 μg sugar/ml and 10 mM, respectively (—○—). Points are means for 2 experiments. (From Matsui *et al.*, 1986b.)

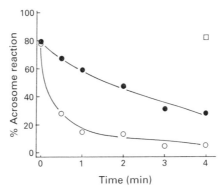

Fig. 6. Acrosome reaction induced by sequential addition of P-ARIS and Fraction M_8. Spermatozoa were incubated with 50 μg sugar P-ARIS/ml and 50 μg Fraction M_8/ml in that (—○—) or the reverse (—●—) order at the intervals indicated. The jelly-induced acrosome reaction is indicated by □. Points are means for 2 experiments. (From Matsui *et al.*, 1986b.)

unpublished data). The activity of Co-ARIS is therefore not simply attributable to the cytolytic action on the plasma membrane.

Physiological importance of sperm-activating peptide

The ability of a jelly solution to induce the acrosome reaction decreases with dilution and reaches zero at about 1 μg sugar/ml. A jelly solution of 0·8 μg sugar/ml remains inactive even after being fortified with ARIS (or P-ARIS) up to 50 μg sugar/ml. When it is fortified with Fraction M_8 to be 20 μg/ml, the ability to induce the acrosome reaction is remarkably increased. This suggests that diffusible components limit the capacity of a jelly preparation (Matsui *et al.*, 1986a). As mentioned earlier, Fraction M_8 is much more effective than a pronase digest of Fraction M_8 or purified Co-ARIS substances as a co-factor for ARIS. In fact, in the presence of a sufficient amount of P-ARIS, 5 μg Fraction M_8/ml, 90 μg Co-ARIS I/ml or 24 μg Co-ARIS II/ml was required for 50%

induction of the acrosome reaction (unpublished data). Furthermore, the amount of P-ARIS required for full induction of the acrosome reaction decreases appreciably if Fraction M_8 is substituted for pure Co-ARIS substances (Matsui *et al.*, 1986b, c; Nishiyama *et al.*, 1987b). Combinations of P-ARIS with Fraction M_8, but not with Co-ARIS, perfectly mimic the jelly in the manner and way of inducing the acrosome reaction (Hoshi *et al.*, 1988).

Although ARIS and Co-ARIS are enough to induce the acrosome reaction in normal sea water, these data suggest that, besides them, sperm-activating peptides play an important role in the physiological induction of the acrosome reaction (Hoshi *et al.*, 1986, 1988). It has been confirmed for a sea urchin that SAP I is indeed involved in the acrosome reaction (Yamaguchi *et al.*, 1989).

Incomplete stimulation of spermatozoa

Once spermatozoa have been treated with insufficient amounts of jelly for inducing the acrosome reaction in normal sea water, or conversely with sufficient amounts of jelly in Ca^{2+}-deficient sea water, for less than 1 min (Figs 5 & 6), they do not undergo the acrosome reaction or the changes in cytoplasmic cations even after the jelly or Ca^{2+} or both are sufficiently fortified. Furthermore, they seem to lose also their ability to react to the jelly coat *in situ*. Similarly, if they are treated with P-ARIS (ARIS) and Fraction M_8 not simultaneously but sequentially, in either order with an interval over minutes, they do not undergo the acrosome reaction and become unresponsive to the jelly. Such effects of 'pretreatment' are found with ARIS, P-ARIS and Fraction M_8, but not with Co-ARIS or with pronase-digested Fraction M_8, suggesting that ARIS as well as an oligopeptide(s), presumably sperm-activating peptide, has the ability to make spermatozoa unresponsive to the jelly (Matsui *et al.*, 1986b). This effect of Fraction M_8 is not attributable to its ability to raise the pH_i, because spermatozoa are still responsive to the jelly even after they are treated with alkaline sea water which increases pH_i significantly.

It is, however, possible to induce the acrosome reaction by increasing intracellular Ca^{2+} (Ca^{2+}_i) and pH_i in those spermatozoa that have become unresponsive to the jelly: they undergo the acrosome reaction like intact ones in response to a calcium ionophore, A23187, plus monensin (Matsui *et al.*, 1986b) and to a Ca^{2+} channel activator, maitotoxin, plus Fraction M_8 or alkaline sea water (Nishiyama *et al.*, 1986; T. Okita, T. Amano & M. Hoshi, unpublished data). The acrosome reaction induced by maitotoxin in combination with Fraction M_8 or alkaline sea water was also susceptible to verapamil. These data suggest that the pretreatment effects are due to an irreversible change(s) in the steps not later than the stimulation of Ca^{2+} channels and Na^+/H^+ exchangers. It is also suggested that verapamil and maitotoxin act on the same channel. This capacity of P-ARIS to render spermatozoa unresponsive to the jelly is species-specific and depends mainly upon the saccharide and sulphate moieties just like its capacity to induce the acrosome reaction in the presence of Co-ARIS, at high Ca^{2+} or at high pH (Matsui *et al.*, 1986b). It seems therefore that the two apparently different effects of ARIS upon spermatozoa actually result from a single action of ARIS. This may also be true for the effects of sperm-activating peptide.

Proposed mechanism of the induction of the acrosome reaction

ARIS, Co-ARIS and sperm-activating peptide are believed to bind to and/or to be adsorbed by the spermatozoa (Matsui *et al.*, 1986b). Whereas it seems natural to assume specific receptors in the sperm plasma membrane for ARIS and sperm-activating peptide, it is more reasonable not to assume such receptors for Co-ARIS substances. Instead, Co-ARIS substances may infiltrate or be inserted into the sperm plasma membrane, because they are saponins exerting cytolytic effects on spermatozoa at high concentrations and because steroidal side chains contribute to their activity much more than saccharide chains (Nishiyama *et al.*, 1987b). It is also consistent with this assumption that ARIS and presumably sperm-activating peptide, but not Co-ARIS substances, show pretreatment effects. Our preliminary data suggesting that Co-ARIS increases the specific binding of P-ARIS to the spermatozoa (K. Kontani, K. Chiba & M. Hoshi, unpublished data) favour such an idea.

Taking account of these results together with the data presented in the preceding sections, we propose that the binding of ARIS to its receptor stimulates verapamil- and maitotoxin-sensitive Ca^{2+} channels and thus increases the Ca^{2+}_i. (This does not exclude a possibility that the receptor is the channel itself.) Co-ARIS may contribute to the Ca^{2+}_i increase by modulating the binding of ARIS and/or the succeeding activation of the channel. On the other hand, sperm-activating peptide stimulates Na^+/H^+ exchange systems and thus increases the pH_i. Sperm-activating peptide may also contribute to some extent in increasing the Ca^{2+}_i (Schackmann & Chock, 1986). It is also our guess at the moment that the pretreatment with ARIS mainly affects the coupling or signal transduction between the binding of ARIS and the activation of Ca^{2+}. Treatments with sperm-activating peptide only may affect that step and/or ARIS-binding itself, which is not a direct result of raising the pH_i.

Upon encountering the jelly coat of an homologous egg, starfish spermatozoa rapidly undergo the acrosome reaction as a result of concomitant increases in Ca^{2+}_i and pH_i which are triggered in concert by the three components in the jelly; i.e. ARIS, Co-ARIS and sperm-activating peptide.

This work was supported in part by grants from the Ministry of Education, Science and Culture of Japan, the Naito Foundation, Yamada Science Foundation, the Foundation for the Promotion of Research on Medical Resources, and the Institute of Developmental and Reproductive Biology in Yamagata.

References

Burnell, D.J. & ApSimon, J.W. (1983) Echinoderm saponins. In *Marine Natural Products, Chemical and Biological Perspectives*, vol. 5, pp. 287–389. Ed. P. J. Scheuer. Academic Press, New York.

Dale, B., Dan-Sohkawa, M., De Santis, A. & Hoshi, M. (1981) Fertilization of the starfish *Astropecten aurantiacus*. *Expl Cell Res.* **132**, 505–510.

Dan, J.C. (1967) Acrosome reaction and lysins. In *Fertilization*, vol. 1, pp. 237–293. Eds C. B. Metz & A. Monroy. Academic Press, New York.

Endo, T., Hoshi, M., Endo, S., Arata, Y. & Kobata, A. (1987) Structures of the sugar chains of a major glycoprotein present in the egg jelly coat of a starfish. *Asterias amurensis*. *Archs Biochem. Biophys.* **252**, 105–112.

Fujimoto, Y., Yamada, T., Ikekawa, N., Nishiyama, I., Matsui, T. & Hoshi, M. (1987) Structure of acrosome reaction-inducing steroidal saponins from the egg jelly of the starfish. *Asterias amurensis*. *Chem. Pharm. Bull.* **35**, 1829–1832.

Hoshi, M., Matsui, T., Nishiyama, I., Fujimoto, Y. & Ikekawa, N. (1986) Egg-jelly components responsible for the induction of acrosome reaction. In *Advances in Invertebrate Reproduction*, vol. 4, pp. 275–282. Eds M. Porchet, J.-C. Andries & A. Dhainaut. Elsevier Science Publishers, Amsterdam.

Hoshi, M., Matsui, T., Nishiyama, I., Amano, T. & Okita, Y. (1988) Physiological inducers of the acrosome reaction. In *Regulatory Mechanisms in Developmental Processes*, pp. 19–24. Eds G. Eguchi, T. S. Okada & L. Saxen. Elsevier Scientific Publishers, Dublin.

Ikadai, H. & Hoshi, M. (1981a) Biochemical studies on the acrosome reaction of the starfish, *Asterias amurensis*. I. Factors participating in the acrosome reaction. *Dev. Growth, Differ.* **23**, 73–80.

Ikadai, H. & Hoshi, M. (1981b) Biochemical studies on the acrosome reaction of the starfish, *Asterias amurensis*. II. Purification and characterization of acrosome reaction-inducing substance. *Dev. Growth, Differ.* **23**, 81–88.

Matsui, T., Nishiyama, I., Hino, A. & Hoshi, M. (1986a) Induction of the acrosome reaction in starfish. *Dev. Growth, Differ.* **28**, 339–348.

Matsui, T., Nishiyama, I., Hino, A. & Hoshi, M. (1986b) Acrosome reaction-inducing substance purified from the egg jelly inhibits the jelly-induced acrosome reaction in starfish: an apparent contradiction. *Dev. Growth, Differ.* **28**, 349–357.

Matsui, T., Nishiyama, I., Hino, A. & Hoshi, M. (1986c) Intracellular pH changes of starfish sperm upon the acrosome reaction. *Dev. Growth, Differ.* **28**, 359–368.

Nishiyama, I., Matsui, T., Yasumoto, T., Oshio, S. & Hoshi, M. (1986) Maitotoxin, a presumed calcium channel activator, induces the acrosome reaction in mussel spermatozoa. *Dev. Growth, Differ.* **28**, 443–448.

Nishiyama, I., Matsui, T. & Hoshi, M. (1987a) Purification of Co-ARIS, a cofactor for acrosome reaction-inducing substance, from the egg jelly of starfish. *Dev. Growth, Differ.* **29**, 161–169.

Nishiyama, I., Matsui, T., Fujimoto, Y., Ikekawa, N. & Hoshi, M. (1987b) Correlation between the molecular structure and the biological activity of Co-ARIS, a cofactor for acrosome reaction-inducing substance. *Dev. Growth, Differ.* **29**, 171–176.

Schackmann, R.W. & Chock, P.B. (1986) Alteration of intracellular $[Ca^{2+}]$ in sea urchin sperm by the egg peptide speract. *J. biol. Chem.* **261**, 8719–8728.

Schackmann, R.W. & Shapiro, B.M. (1981) A partial sequence of ionic changes associated with the acrosome reaction of *Strongylocentrotus purpuratus*. *Devl Biol.* **81**, 145–154.

Suzuki, N. (1989) Sperm activating peptides from sea urchin eggs. In *Bioorganic Marine Chemistry*, vol. 3, pp. 47–70. Ed. P. J. Scheuer. Springer Verlag, Berlin.

Tilney, L.G. (1985) The acrosome reaction. In *Biology of Fertilization*, vol. 2, pp. 157–213. Eds C. B. Metz & A. Monroy. Academic Press, Orlando.

Uno, Y. & Hoshi, M. (1978) Separation of the sperm agglutinin and the acrosome reaction-inducing substance in egg jelly of starfish. *Science, NY* **200**, 58–59.

Yamaguchi, M., Kurita, M. & Suzuki, N. (1989) Induction of the acrosome reaction of *Hemicentrotus pulcherrimus* spermatozoa by the egg jelly molecules, fucose-rich glycoconjugate and sperm-activating peptide I. *Dev. Growth, Differ.* **31**, 233–239.

J. Reprod. Fert., Suppl. **42** (1990), 33–49

Zona pellucida-mediated signal transduction in mammalian spermatozoa

G. S. Kopf

Division of Reproductive Biology, Department of Obstetrics and Gynecology, University of Pennsylvania School of Medicine, Philadelphia, Pennsylvania 19104-6080, USA

Keywords: spermatozoa; signal transduction; zona pellucida; acrosome reaction; mammal

Introduction

Aside from its importance in understanding the process of fertilization, studies of sperm–egg interaction both before and after gamete fusion provide an elegant model with which to elucidate general mechanisms of intercellular communication and cellular activation. Sperm–egg interaction in invertebrate and vertebrate species consists of a series of highly orchestrated and regulated events that initially involve an egg-induced activation of the spermatozoon and ultimately result in a sperm-induced activation of the egg. Both of these activation events are regulated in a manner similar to the way somatic cell function is regulated by hormones, neurotransmitters and growth factors, i.e. through ligand–receptor–second messenger systems. Sperm functions such as motility, metabolism, capacitation (in mammals) and the acrosome reaction are modulated by factors associated with the egg, its acellular or cellular investments, or fluids bathing both the male and female reproductive tracts. In some species the identity, structure and function of these factors are known, and their mode of action is starting to be elucidated. Likewise, sperm–egg fusion results in the awakening of a metabolically and synthetically quiescent egg, thereby initiating a series of events that ultimately allows the fertilized egg to embark on an active mitotic cycle with the subsequent development of the preimplantation embryo. Although details of this sperm-induced egg activation process are only starting to be understood it appears that elements of this process may also occur through signal transduction pathways heretofore described in somatic cells.

We are interested in the biochemical events that mediate egg-induced sperm activation and sperm-induced egg activation in the mammal, with the aim of elucidation of the molecular basis of intercellular communication and signal transduction between these two gametes before, during, and after fertilization. In this paper I shall discuss experiments which focus on the molecular basis of sperm–zona pellucida interaction and induction of an exocytotic event in spermatozoa, the acrosome reaction. Although our experimental model system is the mouse and most of the discussion will focus on this particular model, other species will also be considered in the context of the discussion.

Necessity for ligand–receptor–effector systems in mammalian spermatozoa

In the mammal, sperm–female reproductive tract interaction and sperm–egg interaction before sperm–egg fusion occurs at different levels *in vivo* and is the culmination of a number of integrated processes designed to deliver the most viable, functionally active spermatozoa to the site of fertilization, e.g. the ampullary region of the oviduct. As spermatozoa traverse the female reproductive tract, there are species-specific selection processes that limit the delivery of these cells to the site of fertilization. These processes can be considered anatomical, as well as environmental, and may include cervical and/or uterotubal junction–sperm interactions, cervical mucus–sperm interactions, reproductive tract pH, circulating anti-sperm antibodies, the ability of the spermatozoa to undergo capacitation, and the acrosome reaction itself (see Kopf & Gerton, 1990). Spermatozoa arriving at the ampullary region of the oviduct encounter additional selection processes in the form of cellular investments (i.e. cumulus oophorus and corona radiata) and extracellular matrices (i.e. cumulus cell matrix glycosaminoglycans, zona pellucida). Although the presence of the cumulus oophorus throughout the fertilizable lifespan of an ovulated mammalian egg *in vivo* is species-dependent, the presence of the zona pellucida during this time period is universal. The aforementioned selection processes may serve, therefore, to ensure that sperm–egg interaction occurs between gametes that are most competent to fuse in a successful manner. Cellular selection, which is an important general biological phenomenon, is particularly important in fertilization since spermatozoa represent a heterogeneous cell population with regard to cellular age, morphology, motility characteristics, and ability to undergo capacitation. Heterogeneity of the sperm population at the biochemical level, reflected in differences in membrane characteristics and ability to respond to external stimuli, is also likely to exist.

As a consequence of these aforementioned selection pressures the number of spermatozoa arriving at the site of fertilization *in vivo* is extremely low. Studies by a number of investigators have concluded that the sperm–egg ratio at the site of fertilization is of the order of 1:1–100:1 (Kopf & Gerton, 1990). Since these spermatozoa most probably represent the most viable portion of the cell population, one would presume that subsequent cellular recognition and interaction (i.e. species-specific sperm–egg binding), as well as gamete activation (i.e. induction of acrosomal exocytosis) would involve unique, biologically potent molecules associated with both the spermatozoon and the egg. Furthermore, the egg-associated ligand(s) that would modulate sperm function would be expected to act at a short range. It is clear that the zona pellucida plays a critical role in mediating initial sperm–egg interactions proper and in many species it also mediates acrosomal exocytosis (for an in-depth review of this subject see Wassarman, 1988; Kopf & Gerton, 1990). Since fertilization is a classical example of cell–cell interaction, it might be expected that these interactions would be mediated by specific ligand–receptor interactions which ultimately modulate cellular function through receptor-coupled intracellular effectors, i.e. second messengers. The mouse is an ideal model system with which to study mammalian sperm signal transduction since it is clear that the zona pellucida mediates both sperm binding to the egg and acrosomal exocytosis (Wassarman, 1987). It is now possible to isolate large quantities of zona pellucida glycoproteins and to examine the effects of the purified components of this extracellular matrix on specific sperm functions.

Structure of the mouse egg zona pellucida and its function as a ligand regulating sperm function

Species-specific sperm–egg recognition and interaction, sperm activation (i.e. acrosomal exocytosis), and an egg-induced block to polyspermy in the mouse all appear to be mediated by the extracellular matrix surrounding the egg called the zona pellucida (Wassarman, 1987, 1988). The zona pellucida of the mouse egg is composed of three sulphated glycoproteins designated as ZP1, ZP2 and ZP3, and is truly an egg-associated product since it is synthesized and secreted throughout the period of oocyte growth (Bleil & Wassarman, 1980a, b; Shimizu *et al.*, 1983). Each of these glycoproteins has specific functions. ZP1 ($M_r = 200\,000$) is a dimer connected by intermolecular disulphide bonds and appears to function to maintain the three dimensional structure of the zona pellucida by cross-linking filaments composed of repeating structures of ZP2/ZP3 heterodimers. ZP2 ($M_r = 120\,000$ under non-reducing and reducing conditions) may mediate the binding of acrosome-reacted spermatozoa to the zona pellucida (Bleil *et al.*, 1988; Wassarman, 1988). Upon fertilization, the egg effects a modification of ZP2 to a form called ZP2$_f$ (Wassarman, 1987, 1988) which is brought about by the action of a protease most probably secreted from the egg as a consequence of cortical granule exocytosis (Moller & Wassarman, 1989). ZP2$_f$ has an $M_r = 120\,000$ under non-reducing conditions, which shifts under reducing conditions to $M_r = 90\,000$, suggesting that the proteolysis of the ZP2 molecule results in the generation of fragments that are held together by disulphide bonds. The biological consequence of the conversion of ZP2 to $ZP2_f$ is that $ZP2_f$ no longer will bind to acrosome-reacted spermatozoa (Bleil *et al.*, 1988). ZP3 ($M_r = 83\,000$) accounts for both the sperm-binding and the acrosome reaction-inducing activities of the zona pellucida of unfertilized eggs (Wassarman, 1987, 1988). The sperm-binding activity appears to be conferred by O-linked carbohydrate moieties and not by its polypeptide chain (Florman *et al.*, 1984; Florman & Wassarman, 1985). Alpha-linked terminal galactose residues at the non-reducing termini of these O-linked oligosaccharide chains play a critical role in this binding activity (Bleil & Wassarman, 1988). The acrosome reaction-inducing activity of ZP3, in contrast, appears to be conferred by both the carbohydrate and protein portions of the molecule, although the exact nature of the interaction between the protein and carbohydrate required for biological activity is not clear at this time (Florman *et al.*, 1984). Fertilization is associated with a loss of both the sperm-binding and acrosome reaction-inducing activities of the ZP3 molecule (Wassarman, 1987, 1988). The loss of these two important biological activities is associated with a minor biochemical modification of the ZP3 molecule since the electrophoretic mobility of ZP3 from fertilized eggs is similar to that of ZP3 from unfertilized eggs.

The properties of ZP1, ZP2 and ZP3 from unfertilized and fertilized eggs provide a framework with which to formulate a model to explain the interaction of spermatozoa with this specialized extracellular matrix. Since only acrosome-intact mouse spermatozoa bind to the zona pellucida (Saling *et al.*, 1979), one would propose the existence of a specific receptor(s) for ZP3 on the plasma membrane overlying the sperm acrosome which mediates sperm binding and the induction of acrosomal exocytosis. Since acrosome-reacted spermatozoa do not interact with ZP3, secondary interactions of these spermatozoa with the zona pellucida would then occur through the interaction of a putative receptor(s) for ZP2 on the sperm inner acrosomal membrane. Upon penetration of the zona pellucida by acrosome-reacted spermatozoa, these cells traverse the perivitelline space and then bind and fuse with the plasma membrane of the egg. After sperm–egg fusion, the egg undergoes the cortical granule reaction, which results in the release of cortical granule-associated enzymes (Wassarman, 1987). These enzymes convert ZP2 to $ZP2_f$ and modify ZP3, such that acrosome-intact spermatozoa no longer bind to the zona pellucida (via ZP3) and acrosome-reacted spermatozoa that are bound to the zona pellucida (via ZP2) no longer interact and penetrate the zona pellucida since they are unable to establish secondary binding interactions with $ZP2_f$. Such egg-induced modifications of this extracellular matrix constitute the zona pellucida block to polyspermy. Inherent in such a model is the highly specific and co-ordinated nature of the interactions of acrosome-intact and acrosome-reacted spermatozoa with ZP3 and ZP2, respectively. Such interactions would presumably be mediated via specific sperm-associated receptors for these extracellular matrix glycoproteins.

There are several lines of evidence which support the idea that sperm–zona pellucida interaction in the mouse may occur through specific receptor-mediated events. For example, ZP3 possesses a number of properties which make it ideally suited as a ligand to mediate the initial steps of sperm–egg interaction proper (e.g. sperm binding) and subsequent sperm activation (e.g. induction of the acrosome reaction). Although conserved at the genomic level in a variety of species (Ringuette *et al.*, 1988), ZP3 subserves very specific functions as a component of the egg-associated extracellular matrix (Wassarman, 1987, 1988). (1) ZP3 is synthesized only by the growing oocyte. (2) There is little apparent amino acid sequence homology between ZP3 and any other known proteins or glycoproteins so far examined (Ringuette *et al.*, 1988). (3) The crosslinking of ZP2/ZP3 hetero-dimers by ZP1 in an orderly fashion gives rise to structural domains that ensure that the ZP3 ligand is immobilized and can therefore only act at short distances. (4) Both the sperm-binding and acrosome reaction-inducing activities of ZP3 are observed in the nanomolar range (Florman & Wassarman, 1985; Bleil & Wassarman, 1986). (5) Mouse spermatozoa appear to possess comple-mentary binding sites (receptors?) for ZP3 that are localized over the acrosomal cap region and are present in numbers (10 000–50 000 binding sites/cell) similar to those of receptors in many hormonally responsive cells (Bleil & Wassarman, 1986). (6) ZP3 covalently bound to silica beads specifically binds to acrosome-intact spermatozoa via the sperm head (Vazquez *et al.*, 1989), further supporting the idea that the sperm-associated ZP3 binding moiety(ies) is associated with the plasma membrane overlying the acrosomal region. In addition, specific binding of ^{125}I-labelled ZP2 to the inner acrosomal membrane of acrosome-reacted, but not acrosome-intact, mouse spermatozoa has been demonstrated (Wassarman, 1987; Bleil *et al.*, 1988), suggesting that this particular membrane may possess specific receptors for this zona pellucida glycoprotein.

Evidence for receptor-mediated regulation of sperm function

Presently, sea urchin spermatozoa remain the only experimental system in which receptor-mediated sperm signal transduction has been unequivocally demonstrated (Garbers, 1989a). In this system peptides associated with the jelly coat of the sea urchin egg (resact, speract) interact with specific cell-surface receptors in a species-specific manner to elevate sperm cGMP concentrations (Hansbrough & Garbers, 1981; Suzuki *et al.*, 1981; Dangott & Garbers, 1984). The receptor for these peptides appears to be identical with or closely associated with the membrane-bound enzyme guanylate cyclase (Shimomura *et al.*, 1986; Bentley *et al.*, 1988). Peptide–receptor interaction has been demonstrated to result in sperm chemotaxis, as well as changes in motility and metabolism (Garbers, 1989a). Spermatozoa therefore respond to external stimuli in their environment through receptor-mediated processes coupled to intracellular effector systems. The membrane-bound form of guanylate cyclase also appears to be the cell surface receptor for atrial natriuretic factor (ANF) in specific mammalian tissues (Garbers, 1989b). The conservation of receptor function of an enzyme from both an invertebrate germ cell and mammalian somatic cells is notable, and is even more interesting in light of recent observations that both of these enzymes have considerable sequence homology to one another and also belong to the superfamily of protein kinases (Garbers, 1989b), members of which include cell surface receptors for growth factors (Yarden & Ullrich, 1988).

Studies directed at determining the nature of specific receptors on the mammalian sperm surface for egg-associated factors are only starting to yield potentially important information. Most of this work has been carried out using the mouse as the experimental prototype. Although ZP2 and ZP3 possess properties of ligands which modulate specific cellular functions, little is known about the biochemical nature of 'putative' complementary receptors on the sperm surface for these ligands. Several investigators have attempted to define such sperm-associated binding sites for the zona pellucida indirectly by examining whether specific agents interfere with sperm–zona pellucida interaction. Sperm surface-associated protease inhibitor-sensitive sites (Saling, 1981; Aarons *et al.*, 1984; Benau & Storey, 1987), galactosyltransferase activity (Shur & Hall, 1982a, b; Lopez *et al.*, 1985), and fucosyltransferase activity (Apter *et al.*, 1988) have all been postulated to participate in the binding of spermatozoa to the zona pellucida, presumably through ZP3. Interpretation of such experiments with regard to the identity of sperm-associated receptors for the zona pellucida (or more specifically, ZP3) is limited since they represent indirect approaches to the identification of putative receptors.

More direct approaches have also been taken to identify such sperm-associated receptors. Bleil & Wassarman (1986) utilized whole mount autoradiography to examine the binding of ^{125}I-labelled ZP3 to mouse spermatozoa under various conditions: binding appeared to be solely associated with the plasma membrane overlying the acrosomal region and was not observed on acrosome-reacted spermatozoa. Binding of the radiolabelled ligand could be blocked by unlabelled ZP3 but not ZP2, and ZP3 binding did not occur on somatic cells. Although the use of whole-mount autoradiography has limitations with regard to characterization of the moiety(ies) involved in ZP3 binding to spermatozoa these results suggest that a specific sperm-associated binding site(s) for this ligand exists. Leyton & Saling (1989a) demonstrated that polyclonal anti-phosphotyrosine antibodies react with mouse sperm plasma membrane proteins of $M_r = 52\,000$, $75\,000$ and $95\,000$. Indirect immunofluorescence using this antibody demonstrates that positive immunoreactivity is localized to the acrosomal region of the sperm head. ZP3 binds, on nitrocellulose blots, to the $M_r = 95\,000$ protein and these workers infer that the $M_r = 95\,000$ protein which binds ZP3 also reacts with the anti-phosphotyrosine antibodies. Although these investigators suggest that the $M_r = 95\,000$ protein may be a receptor for ZP3 which acts either as a substrate for tyrosine phosphorylation or possesses tyrosine kinase activity itself, they provide little evidence for binding specificity in these studies. Clearly, additional studies will be necessary to establish whether this protein is a specific ZP3 receptor. However, these results are interesting in light of the fact that some somatic cell receptors possess intrinsic protein kinase activity (Yarden & Ullrich, 1988). Bleil & Wassarman (1989) demonstrated that purified ZP3 or glycopeptides of ZP3 possessing sperm binding activity can be specifically crosslinked to a $M_r = 56\,000$ protein of acrosome-intact mouse spermatozoa. This protein interacts specifically with ZP3, but not ZP2, affinity columns. The $M_r = 56\,000$ protein also interacts specifically with galactose affinity columns, but not with N-acetylglucosamine affinity columns. Whole-mount autoradiography using radiolabelled, cross-linked ZP3 glycopeptides which possess sperm binding activity demonstrates a localization to the head region of acrosome-intact spermatozoa. This experimental approach provides, to date, the most promise with regard to establishing the biochemical identity of such sperm-associated receptors for zona pellucida glycoproteins.

Nature of the interaction between zona pellucida ligands and the sperm surface

As described above, little is known about the molecular nature of the ligands associated with ZP2 and ZP3, as well as their complementary binding sites on the sperm surface, which mediate sperm binding (of acrosome-intact and acrosome-reacted spermatozoa) and acrosomal exocytosis. It would seem premature, therefore, to discuss the nature of such interactions. However, recent data have emerged from a few laboratories, including our own, that might reveal information as to the type of interactions which may occur between ZP3 and the mouse sperm surface to mediate these important pre-fertilization sperm–egg interactions. These studies have evolved from the observations that ZP3 has dual functions in initial sperm–egg interaction, e.g. it is responsible both for the binding of acrosome-intact spermatozoa and for initiating acrosomal exocytosis.

Dissociation of events mediating sperm–ZP3 binding and ZP3-induced acrosomal exocytosis

Previous investigations have demonstrated that the sperm binding activity and the acrosome reaction-inducing activity of ZP3 can be either partly or completely dissociated from one another by agents that act either at the level of the spermatozoon or at the level of ZP3. When acrosomal exocytosis is blocked, the inhibition by these agents appears to occur at a specific stage of the zona pellucida-induced acrosome reaction. In these particular experiments the acrosomal status of mouse spermatozoa was monitored using the fluorescent probe chlortetracycline (CTC) (Saling & Storey, 1979; Ward & Storey, 1984; Lee & Storey, 1985). CTC is fluorescent when present in a hydrophobic environment and complexed with calcium, and mouse spermatozoa treated with CTC exhibit characteristic patterns of fluorescence that have been correlated with different stages leading to the completion of the acrosome reaction. Capacitated, acrosome-intact spermatozoa display a characteristic 'B pattern', which is characterized by bright fluorescence over the anterior portion of the head and midpiece. An 'S pattern', which represents a true intermediate stage that appears before the completion of the acrosome reaction, is characterized by bright fluorescence over the midpiece and punctate fluorescence over the anterior portion of the head. The appearance of this pattern correlates with the loss of a transmembrane pH gradient (Lee & Storey, 1985; Endo *et al.*, 1988). An 'AR pattern' is characteristic of spermatozoa that have completed the acrosome reaction and is characterized by a lack of fluorescence over the anterior portion of the sperm head. The B and AR patterns have been characterized as acrosome-intact and acrosome reacted, respectively, by electron microscopy (Saling *et al.*, 1979; Florman & Storey, 1982a). The zona pellucida-induced acrosome reaction in mouse spermatozoa, as monitored by the CTC assay, therefore consists of B to S and S to AR transitions which may be independently regulated (Lee *et al.*, 1987).

3-Quinuclidinyl benzilate (QNB), a classical muscarinic-cholinergic antagonist, has been shown to bind to a single class of high-affinity sites on mouse spermatozoa and to inhibit the zona pellucida-induced acrosome reaction without affecting the ability of the spermatozoon to bind to the zona pellucida (Florman & Storey, 1981, 1982a, b). Spermatozoa incubated with QNB are inhibited from undergoing a B to S transition in response to either solubilized zonae pellucidae or purified ZP3 (Lee & Storey, 1985; Endo *et al.*. 1988). Although specific binding of this antagonist to spermatozoa can be demonstrated, the characteristics of this binding are different from the binding characteristics of a classical muscarinic-cholinergic receptor, and the molecular nature of this sperm-associated site has yet to be determined. M-42, a monoclonal antibody against a sperm protein of $M_r = 200\,000/220\,000$, represents a second reagent that has been demonstrated to inhibit the zona pellucida-induced acrosome reaction without affecting sperm binding to this extra-cellular matrix (Leyton *et al.*, 1989). The inhibitory effect of this antibody is at the B to S transition, does not block more distal events leading to acrosomal exocytosis (e.g. S to AR transitions), and is observed with solubilized zonae pellucidae as well as purified ŻP3. Pertussis toxin represents a third agent that, when added to capacitated mouse spermatozoa inhibits specifically the B to S transition induced by structurally-intact zonae pellucidae, solubilized zonae pellucidae, or purified ZP3 with-out affecting sperm binding (Endo *et al.*, 1987b, 1988). This bacterial toxin has been demonstrated to inactivate functionally a number of guanine nucleotide binding regulatory proteins (G proteins) by its ability to catalyse the ADP-ribosylation of the α subunit of these proteins and is thought to inactivate the G_i-like protein present in mouse spermatozoa (Kopf *et al.*, 1986; see also below). All of these agents, when added to spermatozoa, inhibit a specific stage(s) of the acrosome reaction induced solely by the zona pellucida (or ZP3) without affecting reactions involved in sperm–zona pellucida binding (mediated by ZP3). Furthermore, incubation of mouse spermatozoa with either biologically active phorbol diesters or diacylglycerols, which are activators of the Ca^{2+} and phospholipid-dependent protein kinase (protein kinase C; PK-C), in the presence of zonae pellucidae accelerates the B to S transition, but inhibits the S to AR transition, suggesting that these two transitions can be independently regulated (Lee *et al.*, 1987). These PK-C activators do not affect the ability of spermatozoa to bind to the zona pellucida and, therefore, can affect the different stages of the acrosome reaction without affecting reactions involved in zona pellucida binding.

Biologically active phorbol diesters and diacylglycerols also effect egg-induced dissociations of the two biological activities of ZP3, and these observations have likewise provided insight to the nature of sperm–ZP3 interaction. These agents, when added to zona pellucida-intact mouse eggs, cause egg-induced modifications of ZP2 to $ZP2_f$ and a modification of ZP3, such that the sperm-binding activity of ZP3 is completely retained and the acrosome reaction-inducing component of ZP3 is partly modified (Endo *et al.*, 1987a, c). Spermatozoa incubated with solubilized zonae pellucidae or purified ZP3 from these treated eggs bind normally and undergo the B to S transition with normal kinetics, but are inhibited from completing the acrosome reaction as a consequence of their inability to undergo an S to AR transition. Spermatozoa suspended in the intermediate S pattern are not irreversibly stuck in this pattern since solubilized zonae pellucidae from untreated eggs (but not treated or fertilized eggs) can bring about an S to AR transition (Kligman *et al.*, 1988; Leyton *et al.*, 1989).

These observations, taken together, demonstrate that: (1) sperm binding to the zona pellucida and the zona pellucida-induced acrosome reaction are two independent processes, and (2) the zona pellucida-induced acrosome reaction in the mouse may consist of discrete, independently regulated events, as monitored by the CTC assay. The reaction(s) comprising these different events (i.e. comprising the B to S and S to AR transitions) can be inhibited by a number of agents in a very specific manner. The concept that this exocytotic process proceeds in discrete steps is consistent with known regulatory events comprising exocytotic reactions in other cells (Gomperts & Tatham, 1988).

The interaction of ZP3 with the sperm surface may involve multivalent interactions

Insight into the nature of the interaction of ZP3 with the sperm surface to modulate both sperm binding and the induction of a complete acrosome reaction can be inferred when attempting to explain the effects of PK-C activators on egg-induced modifications of ZP3. Since preliminary experiments indicate that treatment of eggs with PK-C activators results in a partial reduction of cortical granules (T. Ducibella, G. S. Kopf & R. M. Schultz, unpublished observations), it is reasonable to assume that these agents are acting to stimulate cortical granule exocytosis. A model has been proposed to explain the results of these PK-C activators (Kopf *et al.*, 1989), and takes into account the properties of sperm binding and the induction of the acrosome reaction observed with various concentrations of solubilized zonae pellucidae or purified ZP3 (Bleil & Wassarman, 1983). This model is based on the fact that multiple interactions between ZP3 molecules and sperm surface sites may be required *in toto* for binding and the induction of the acrosome reaction. This model also proposes that there are differences in the concentration dependence of ZP3 to express sperm binding activity and acrosome reaction-inducing activity. Specifically, the concentration response curve for ZP3 acrosome reaction-inducing activity is shifted to the right of the concentration response curve for ZP3 sperm-binding activity. Finally, this model predicts that ZP3 is composed of multiple 'functional ligands', and that the interaction of these ligands with the sperm surface is responsible for both the sperm binding activity and the ability to induce a complete acrosome reaction. These functional ligands do not necessarily have to be identical. Successful sperm binding to ZP3 requires the interaction with a single ligand of the ZP3 molecule, and this accounts for the concentration-dependence relationship of ZP3 to effect sperm binding that is described by a hyperbolic function (Bleil & Wassarman, 1983). Such a hyperbolic function is suggestive of single-site interactions between the sperm surface and ZP3 to mediate sperm binding. Once this interaction to mediate binding has occurred interactions of the spermatozoa with multiple ligands of the ZP3 molecule are required to induce a complete acrosome reaction. This is consistent with the observation that the concentration dependence of ZP3 to induce acrosomal exocytosis is described by a sigmoidal function (Bleil & Wassarman, 1983). Such a function is suggestive of co-operative or multi-site interactions between the sperm surface and ZP3 to mediate the complete acrosome reaction. Fertilization normally results in a modification or inactivation of a majority (or all) of the ligands associated with the ZP3 molecule and hence the loss of both biological activities. In contrast, the partial release of cortical granules that is stimulated by PK-C activators results in a submaximal modification of these ligands. Consequently, ZP3 still possesses sperm binding activity, but the suboptimal numbers of active ligands remaining are not sufficient to permit the multiple interactions with the sperm surface necessary to induce a complete acrosome reaction. As a result, spermatozoa initiate (B to S transition) but do not complete the acrosome reaction because they remain arrested at the S pattern. This partial inhibition can be relieved when zonae pellucidae (or ZP3) which contain a sufficient number of active ligands (e.g. from unfertilized eggs) are now added to the spermatozoa arrested at the S pattern (Kligman *et al.*, 1988; Leyton *et al.*, 1989). Induction of the complete acrosome reaction, therefore, may involve multiple interactions between sperm-associated ZP3 binding components and the ZP3 molecule.

Such interactions have also been proposed by using a different experimental approach (Leyton & Saling, 1989b). Using monospecific polyclonal antibodies to ZP2 and ZP3 it was suggested that the aggregation of sperm-associated receptors for ZP3 may play a role in the ZP3-induced acrosome reaction. Briefly, ZP3 glycopeptides, which possess sperm binding activity but do not possess the ability to induce an acrosome reaction when added to spermatozoa alone, bring about an acrosome reaction when incubated with spermatozoa in the presence of anti-ZP3 IgG. This effect is not observed with anti-ZP2 IgG or with monovalent anti-ZP3 Fab fragments. However, if spermatozoa are incubated with ZP3 glycopeptides and anti-ZP3 Fab fragments in the presence of an anti-IgG, the ability of the spermatozoa to undergo acrosome reactions is restored. Although the addition of anti-ZP3 IgG to capacitated B pattern spermatozoa does not induce an acrosome reaction, the addition of this antibody to spermatozoa that are suspended in the S pattern (obtained by incubation of spermatozoa with zonae pellucidae from phorbol diester-treated eggs) brings about this exocytotic event. These investigators concluded that the aggregation of sperm-associated receptors for ZP3, which were recognized by the ZP3 glycopeptides or by zonae pellucidae from phorbol diester-treated eggs and then crosslinked by the addition of the anti-ZP3 IgG fraction, is required for the induction of the complete acrosome reaction.

The idea that receptor aggregation is required to elicit ligand-dependent signal transduction and a cellular response is not unique (Yarden & Schlessinger, 1987). Since it has been recently demonstrated that extracellular matrices from a variety of tissues may contain domains that aggregate acetylcholine receptors (Godfrey *et al.*, 1988), it is certainly possible that the zona pellucida, itself an extracellular matrix, also possesses this property. These concepts are summarized in Fig. 1. In this figure the ZP3 ligand involved in sperm binding is shown as being different from those ligands participating in acrosomal exocytosis. This does not necessarily have to be the case but is presented in this manner for clarity.

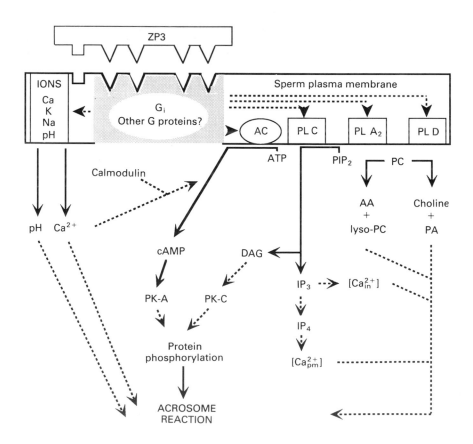

Fig. 1. Hypothetical model of ZP3–receptor–effector interactions leading to acrosomal exocytosis in mouse spermatozoa. Although this model incorporates results obtained from experiments using different species, many of the elements shown in this figure have been taken from observations made using the zona pellucida-induced acrosome reaction of mouse spermatozoa as a model system. In this model, the ZP3 molecule is composed of multiple 'functional ligands' (u, v) which interact with complementary cell surface receptors present in the sperm plasma membrane. These ligands are shown here as being different from one another, but this does not necessarily have to be the case. Successful sperm binding to ZP3 requires the interaction with a single ligand (u). Once this interaction has occurred multiple interactions of the spermatozoa with additional ligands (v) associated with the ZP3 molecule are then required to induce a complete acrosome reaction. The interaction of spermatozoa with ZP3 to promote binding presumably allows for the proper orientation of the ZP3-associated functional ligands and complementary sperm cell surface receptors involved in mediating the acrosome reaction. Four ZP3-associated ligands are shown here which are involved in inducing the acrosome reaction. The actual numbers of ligands involved are not known and are shown in this fashion for illustrative purposes only. Once the proper interaction of these ZP3 ligands with their complementary receptors has been accomplished, signal transduction and second messenger/ion conductance changes occur which ultimately lead to the acrosome reaction (shown in the figure by a change in the shading of the sperm plasma membrane). The interaction of multiple ZP3 ligands to bring about this exocytotic event may be accomplished by some type of functional coupling of the receptors for these different ligands, i.e. perhaps by receptor aggregation.

The signalling systems distal to ZP3–receptor–G protein interactions may be asociated with a number of different regions of the sperm head, including the plasma, outer, and inner acrosomal membranes, as well as the regions confined within these membranes. An acrosomal-associated G_i-like protein (G_i) (or other possible presently unidentified G proteins) functions as a signal transducing element distal to ZP3–receptor interactions, and couples receptor occupancy to changes in ionic conductance and/or a variety of intracellular second messenger cascade systems. These second messenger systems may include the adenylate cyclase (**AC**) system. This enzyme might be regulated by extracellular Ca^{2+}, through the Ca^{2+} binding protein, calmodulin. Alternatively, AC may be regulated by the G_i-like protein in some manner. Generation of cyclic AMP (**cAMP**), with resultant stimulation of a cAMP-dependent protein kinase (**PK-A**), could lead to protein phosphorylation and acrosomal exocytosis. An alternative/additional signalling pathway that may play a role in the induction of the acrosome reaction is through the polyphosphoinositide-specific phospholipase C (**PLC**), which hydrolyses phosphatidylinositol 4,5-bisphosphate (**PIP$_2$**) to form *sn*-1,2-diacylglycerol (**DAG**) and inositol 1,4,5-trisphosphate (**IP$_3$**). IP$_3$ formation may regulate intracellular sperm Ca^{2+} concentrations through effects on intracellular non-mitochondrial Ca^{2+} stores ($[Ca^{2+}_{in}]$) such as the plasma or outer acrosomal membranes. In addition, formation of inositol 1,3,4,5-tetrakisphosphate (**IP$_4$**) by the phosphorylation of IP$_3$ may ultimately regulate sperm Ca^{2+} uptake through effects on plasma membrane channels ($[Ca^{2+}_{pm}]$). Liberated DAG activates a Ca^{2+} and phospholipid-dependent protein kinase (**PK-C**) that then phosphorylates proteins which may ultimately lead to the induction of the acrosome reaction. Hydrolysis of other phospholipids such as phosphatidylcholine (**PC**) may occur through the action of phospholipase A$_2$ (**PLA$_2$**) or phospholipase D (**PLD**), resulting in the generation of either lysophosphatidylcholine (**lyso-PC**) plus arachidonic acid (**AA**) or phosphatidic acid (**PA**) plus choline, respectively. These enzymes have also been proposed to be regulated by G proteins. Membrane-associated lysophospholipids may promote acrosomal exocytosis by virtue of their fusigenic properties. PA may promote the acrosome reaction by virtue of its ability to function as an ionophore. PA formation may also occur through the phosphorylation of DAG. G protein mediated effects on ion conductance might directly or indirectly lead to changes in intracellular pH and/or the regulation of the aforementioned signalling systems. Integration of a number of these signalling systems may be required for the successful induction of acrosomal exocytosis. Solid arrows ($\rightarrow$) indicate pathways that have already been demonstrated to exist in spermatozoa (invertebrate and/or mammalian) and broken arrows ($--\rightarrow$) indicate potential interactions that have been proposed to regulate sperm function.

Nature of sperm signal transduction mechanisms modulating zona pellucida-mediated acrosomal exocytosis

The unique structure of ZP3, its biological potency, its association with ZP1 and ZP2 in the zona pellucida to form an immobilized ligand in a highly ordered three-dimensional matrix capable of acting at limited distances, and the probable existence on the plasma membrane of acrosome-intact spermatozoa of a complementary ZP3 receptor(s) satisfy a number of criteria that would have to be met if one were to construct a macromolecule that would control specific cell–cell recognition events in a receptor-mediated fashion. As described above the interaction of ZP3 with the sperm surface to effect both binding and the acrosome reaction may represent a highly co-operative process in which the aggregation of occupied ZP3 receptors on the sperm surface results in signal transduction leading to acrosomal exocytosis. Although the components of this system are only starting to be recognized and characterized, an additional question comes to mind, pertaining to the mechanism(s) by which a ligand such as ZP3 effects informational flow across the sperm plasma membrane to initiate acrosomal exocytosis.

Identification of guanine nucleotide-binding regulatory proteins in spermatozoa

The guanine nucleotide-binding regulatory proteins (G proteins), which include G_s, G_i, G_o, and transducin, occupy critical roles as signal transducing elements in coupling many ligand–receptor interactions with the generation of intracellular second messengers (Casey & Gilman, 1988). These heterotrimeric plasma membrane-associated proteins are composed of distinct α-subunits, which contain a GTP-binding domain, and more highly conserved β- and γ-subunits. The α-subunits can be covalently modified by ADP-ribosylation in the presence NAD^+ by the action of a variety of bacterial toxins, including cholera toxin, pertussis toxin, and botulinum toxin. The ability to undergo toxin-catalysed ADP-ribosylation has been used by many investigators to identify general classes of G proteins. Activation of G proteins occurs upon GTP binding to the α-subunit, causing dissociation of α-GTP from the βγ dimer. These dissociated subunits then exert their regulatory actions on respective targets, ultimately resulting in ligand coupling to intracellular signalling systems. G proteins regulate the hormonally responsive adenylate cyclase of somatic cells, the cyclic GMP phosphodiesterase of retinal rod outer segments, atrial K^+ channels, Ca^{2+} channels, and have been implicated in regulating phospholipase C, phospholipase A_2 and phospholipase D (Casey & Gilman, 1988; Ross, 1989). Since many of these intracellular signalling mechanisms have been reported to control various sperm functions (Garbers & Kopf, 1980; Tash & Means, 1983), it is possible that spermatozoa utilize G proteins as signal transducing elements in mediating cellular function in response to the extracellular environment. We have therefore investigated whether spermatozoa contain these signal transducing proteins (Kopf *et al.*, 1986).

Extracts from invertebrate and mammalian spermatozoa were assessed for the presence of the α-subunits of G proteins by bacterial toxin-catalysed ADP ribosylation. Sperm extracts were examined for the presence of pertussis toxin substrates. Pertussis toxin catalyses the ADP-ribosylation of the α-subunits of G_i, G_o and transducin and will functionally inactivate these proteins. Invertebrate (abalone) and mammalian (man, mouse, guinea-pig, cattle) spermatozoa contain a single pertussis toxin substrate of $M_r = 41\,000$. Peptide mapping of the mouse and human sperm $M_r = 41\,000$ substrates by limited proteolytic digestion demonstrates a similarity to $α_i$ of mouse S-49 lymphoma cells (Kopf *et al.*, 1986). These data suggest that the pertussis toxin substrates of $M_r = 41\,000$ from mouse and human spermatozoa are $α_i$-like. Subsequent observations by Jones *et al.* (1989) demonstrated that mouse spermatozoa contain two closely migrating pertussis toxin substrates which can only be resolved when sodium dodecyl sulphate containing a substantial portion of C_{14} and C_{16} alkyl sulphates is used for polyacrylamide gel electrophoresis. The nature of these multiple forms is not presently known and is currently under investigation. The presence of a G_i-like protein in mouse spermatozoa was further substantiated using an antiserum directed against the β-subunit common to the different heterotrimeric G-proteins (Kopf *et al.*,

1986). Analysis of one-dimensional polyacrylamide gels of mouse sperm membrane extracts using Western blotting demonstrates the presence of a single immunoreactive band of $M_r = 35\,000/36\,000$, which co-migrates with the β-subunit of G proteins from somatic cell membranes.

Spermatozoa were also analysed for the presence of specific substrates for cholera toxin-catalysed ADP-ribosylation, indicative of the presence of G_s protein. No specific substrates are detected in any of the fractions assayed under a variety of conditions. Our inability to detect G_s protein in spermatozoa is consistent with the data of others (Hildebrandt *et al.*, 1985), and is also supported by the work of investigators who have examined the guanine nucleotide regulation of the sperm adenylate cyclases (Garbers & Kopf, 1980). It is possible the G_s protein is present in spermatozoa but that the current methods used to probe for its existence are inadequate at this time. However, the inability to reconstitute sperm adenylate cyclase activity with purified G_s protein from an exogenous source implies that this enzyme may have unique regulatory properties, and that G_s protein may not play a regulatory role in sperm function (Hildebrandt *et al.*, 1985).

In conclusion mouse spermatozoa, as well as spermatozoa from a number of other species, contain G proteins. In most species the G protein appears to be G_i-like. The existence of these signal transducing proteins in spermatozoa has been confirmed (Bentley *et al.*, 1986; Garty *et al.*, 1988). Additional biochemical, immunological and molecular studies are currently in progress to determine the relationship of the sperm G proteins to somatic cell G proteins, and to determine whether the sperm G proteins are localized to different regions of the cell.

Experiments utilizing polyclonal antisera generated against conserved peptide sequences common to the α-subunits of various G proteins were designed to characterize further the nature of mammalian sperm G proteins and to determine whether they display distinct regionalization in this highly differentiated cell (Glassner *et al.*, 1989). Both mouse and guinea-pig spermatozoa display positive immunofluorescence in the acrosomal region using an antiserum directed against specific peptide regions common to all G_α proteins (anti-CFDVGGQRSERKK). This fluorescence disappears when spermatozoa undergo the acrosome reaction, either spontaneously or in response to zona pellucida glycoproteins, suggesting that the immunoreactive material is associated with the plasma/outer acrosomal membrane overlying the acrosome. Negligible midpiece and tail staining is observed with this antiserum. This antiserum also immunoprecipitates a pertussis toxin catalysed [^{32}P]ADP-ribosylated protein(s) of $M_r = 41\,000$ from mouse spermatozoa. The assocation of G proteins with the sperm acrosome was further confirmed in guinea-pig spermatozoa by demonstrating that purified plasma/outer acrosomal membrane fractions isolated from cells acrosome-reacted with A-23187 contain a substrate(s) of $M_r = 41\,000$ for pertussis toxin catalysed ADP-ribosylation. These data demonstrate that G protein α-subunits are present in the acrosomal region of mammalian spermatozoa consistent with their postulated role in regulating zona pellucida-mediated acrosomal exocytosis (see below). Clearly, additional studies using more specific probes are required to determine what $G_{i\alpha}$ subtype is present in spermatozoa.

The role of the sperm G_i-like protein in the zona pellucida-mediated acrosome reaction

The physiological role of the sperm G_i-like protein in the zona pellucida-induced acrosome reaction was next examined (Endo *et al.*, 1987b, 1988). Spermatozoa were treated with pertussis toxin and the ability of the spermatozoa to bind to structurally intact zonae pellucidae and undergo the acrosome reaction was then examined. Pertussis toxin can cross the plasma membrane and functionally inactivate G_i by ADP-ribosylating its α-subunit (Casey & Gilman, 1988). Intact mouse spermatozoa were incubated with pertussis toxin under conditions conducive to capacitation and it was demonstrated that the toxin could enter the cell and ADP-ribosylate the G_i-like protein. Pertussis toxin does not affect the ability of the mouse spermatozoon to become capacitated and these spermatozoa bind to structurally intact zonae pellucidae to the same extent as do control spermatozoa incubated in the absence of this toxin. In addition, sperm motility and viability are not affected at any concentration of pertussis toxin tested. However, the zona pellucida-induced acrosome reaction, as monitored by the CTC assay described above, is inhibited in a concentration-dependent manner by pertussis toxin, with half-maximal effects at 0·1–1·0 ng pertussis toxin/ml. Pertussis toxin inhibits the acrosome reaction due to an effect on the ability of the spermatozoon to progress from the B-pattern to the intermediate S-pattern; the spermatozoa therefore remain in the B-pattern. Inactivated pertussis toxin does not inhibit the zona pellucida-induced acrosome reaction, and cholera toxin is also without effect. These inhibitory effects of pertussis toxin on the zona pellucida-induced acrosome reaction are also confirmed at the electron microscopic level. These data suggest that functional inactivation of the mouse sperm G_i-like protein by pertussis toxin prevents the zona pellucida-induced acrosome reaction and that the inhibition appears, at least, to be at the level of the B to S transition.

The specificity of the pertussis toxin effect on the zona pellucida-induced sperm acrosome reaction was further defined in additional experiments. The effects of non-hydrolysable GTP and GDP analogues on the pertussis toxin mediated inhibition of the zona pellucida-induced acrosome reaction were examined, since the β-subunit of the G_i αβγ heterotrimer appears to be required for the pertussis toxin-catalysed ADP-ribosylation of the $α_i$-subunit (Neer et al., 1984). The rationale for this approach is as follows. Non-hydrolysable analogues of GTP (e.g. guanosine-5′-O-3-thiotriphosphate; GTPγS) bind to the $α_i$-subunit with high affinity and dissociate the heterotrimer into GTPγS-$α_i$ and βγ subunits (Casey & Gilman, 1988). It would be expected that if GTPγS penetrated intact spermatozoa and bound to the α-subunit of the sperm G_i-like protein, the resultant subunit dissociation would prevent subsequent pertussis toxin-catalysed ADP-ribosylation of the α-subunit and, as a result, prevent functional inactivation of the protein. There is a precedent for cellular permeability of GTPγS (Minke & Stephenson, 1985). In contrast, incubation of intact spermatozoa with a non-hydrolysable GDP analogue (e.g. guanosine-5′-O-2-thiodiphosphate: GDPβS) would not be expected to inhibit the pertussis toxin-catalysed ADP-ribosylation since this analogue does not cause subunit dissociation. When intact spermatozoa are capacitated in the presence of 100 μM-GTPγS before the addition of 10 ng pertussis toxin/ml, sperm binding to the zona pellucida and the subsequent acrosome reaction occurs to the same extent as for control spermatozoa incubated in the absence of both of these agents; this contrasts sharply with the inhibitory effects on the acrosome reaction observed when spermatozoa are incubated with pertussis toxin alone. Capacitation of spermatozoa in the presence of 100 μM-GDPβS before the addition of pertussis toxin, on the other hand, does not abolish the pertussis toxin-mediated inhibition of the zona pellucida-induced acrosome reaction. These data suggest that the pertussis toxin-sensitive component of mouse spermatozoa is a G_i-like protein, which upon activation by GTPγS (but not GDPβS) loses its ability to become functionally inactivated by pertussis toxin-catalysed ADP-ribosylation. Since the only pertussis toxin substrate found to be present in mouse spermatozoa is the $M_r = 41\,000$ α-subunit of the G_i-like protein, it is likely that this protein is the pertussis toxin-sensitive component.

These initial experiments utilized mechanically isolated, structurally intact zonae pellucidae in which the acrosome reaction was monitored by spermatozoa bound to the zona pellucida. Although ZP3 has been demonstrated to account quantitatively for both the sperm receptor and acrosome-inducing activities of the mouse zona pellucida, it could be argued that pertussis toxin treatment of the spermatozoa could affect the sperm surface such that a non-physiological interaction between the spermatozoa and the structurally intact zona pellucida would occur; such a non-physiological interaction could certainly be exacerbated by the steric constraints of an intact zona pellucida. This interaction might ultimately result in a non-specific inhibitory effect on the acrosome reaction. The locus of such an effect would most probably be downstream from the sperm binding site(s) since sperm binding to structurally intact zonae pellucidae is not affected by pertussis toxin pretreatment of the spermatozoa. The argument might also be made that when using such a sperm–zona pellucida binding assay, the apparent inhibition of the acrosome reaction could result from a preferential binding to the zona pellucida of a subset of pertussis toxin-treated spermatozoa destined not to complete the acrosome reaction. To rule out these possibilities the effect of pertussis toxin treatment of spermatozoa on the acrosome reaction induced by purified ZP3 was examined (Endo *et al.*, 1988).

When compared to spermatozoa capacitated in the absence of pertussis toxin, spermatozoa capacitated in the presence of pertussis toxin are inhibited from undergoing the acrosome reaction in response to ZP3. As with structurally intact zonae pellucidae, this inhibition occurs at the B to S transition. In contrast to the inhibitory effects of pertussis toxin on the ZP3-induced acrosome reaction, the ability of spermatozoa to undergo either a spontaneous acrosome reaction (i.e. in the absence of solubilized ZP3) or a non-physiologically induced acrosome reaction (A-23187-induced) is not affected by the pertussis toxin treatment. Thus, the inhibitory effect of pertussis toxin on the zona pellucida-induced acrosome reaction does not occur via a non-specific inhibitory effect that is observed when monitoring acrosome reactions of spermatozoa bound to structurally intact zonae pellucidae. More importantly, only acrosome reactions induced by the physiologically relevant ZP3 molecule are inhibited by pertussis toxin. These results are consistent with the idea that the pertussis toxin-sensitive site (G_i-like protein) in mouse spermatozoa plays an important intermediary role in the acrosome reaction induced specifically by ZP3, the biologically relevant molecule present in the zona pellucida. Similar observations in the mouse using ZP3 have been subsequently reported by other investigators (Vazquez *et al.*, 1989), and Florman *et al.* (1989) have demonstrated that pertussis toxin inhibits the bovine sperm acrosome reaction induced by solubilized zonae pellucidae.

If one considers the zona pellucida-induced acrosome reaction as an example of stimulus–secretion coupling which occurs in a receptor-mediated fashion, one would propose that receptor–G protein interaction subsequently leads to the generation of intracellular second messengers and/or the modulation of ionic changes within the spermatozoa. Two criteria would have to be met to establish the signal transducing function of this GTP binding protein in such a system. First, the occupation of a putative receptor for the acrosome reaction-inducing component of the zona pellucida (e.g. ZP3 in the mouse) should result in G protein activation in a manner described for other ligand–receptor–G protein interactions. Second, the resultant G protein interaction should then modulate second messenger/ionic changes distal to receptor occupancy (see below). There is presently evidence to support both of these possibilities.

We have addressed the first question by measuring high-affinity GTPase activity in mouse sperm homogenates in both the absence and presence of acid-solubilized zona pellucida glycoproteins to determine whether this extracellular matrix can activate the sperm-associated G_i-like protein (Wilde & Kopf, 1990). This particular experimental approach is based on the fact that in other systems receptor activation of G proteins is accompanied by the dissociation of the α-subunit from the βγ-subunits of the heterotrimeric G protein, which results in the expression of a latent high-affinity GTPase activity associated with the α-subunit. An increase in GTP hydrolysis (50% over basal activity) is observed when sperm homogenates are incubated in the presence of acid-solubilized zonae pellucidae. The zona pellucida-induced activation of this enzyme occurs as a consequence of an increase in the V_{max} of the enzyme, with little effect on the $K_{m\ app}$ of the enzyme for GTP, indicating that increased GTP turnover occurs in response to this extracellular matrix. Accompanying this increase in enzyme activity is a reduction in the ability of pertussis toxin to catalyse *in vitro* [^{32}P]ADP-ribosylation of the $M_r = 41\ 000$ G_i-like protein, suggesting that the increase in GTPase activity is associated with the activation of a pertussis toxin-sensitive sperm G protein(s). Concentrations of 0·2 zonae pellucidae/μl are required for half-maximal activation of the enzyme which is similar to the concentration required for sperm–zona pellucida binding but an order of magnitude below the concentration required for zona pellucida-induced acrosomal exocytosis. These data suggest that a component(s) of the zona pellucida (perhaps ZP3) may function by binding to a sperm surface-associated receptor and subsequently activating a G protein which is coupled to intracellular signal transduction cascade(s) required for induction of acrosomal exocytosis.

Taken together, the experiments described above provide evidence that the sperm G_i-like protein plays a role in zona pellucida-mediated signal transduction leading to acrosomal exocytosis which occurs when these cells interact with the extracellular matrix of the mature egg before fertilization.

Intracellular effector systems modulating zona pellucida-mediated acrosomal exocytosis

Although the sperm-associated G_i-like protein appears to play an important intermediary role in the ZP3-induced acrosome reaction, the intracellular signalling systems that this particular signal-transducing protein are coupled to are not known at this time. Moreover, the biochemical responses of mouse spermatozoa to ZP3 have not been examined to date. As stated above, G proteins have been demonstrated to regulate a variety of intracellular second messenger systems, as well as ion channels, in a variety of cell types.

Using the lipophilic fluorescent probe 9-amino-3-chloro-7-methoxyacridine (ACMA) to monitor transmembrane pH gradients in mouse spermatozoa, Lee & Storey (1985) demonstrated that the zona pellucida-induced B to S transition, as monitored by using CTC fluorescence, is accompanied by a parallel abolition of a transmembrane pH gradient as evidenced by the loss of ACMA fluorescence associated with the intact spermatozoon. The loss of this transmembrane pH gradient is not a consequence of major permeability changes such as fusion of the plasma and outer acrosomal membranes. Presently, it is not clear whether the loss of this gradient is a cause, or a consequence, of the B to S transition. Nevertheless, it can be concluded that the zona pellucida-induced B to S transition is associated with a modification of ion permeability in these cells. Since pertussis toxin specifically inhibits the B to S transition the effects of this toxin on the loss of ACMA fluorescence of spermatozoa bound to structurally intact zonae pellucidae was examined (Endo et al., 1988). It was demonstrated that the pertussis toxin-induced inhibition of the B to S transition is accompanied by a parallel retention of ACMA fluorescence at all of the time points tested. These data demonstrate that the pertussis toxin-sensitive site is upstream from those event(s) associated with the loss of the transmembrane pH gradient normally accompanying the zona pellucida-induced B to S transition, and suggest that the G_i-like protein might modulate such changes in ion permeability. Additional studies will be required to confirm whether such changes in ionic permeability are coupled to this protein, and whether other ionic changes might be coupled in a G protein-mediated fashion. This is important in light of two recent observations. Lee & Storey (1989) have demonstrated that the zona pellucida-induced acrosome reaction in the mouse is accompanied by changes in Ca^{2+} permeability. In addition, Florman et al. (1989) have demonstrated that the pH and Ca^{2+} changes observed in bovine spermatozoa incubated in the presence of solubilized zonae pellucidae can be partly inhibited by pertussis toxin, suggesting that the G_i-like protein in these spermatozoa may regulate ionic changes in response to zonae pellucidae.

Other studies have suggested that alterations in phospholipid metabolism and/or cyclic nucleotide metabolism may play important intermediary roles in the sperm acrosome reaction (Kopf & Gerton, 1990). Lee et al. (1987) demonstrated that biologically active phorbol diesters and diacylglycerols can alter the kinetics of the different stages of the zona pellucida-mediated acrosome reaction in mouse spermatozoa, thus providing evidence for the potential role of protein kinase C in regulating this exocytotic event. However, the products of polyphosphoinositide turnover (e.g. inositol 1,4,5-trisphosphate and 1,2-diacylglycerol) have not yet been examined in spermatozoa challenged with zonae pellucidae. Noland et al. (1988) have reported that solubilized zonae pellucidae from mouse eggs induce transient elevations in mouse sperm cAMP concentrations which are dependent on the presence of extracellular Ca^{2+}. These cAMP elevations appear correlated with the induction of the acrosome reaction by the zona pellucida, and suggest that cAMP may be a potential participant in the signalling pathway leading to acrosomal exocytosis. Since these intracellular signalling systems are coupled to G proteins in a receptor mediated fashion in other cell types, it will be of interest to determine whether such second messenger systems are modulated by the sperm G_i-like protein. A working model of the events comprising the ZP3-induced acrosome reaction is shown in Fig. 1.

Conclusion

Spermatozoa from all species studied so far contain G proteins. The presence of such signal-transducing proteins in these cells suggests that the regulation of sperm function might have control elements which are similar to ligand:receptor:G protein:second messenger systems common to many somatic cells. This hypothesis is supported by experiments which demonstrate an inter-mediary role for the mouse sperm G_i-like protein in ZP3-induced acrosomal exocytosis. The specific function of the G_i-like protein in this important physiological event is not known at this time, although possible roles in regulating ionic movements, cyclic nucleotide metabolism and polyphosphoinositide turnover should be considered. Studies directed at the localization and bio-chemical identity of the mouse sperm G_i-like protein, as well as the nature of the second messenger system(s)/ionic events modulated by this protein, are in progress and should help to delineate the sequence of events involved in some of the early steps of sperm–zona pellucida interaction. Based on our studies of the biochemical mechanisms controlling the egg-induced polyspermy block, it appears that the induction of the acrosome reaction may involve multiple interactions between ZP3 moieties and complementary binding sites (receptors) on the sperm surface. This is consistent with other studies, suggesting that aggregation of sperm-associated ZP3 receptors may be responsible for the induction of the complete acrosome reaction. The mechanism by which these interactions occur, the identity of the sperm-associated receptor(s) for ZP3, and the role of signal transduction and intracellular second messenger pathways in coupling these interactions at the sperm surface with resultant physiological responses leading to acrosomal exocytosis will be of great interest for future research.

I gratefully acknowledge the work and financial support of the following: Yoshihiro Endo (Rockefeller Foundation), David L. Garbers (NIH HD 10254: Howard Hughes Medical Institute), George L. Gerton (NIH HD 20736), Michael A. Lee (NIH HD 06274), Tom D. Noland, Mary Wilde (T32HD 07305) and Marilyn J. Woolkalis (NIH PO1-GM 34781). This work is supported by the NIH (HD 19096; HD 06274; HD 22732) and a grant from the Andrew Mellon Foundation.

References

Aarons, D., Speake, J.L. & Poirier, G.R. (1984) Evidence for a proteinase inhibitor binding component associated with murine spermatozoa. *Biol. Reprod.* **31**, 811–817.

Apter, F.M., Baltz, J.M. & Millette, C.F. (1988) A possible role for cell surface fucosyltransferase (FT) activity during sperm-zona pellucida binding in the mouse. *J. Cell Biol.* **107**, 175a, abstr.

Benau, D.A. & Storey, B.T. (1987) Characterization of the mouse sperm plasma membrane zona-binding site sensitive to trypsin inhibitors. *Biol. Reprod.* **36**, 282–292.

Bentley, J.K., Garbers, D.L., Domino, S.E., Noland, T.D. & VanDop, C. (1986) Spermatozoa contain a guanine nucleotide binding protein ADP-ribosylated by pertussis toxin. *Biochem. Biophys. Res. Commun.* **138**, 728–734.

Bentley, J.K., Khatra, A.S. & Garbers, D.L. (1988) Receptor-mediated activation of detergent solubilized guanylate cyclase. *Biol. Reprod.* **39**, 639–647.

Bleil, J.D. & Wassarman, P.M. (1980a) Structure and function of the zona pellucida: Identification and characterization of the proteins of the mouse oocyte's zona pellucida. *Devl Biol.* **76**, 185–202.

Bleil, J.D. & Wassarman, P.M. (1980b) Synthesis of zona pellucida proteins by denuded and follicle-enclosed mouse oocytes during culture *in vitro*. *Proc. natn. Acad. Sci., USA* **77**, 1029–1033.

Bleil, J.D. & Wassarman, P.M. (1983) Sperm-egg inter-actions in the mouse: sequence of events and induc-tion of the acrosome reaction by a zona pellucida glycoprotein. *Devl Biol.* **95**, 317–324.

Bleil, J.D. & Wassarman, P.M. (1986) Autoradiographic visualization of the mouse egg's sperm receptor bound to sperm. *J. Cell Biol.* **102**, 1363–1371.

Bleil, J.D. & Wassarman, P.M. (1988) Galactose at the non-reducing terminus of O-linked oligosaccharides of mouse egg zona pellucida glycoprotein ZP3 is essential for the glycoprotein's sperm receptor activity. *Proc. natn. Acad. Sci., USA* **85**, 6778–6782.

Bleil, J.D. & Wassarman, P.M. (1989) Identification of a mouse sperm protein that recognizes ZP3. *J. Cell Biol.* **109**, 125a, abstr.

Bleil, J.D., Greve, J.M. & Wassarman P.M. (1988) Identification of a secondary sperm receptor in the mouse egg zona pellucida: Role in maintenance of binding of acrosome-reacted sperm to eggs. *Devl Biol.* **128**, 376–385.

Casey, P.J. & Gilman, A.G. (1988) G protein involvement in receptor-effector coupling. *J. biol. Chem.* **263**, 2577–2580.

Dangott, L.J. & Garbers, D.L. (1984) Identification and partial characterization of the receptor for speract. *J. biol. Chem.* **259**, 13712–13716.

Endo, Y., Schultz, R.M. & Kopf, G.S. (1987a) Effects of phorbol esters and a diacylglycerol on mouse eggs: Inhibition of fertilization and modification of the zona pellucida. *Devl Biol.* **119**, 199–209.

Endo, Y., Lee, M.A. & Kopf, G.S. (1987b) Evidence for the role of a guanine nucleotide-binding regulatory protein in the zona pellucida-induced mouse sperm acrosome reaction. *Devl Biol.* **119**, 210–216.

Endo, Y., Mattei, P., Kopf, G.S. & Schultz, R.M. (1987c) Effects of a phorbol ester on mouse eggs: Dissociation of sperm receptor activity from acrosome reaction-inducing activity of the mouse zona pellucida protein, ZP3. *Devl Biol.* **123**, 574–577.

Endo, Y., Lee, M.A. & Kopf, G.S. (1988) Characterization of an islet activating protein-sensitive site in mouse sperm that is involved in the *zona pellucida*-induced acrosome reaction. *Devl Biol.* **129**, 12–24.

Florman, H.M. & Storey, B.T. (1981) Inhibition of in vitro fertilization of mouse eggs: 3-quinuclidinyl benzilate specifically blocks penetration of zonae pellucidae by mouse spermatozoa. *J. exp. Zool.* **216**, 159–167.

Florman, H.M. & Storey, B.T. (1982a) Mouse gamete interactions: the zona pellucida is the site of the acrosome reaction leading to fertilization in vitro. *Devl Biol.* **91**, 121–130.

Florman, H.M. & Storey, B.T. (1982b) Characterization of cholinomimetic agents that inhibit in vitro fertilization in the mouse. *J. Androl.* **3**, 157–164.

Florman, H.M. & Wassarman, P.M. (1985) O-linked oligosaccharides of mouse egg ZP3 account for its sperm receptor activity. *Cell* **41**, 313–324.

Florman, H.M., Bechtol, K.B. & Wassarman, P.M. (1984) Enzymatic digestion of the functions of the mouse egg's receptor for sperm. *Devl Biol.* **106**, 243–255.

Florman, H.M., Tombes, R.M., First, N.L. & Babcock, D.F. (1989) An adhesion-associated agonist from the zona pellucida activates G protein-promoted elevations of internal Ca^{2+} and pH that mediate mammalian sperm acrosomal exocytosis. *Devl Biol.* **135**, 133–146.

Garbers, D.L. (1989a) Molecular basis of fertilization. *Ann. Rev. Biochem.* **58**, 719–742.

Garbers, D.L. (1989b) Guanylate cyclase, a cell surface receptor. *J. biol. Chem.* **264**, 9103–9106.

Garbers, D.L. & Kopf, G.S. (1980) The regulation of spermatozoa by calcium and cyclic nucleotides. *Adv. Cyclic Nuc. Res.* **13**, 251–306.

Garty, N.B., Galiani, D., Aharonheim, A., Ho, Y.K., Phillips, D.M., Dekel, N. & Salomon, Y. (1988) G proteins in mammalian gametes: an immunocytochemical study. *J. Cell Sci.* **91**, 21–31.

Glassner, M., Abisogun, A.O., Kligman, I., Woolkalis, M.J., Gerton, G.L. & Kopf, G.S. (1989) Immunocytochemical and biochemical analysis of guanine nucleotide-binding regulatory proteins (G proteins) in mammalian spermatozoa. *J. Cell Biol.* **109**, 250a, abstr.

Godfrey, E.W., Dietz, M.E., Morstad, A.L., Wallskog, P.A. & Yorde, D.E. (1988) Acetylcholine receptor-aggregating proteins are associated with the extracellular matrix of many tissues in Torpedo. *J. Cell Biol.* **106**, 1263–1272.

Gomperts, B.D. & Tatham, P.E.R. (1988) GTP-binding proteins in the control of exocytosis. *Cold Spring Harbor Symp. Quant. Biol.* **53**, 983–992.

Hansbrough, J.R. & Garbers, D.L. (1981) Speract; purification and characterization of a peptide associated with eggs that activates spermatozoa. *J. biol. Chem.* **256**, 2235–2241.

Hildebrandt, J.D., Codina, J., Tash, J.S., Kirchick, H.J., Lipschultz, L., Sekura, R.D. & Birnbaumer, L. (1985) The membrane-bound spermatozoal adenylyl cyclase system does not share coupling characteristics with somatic cell adenylyl cyclases. *Endocrinology* **116**, 1357–1366.

Jones, J., Kopf, G.S. & Schultz, R.M. (1989) Variability in electrophoretic mobility of G_i-like proteins; effect of SDS. *FEBS Lett.* **243**, 409–412.

Kligman, I., Storey, B.T. & Kopf, G.S. (1988) The zona pellucida-mediated acrosome reaction of mouse sperm: characterization of an intermediate stage prior to the completion of the acrosome reaction. *Proc. 10th Testis Workshop*, Baltimore, p. 75, abstr.

Kopf, G.S. & Gerton, G.L. (1990) The mammalian sperm acrosome and the acrosome reaction. In *The Biology and Chemistry of Mammalian Fertilization*, in press. Ed. P. M. Wassarman. CRC Uniscience Series, CRC Press, Inc., Boca Raton.

Kopf, G.S., Woolkalis, M.J. & Gerton, G.L. (1986) Evidence for a guanine nucleotide-binding regulatory protein in invertebrate and mammalian sperm: identification by islet-activating protein-catalyzed ADP-ribosylation and immunochemical methods. *J. biol. Chem.* **261**, 7327–7331.

Kopf, G.S., Endo, Y., Mattei, P., Kurasawa, S. & Schultz, R.M. (1989) Egg-induced modifications of the murine zona pellucida. In *Mechanisms of Egg Activation*, pp. 249–272. Eds R. L. Nuccitelli, W. H. Clark & G. N. Cherr. Plenum Publishing Corp., New York.

Lee, M.A. & Storey, B.T. (1985) Evidence for plasma membrane impermeability to small ions in acrosome-intact mouse spermatozoa bound to mouse *zonae pellucidae*, using an aminoacridine fluorescent probe: time course of the *zona*-induced acrosome reaction monitored by both chlortetracycline and pH probe fluorescence. *Biol. Reprod.* **33**, 235–246.

Lee, M.A. & Storey, B.T. (1989) Endpoint of first stage of zona pellucida-induced acrosome reaction in mouse spermatozoa characterized by acrosomal H^+ and Ca^{2+} permeability: population and single cell kinetics. *Gamete Res.* **24**, 303–326.

Lee, M.A., Kopf, G.S. & Storey, B.T. (1987) Effects of phorbol esters and a diacylglycerol on the mouse sperm acrosome reaction induced by the zona pellucida. *Biol. Reprod.* **36**, 617–627.

Leyton, L. & Saling, P.M. (1989a) 95 kD sperm proteins bind ZP3 and serve as tyrosine kinase substrates in response to zona binding. *Cell* **57**, 123–130.

Leyton, L. & Saling, P.M. (1989b) Evidence that aggregation of mouse sperm receptors by ZP3 triggers the acrosome reaction. *J. Cell Biol.* **108**, 2163–2168.

Leyton, L., Robinson, A. & Saling, P.M. (1989) Relationship between the M42 antigen of mouse sperm and the acrosome reaction induced by ZP3. *Devl Biol.* **132**, 174–178.

Lopez, L.C., Bayna, E.M., Litoff, D., Shaper, N.L., Shaper, J.H. & Shur, B.D. (1985) Receptor function of mouse sperm surface galactosyltransferase during fertilization. *J. Cell. Biol.* **101**, 1501–1510.

Minke, B. & Stephenson, R.S. (1985) The characteristics of chemically induced noise in *Musca* photoreceptors. *J. comp. Physiol. A.* **156**, 339–356.

Moller, C.C. & Wassarman, P.M. (1989) Characterization of a proteinase that cleaves zona pellucida glycoprotein ZP2 following activation of mouse eggs. *Devl Biol.* **132**, 103–112.

Neer, E.J., Lok, J.M. & Wolf, L.G. (1984) Purification and properties of the inhibitory guanine nucleotide regulatory unit of brain adenylate cyclase. *J. biol. Chem.* **259**, 14222–14229.

Noland, T.D., Garbers, D.L. & Kopf, G.S. (1988) An elevation in cyclic AMP concentration precedes the *zona pellucida*-induced acrosome reaction of mouse spermatozoa. *Biol. Reprod.* **38** (Suppl.), 94, abstr.

Ringuette, M.J., Chamberlin, M.E., Baur, A.W., Sobieski, D.A. & Dean, J. (1988) Molecular analysis of cDNA coding for ZP3, a sperm binding protein of the mouse zona pellucida. *Devl Biol.* **127**, 287–295.

Ross, E.M. (1989) Signal sorting and amplification through G protein-coupled receptors. *Neuron* **3**, 141–152.

Saling, P.M. (1981) Involvement of trypsin-like activity in binding of mouse spermatozoa to zonae pellucidae. *Proc. natn. Acad. Sci., USA* **78**, 6231–6235.

Saling, P.M. & Storey, B.T. (1979) Mouse gamete interactions during fertilization *in vitro*: chlortetracycline as fluorescent probe for the mouse sperm acrosome reaction. *J. Cell Biol.* **83**, 544–555.

Saling, P.M., Sowinski, J. & Storey, B.T. (1979) An ultrastructural study of epididymal mouse spermatozoa binding to zonae pellucidae *in vitro*: sequential relationship to the acrosome reaction. *J. exp. Zool.* **209**, 229–238.

Shimizu, S., Tsuji, M. & Dean, J. (1983) *In vitro* biosynthesis of three sulfated glycoproteins of murine zonae pellucidae by oocytes grown in follicle culture. *J. biol. Chem.* **258**, 5858–5863.

Shimomura, H., Dangott, L.J. & Garbers, D.L. (1986) Covalent coupling of a resact analogue to guanylate cyclase. *J. biol. Chem.* **261**, 15778–15782.

Shur, B.D. & Hall, N.G. (1982a) Sperm surface galactosyltransferase activities during in vitro capacitation. *J. Cell Biol.* **95**, 567–573.

Shur, B.D. & Hall, N.G. (1982b) A role for mouse surface galactosyltransferase in sperm binding to the egg zona pellucida. *J. Cell Biol.* **95**, 574–579.

Suzuki, N., Nomura, K., Ohtake, H. & Isaka, S. (1981) Purification and the primary structure of sperm-activating peptides from the jelly coat of sea urchin eggs. *Biochem. Biophys. Res. Commun.* **99**, 1238–1244.

Tash, J.S. & Means, A.R. (1983) Cyclic adenosine 3′,5′-monophosphate, calcium and protein phosphorylation in flagellar motility. *Biol. Reprod.* **28**, 75–104.

Vazquez, M.H., Phillips, D.M. & Wassarman, P.M. (1989) Interaction of mouse sperm with purified sperm receptors covalently linked to silica beads. *J. Cell Sci.* **92**, 713–722.

Ward, C.R. & Storey, B.T. (1984) Determination of the time course of capacitation in mouse spermatozoa using a chlortetracycline fluorescence assay. *Devl Biol.* **104**, 287–296.

Wassarman, P.M. (1987) Early events in mammalian fertilization. *Ann. Rev. Cell Biol.* **3**, 109–142.

Wassarman, P.M. (1988) Zona pellucida glycoproteins. *Ann. Rev. Biochem.* **57**, 415–442.

Wilde, M.W. & Kopf, G.S. (1990) Activation of a G-protein in mammalian sperm by an egg-associated extracellular matrix, the zona pellucida. *J. Cell Biol.* **109**, 251a, abstr.

Yarden, Y. & Schlessinger, J. (1987) Epidermal growth factor induces rapid, reversible aggregation of the purified epidermal growth factor receptor. *Biochemistry, NY* **26**, 1443–1451.

Yarden, Y. & Ullrich, A. (1988) Growth factor receptor tyrosine kinases. *Ann. Rev. Biochem.* **57**, 443–448.

J. Reprod. Fert., Suppl. **42** (1990), 51–67

Phosphoinositides and their products in the mammalian sperm acrosome reaction

R. A. P. Harrison and E. R. S. Roldan

Department of Molecular Embryology, AFRC Institute of Animal Physiology and Genetics Research, Babraham, Cambridge CB2 4AT, UK

Summary. At fertilization, the spermatozoon exocytoses its acrosomal granule in a Ca^{2+}-dependent process known as the acrosome reaction. In mammalian spermatozoa, possibly because the acrosome is large and membrane fusion takes place between the outer acrosomal membrane and the overlying plasma membrane extensively over the anterior of the sperm head, the exocytotic process is slow and therefore amenable to biochemical dissection. By prelabelling sperm phospholipids with ^{32}P and inducing the acrosome reaction with Ca^{2+} and the ionophore A23187, we have been able to show that membrane fusion occurs as the result of a sequence of events following Ca^{2+} entry; Ca^{2+} is required for at least 3 of these events. The process is initiated by a large-scale breakdown of polyphosphoinositides that is catalysed by a Ca^{2+}-dependent phospholipase C. Of the resultant products, diacylglycerol is the essential one. Although its precise role remains to be established, this compound appears to stimulate a later process; it does not seem to act directly as a fusogen, nor does it act through a metabolite. However, it does not act through protein kinase C. At present we believe that diacylglycerol may simultaneously activate phospholipase A_2 and inhibit lyso-phosphatide acyltransferase, to cause a large-scale build-up of fusogenic lysophospholipids in the acrosomal region; Ca^{2+} may bring about membrane fusion when the levels of these lipids have risen above a necessary threshold.

Keywords: phosphoinositides; spermatozoa; acrosome reaction; Ca^{2+}; diacylglycerol

Introduction

In recent years phosphoinositides (i.e. inositol phospholipids) have been shown to be a source of 'second messengers' in very many cellular systems, especially with respect to secretory or exocytotic processes. The current generally accepted concept (shown schematically in Fig. 1) is that external agonists act through plasma-membrane receptors to stimulate a specific phospholipase C that hydrolyses the polyphosphoinositides (PtdInsP and PtdInsP$_2$: see Table 1 for abbreviations used in this paper); the products of this hydrolysis, DAG and inositol polyphosphates (in particular, Ins(1,4,5)P$_3$ derived from PtdInsP$_2$) act as second messengers in Ca^{2+}-dependent processes, DAG by stimulating Ca^{2+}-dependent protein kinase C and Ins(1,4,5)P$_3$ by stimulating Ca^{2+} release from non-mitochondrial intracellular stores (see Berridge, 1987). The great importance of Ca^{2+} as a regulating ion has attracted much attention to the metabolism of the phosphoinositides and their phospholipase C-generated products, and the general concept outlined above has proved to have several variations. Within the past 3 years, research by us and by others has revealed that phosphoinositides may also be involved in the sperm acrosome reaction, a Ca^{2+}-dependent exocytotic event essential to fertilization.

As a morphological change associated with fertilization, the acrosome reaction was first observed in mammalian spermatozoa by Austin & Bishop (1958), although a similar event seems to

Table 1. Abbreviations used in the text

DAG:	diacyl-*sn*-glycerol
InsP$_3$:	*myo*-inositol trisphosphate, with isomeric (D-) numbering as appropriate
InsP$_4$:	*myo*-inositol tetrakisphosphate, with isomeric (D-) numbering as appropriate
PtdOH:	phosphatidate
PtdIns:	phosphatidyl-*myo*-inositol
PtdInsP:	phosphatidyl-*myo*-inositol 4-phosphate
PtdInsP$_2$:	phosphatidyl-*myo*-inositol 4,5-bisphosphate

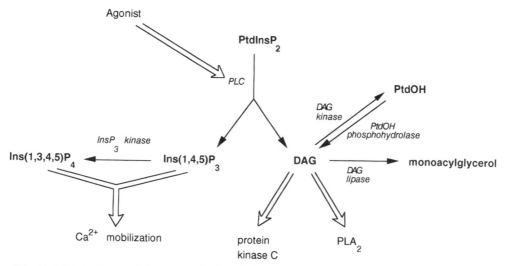

Fig. 1. Metabolism and function of phosphoinositides and their products in a generalized cell. The scheme is a greatly abbreviated one, and shows only the processes relevant to this review. Note that some of the pathways may be absent from mammalian spermatozoa. PLC, phospholipase C; PLA$_2$, phospholipase A$_2$.

have been observed in invertebrate spermatozoa many years before (see Dan, 1967). Austin & Bishop (1958) at once recognized the process as engendering the release or unmasking of lytic enzymes to assist the fertilizing spermatozoon penetrate the egg vestments, in particular the zona pellucida. Subsequently, it was observed that fusion and pore formation between the outer acrosomal membrane and the overlying plasma membrane preceded dispersal of the acrosomal contents (see Fig. 2), and use of the term 'dehiscence' by Colwin & Colwin (1967) implied already the concept that disappearence or modification of the acrosomal contents was an inevitable consequence of this fusion. Since that time, a great deal of research has been carried out on the mammalian acrosome reaction and its consequences (see Yanagimachi, 1988), but progress in understanding its mechanism has been relatively slow.

The requirement for external supplies of Ca^{2+} was first noted by Barros (1974) and by Yanagimachi & Usui (1974), while the involvement of lipid modifications was established particularly by studies such as those of Fleming & Yanagimachi (1981) and Davis (1981), reviewed extensively by Go & Wolf (1983) and Langlais & Roberts (1985). Definition of the reaction as an exocytotic event has also been of considerable significance. This view, together with its implications, has been rather slow to gain general recognition. The acrosome had been seen to be a

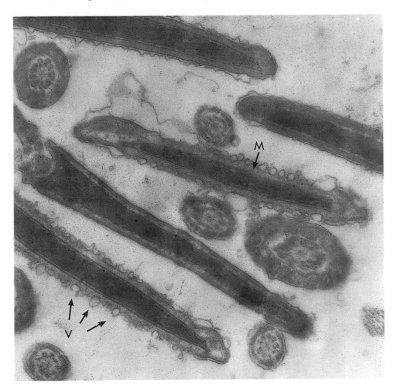

Fig. 2. Ram spermatozoa undergoing ionophore-induced acrosome reactions in the presence of *p*-aminobenzamidine (pAB) and *p*-nitrophenylguanidinobenzoate (NPGB). Spermatozoa were pretreated with 1 mM-pAB and 0·1 mM-NPGB and then induced to undergo an acrosome reaction with 3 mM-Ca^{2+} and 1 μM-A23187. This section is from a sample taken 30 min after initiation of ionophore treatment; experimental details are given by Shams-Borham & Harrison (1981). In 2 of the sperm heads shown, fusion between the plasma membrane and the outer acrosomal membrane has taken place (seen as vesiculation: V), although dispersal of the acrosomal matrix (M) has been prevented by the protease inhibitors pAB and NPGB. × 14 200.

secretory product of the Golgi many years previously (Bowen, 1922), but, at the time that secretory granules were being defined as specific organelles distinct in function from lysosomes and other phagocytic organelles, Allison & Hartree (1970) introduced the concept of the acrosome as a lysosome. Although the hypothesis of a zona lysin coupled with the presence of lytic enzymes in 'acrosomal extracts' encouraged such an analogy, the lysosome concept diverted attention from important work on secretory granules and exocytosis in other cell systems and thus reduced greatly cross-fertilization of mechanistic ideas, particularly with respect to the mammalian reaction. Friend (1977) and Green (1978), however, re-introduced the acrosome as a secretory granule, a concept that was emphasized by Harrison (1983). It is this view which is promoting current progress because it has encouraged students of the spermatozoon to take a broader approach and pay attention to work on exocytosis in other systems, particularly with respect to molecular 'signalling'.

Acrosomal exocytosis is none the less an unusual secretory process. In comparison with other secretory granules, the acrosome is very large and asymmetric, with distinct morphological regions. During the lifetime of the spermatozoon, the outer acrosomal membrane lies in close apposition to the overlying plasma membrane with which it fuses during exocytosis, a situation unlike many other systems, in which the secretory granules move into apposition to the plasma membrane and even 'dock' with the exocytosis site (see De Lisle & Williams, 1986); also, the surface area within which the plasma and outer acrosomal membranes fuse is very large, with fusion taking place along large arborescent pathways (Fléchon et al., 1986; Aguas & Pinto Da Silva, 1989) rather than at a single pore-forming site. Possibly because of its extensive nature, the fusion process in the acrosome reaction is very slow in comparison with other systems: many minutes can elapse between triggering and membrane fusion, even under physiological conditions (Florman & Storey, 1982; Florman & First, 1988; Lee & Storey, 1989). This slow response is a great advantage when analyses of the process are to be made, and renders the sperm acrosome reaction an excellent cellular model for studies on exocytosis.

Under physiological conditions, most cell membranes do not fuse spontaneously, even in the presence of Ca^{2+}. For fusion to occur, the membrane structure requires prior and probably rather complex modification, which must undoubtedly take place in a definite sequence of molecular events. It is the unravelling of this sequence of events with respect to the acrosome reaction that we have attempted in our recent studies. As a basic premise, we decided that it was necessary to analyse changes directly in reacting whole cells rather than to isolate (membrane) fractions from such cells and then analyse the fractions for changes; this was because of the long delay inherent in any isolation procedure and the likelihood of further metabolism occurring during this isolation. Clearly, too, an experimental system was required in which a large proportion of the sperm population would undergo an acrosome reaction synchronously in response to a stimulus. In any other situation, the detection and identification of the sequential events of the acrosome reaction amid other possible changes (capacitation, senescence) would be extremely difficult. At the present time, procedures are still being developed for obtaining sperm populations in which high proportions of the cells are in the capacitated state and capable of exocytosing their acrosomes synchronously in response to a physiological trigger. We therefore chose to use a Ca^{2+}/ionophore-induction system (Shams-Borhan & Harrison, 1981), in which the need for capacitation is obviated. In this system, Ca^{2+} entry into the ejaculated spermatozoon is mediated by the divalent cation ionophore A23187, after which more than 90% of the cells undergo an acrosome reaction (Fig. 3); the response is reasonably synchronous because the vast majority of the population respond within 30 min of starting treatment. Ca^{2+} entry is very rapid (changes in motility pattern occur in all cells within seconds: Shams-Borhan & Harrison, 1981; see also Simpson & White, 1988), and so there is a fixed time-point for the initiation of the sequence of events.

Phosphoinositide breakdown

The essential importance of phospholipids in membrane structure and function generally, and their demonstrable involvement in the acrosome reaction, has led us to direct our attention to changes taking place in these compounds during the ionophore-induced reaction. [A general introduction to the involvement of lipids in the acrosome reaction, together with diagrams of the pathways interconnecting these lipids and their derivatives, has been presented by Roldan & Harrison (1990).] By pre-labelling sperm phospholipids with ^{32}P, we have been able to detect a rapid and extensive breakdown of the labelled polyphosphoinositides following ionophore treatment, with a slower but very large increase in labelled PtdOH (Fig. 4; Roldan & Harrison, 1989).

The breakdown of the polyphosphoinositides has a specific requirement for low concentrations of Ca^{2+}, and appears to be brought about (at least in part) by a phospholipase C, because it is accompanied by a rapid increase in DAG levels (see Table 4) and production of $Ins(1,4,5)P_3$ (Harrison et al., 1990). The enzyme responsible may be the phospholipase C specific for phosphoinositides that has been identified in human spermatozoa by Ribbes et al. (1987) and in bull spermatozoa by Vanha-Perttula & Kasurinen (1989). It is of note that in our system, even in the presence of millimolar concentrations of Ca^{2+}, there is very little degradation of PtdIns itself (see Fig. 4); we suspect that, under the conditions generated by ionophore treatment, either the enzyme has much greater affinity for the phosphorylated derivatives (see Taylor & Exton, 1987; Homma et al., 1988; Baldassare et al., 1989) or that it has access only to these derivatives.

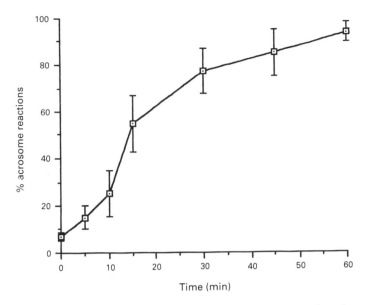

Fig. 3. Time course of the onset of ionophore-induced acrosome reactions in a ram sperm population. Spermatozoa were added to a balanced saline medium containing 3 mM-Ca^{2+} and 1 μM-A23187 at 37°C. At intervals, samples of the suspension were taken, fixed with glutaraldehyde, and the percentage of acrosome reactions assessed by phase-contrast microscopy according to Shams-Borhan & Harrison (1981). Data taken from Roldan & Harrison (1989), shown as means ± s.d. for 4 experiments.

The phosphoinositide breakdown is largely complete within 3 min and seems essential for subsequent exocytosis (Roldan & Harrison, 1989). If EGTA is included with the ionophore so as to chelate Ca^{2+}, no inositide breakdown occurs and no acrosome reactions ensue; subsequent addition of Ca^{2+} initiates the rapid inositide breakdown, and exocytosis follows, with a time curve relative to Ca^{2+} addition indistinguishable from that seen after normal Ca^{2+}/ionophore induction. Moreover, if spermatozoa are treated with neomycin, an aminoglycoside antibiotic that binds specifically to polyphosphoinositides and blocks their metabolism (e.g. Downes & Michell, 1981; Cockcroft & Gomperts, 1985; Whitaker & Aitchison, 1985), not only is the ionophore-induced polyphosphoinositide breakdown very much delayed but no acrosome reactions ensue. However, such blocking of the acrosome reactions only occurs if the neomycin is added before or at the same time as Ca^{2+} and ionophore. If it is added 3 min after the initiation of ionophore treatment (i.e. after phosphoinositide breakdown has taken place), acrosome reactions ensue normally.

When we compared Ca^{2+} involvement in phosphoinositide breakdown with the overall requirements for Ca^{2+} in the acrosome reaction, we were able to distinguish three Ca^{2+}-requiring processes (Roldan & Harrison, 1989). In the standard induction system, millimolar levels of Ca^{2+} are included in the medium at the start of ionophore treatment. If this Ca^{2+} was omitted, the polyphosphoinositide breakdown took place normally (due to the mobilization of low levels of endogenous Ca^{2+}) but no visible acrosome reactions ensued; acrosome reactions occurred normally, however, if the medium was supplemented with millimolar levels of Ca^{2+} or Sr^{2+} (line 1 in Table 2). If low levels of endogenous Ca^{2+} were chelated by inclusion of EGTA at the start of ionophore treatment, there was, of course, no polyphosphoinositide breakdown unless Ca^{2+} was added; in these circumstances, acrosome reactions also occurred only if Ca^{2+} was added (line 2 in Table 2). From these observations, it could be deduced that there was an event subsequent to polyphosphoinositide breakdown which showed a requirement for millimolar levels of either Ca^{2+} or Sr^{2+}. However, if the low levels of mobilized Ca^{2+} in the Ca^{2+}-deficient system were chelated

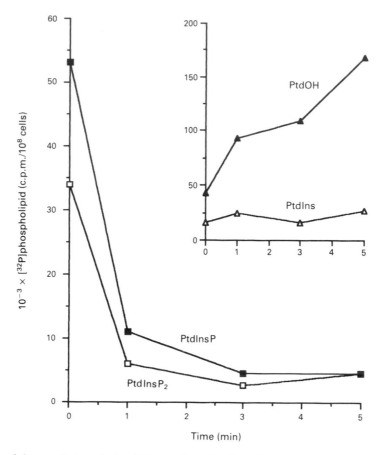

Fig. 4. Breakdown of phosphoinositides and production of phosphatidate following Ca^{2+}/ionophore treatment of ram spermatozoa. Spermatozoa were pre-labelled for 45 min with [^{32}P]orthophosphate and then treated with Ca^{2+} and A23187. At various times after initiation of treatment, samples were precipitated with trichloracetic acid, after which the lipids were extracted, isolated, and analysed for radioactivity. Data from Roldan & Harrison (1989), the results of a typical experiment.

with EGTA after 5 min of ionophore treatment (by which time all polyphosphoinositide had been catabolized), again acrosome reactions ensued only if further Ca^{2+} was added: Sr^{2+} was not able to support reactions (line 3 in Table 2), indicating another process following phosphoinositide breakdown which had a specific requirement for Ca^{2+}. When Ca^{2+} was added later to a Ca^{2+}-deficient system (in which inositide breakdown occurred normally at the start of ionophore treatment), the rate of onset of acrosome reactions relative to Ca^{2+} addition was faster than in the standard system (Table 3), suggesting that there had been a build-up of intermediates. The collective inference from all these observations was therefore that polyphosphoinositide breakdown initiates a train of events necessary for membrane fusion. There are three Ca^{2+}-dependent processes: (a) polyphosphoinositide breakdown itself, with a specific requirement for low levels of Ca^{2+}; (b) a subsequent process with a specific requirement for low levels of Ca^{2+}; and (c) a later process with a requirement for millimolar levels of Ca^{2+} (for which Sr^{2+} can substitute).

The question now arises, which of the products of phosphoinositide breakdown is important for subsequent membrane fusion, and why?

Table 2. Ability of different divalent cations to induce the acrosome reaction in ram spermatozoa in the presence of ionophore

Treatment	% Acrosome reactions after 60 min with cation:			
	None	Ca^{2+}	Sr^{2+}	Ba^{2+}
A23187	8.0 ± 4.2	89.0 ± 1.4	82.5 ± 2.1	6.0 ± 0.0
A23187 + EGTA	3.0 ± 1.4	97.0 ± 5.2	18.3 ± 8.7	6.0 ± 3.6
A23187 for 5 min; then EGTA and the cation added	—	92.3 ± 4.7	23.0 ± 10.8	6.0 ± 2.6

Spermatozoa were treated with 1 μM-A23187, and additions of 1 mM-EGTA and/or the different divalent cations (3 mM) were made either simultaneously with the ionophore or 5 min later. Data from Roldan & Harrison (1989), given as means ± s.d. for 3 experiments.

Table 3. Effect of late addition of Ca^{2+} on the onset of ionophore-induced acrosome reactions in ram spermatozoa

Treatment	% Acrosome reactions after Ca^{2+} addition			
	5 min	10 min	15 min	20 min
A23187 + Ca^{2+}	19.0 ± 4.8	23.5 ± 11.3	38.0 ± 19.2	67.5 ± 12.7
A23187; Ca^{2+} added 10 min later	16.5 ± 8.8	$34.5 \pm 17.2*$	$59.2 \pm 15.6**$	79.5 ± 11.1

Spermatozoa were treated with 1 μM-A23187; 3 mM-Ca^{2+} was added with the ionophore or 10 min later. Data from Roldan & Harrison (1989), given as means ± s.d. for 4 experiments.
$*P < 0.05$, $**P < 0.01$, relative to results with Ca^{2+} added at start of treatment.

Inositol 1,4,5-trisphosphate

In very many cell types, as mentioned above, $Ins(1,4,5)P_3$ is involved in the modulation of cytoplasmic Ca^{2+} levels, either directly by stimulating Ca^{2+} release from intracellular storage organelles or indirectly by stimulating Ca^{2+} entry through the plasma membrane via emptying of these intracellular organelles (Berridge & Irvine, 1989). At the present time, all the experimental indications are that the completion of the sperm acrosome reaction relies entirely upon external Ca^{2+} (see Fraser & Ahuja, 1988). There is no morphological evidence for internal non-mitochondrial storage organelles; in addition, although localized deposits of Ca^{2+} within the head cytoplasm of normal spermatozoa have been detected by some workers using cytochemical methods (Chandler & Battersby, 1976; Berruti *et al.*, 1986; Ruknudin, 1989), such results were not obtained by others using a milder fixation procedure (Watson & Plummer, 1986). The sperm cell may therefore not readily relate to what is currently known of inositol polyphosphate-mediated Ca^{2+} modulation in other cell types. Of course, in our model sperm system, there is no obvious role for inositol polyphosphates because Ca^{2+} mobilization has been facilitated by the ionophore. On the other hand, it is possible that in the physiological process a zona-pellucida agonist might induce initial breakdown of $PtdInsP_2$ to produce $Ins(1,4,5)P_3$ in order to stimulate Ca^{2+} entry by various mechanisms (as discussed by Roldan & Harrison, 1990); the resultant rise in intracellular Ca^{2+} would then activate further and extensive polyphosphoinositide breakdown, leading to subsequent exocytosis as in our ionophore-induced system. However, it has become increasingly clear that in other cell systems $Ins(1,4,5)P_3$ must act in conjunction with its phosphorylated product

Ins(1,3,4,5)P_4 in order to mediate its effects (see Berridge & Irvine, 1989). While seeking evidence for the formation of Ins(1,4,5)P_3 during breakdown of phosphoinositides in the ionophore-induced acrosome reaction in ram spermatozoa, we looked also for Ins(1,3,4,5)P_4; we could not find either Ins(1,3,4,5)P_4 or its usual catabolite Ins(1,3,4)P_3 in extracts from acrosome-reacting spermatozoa, nor could we demonstrate any phosphorylation of Ins(1,4,5)P_3 by sperm homogenates (Harrison et al. 1990). We have concluded that the enzyme required, InsP_3-3-kinase (see Fig. 1), is not present in ram spermatozoa, and therefore that Ins(1,3,4,5)P_4 is not formed from Ins(1,4,5)P_3 when the latter is produced during breakdown of PtdInsP_2. The absence of InsP_4 implies in turn that Ins(1,4,5)P_3 is not involved in Ca^{2+} modulation in these cells, and that other mechanisms regulate net Ca^{2+} influx (see Roldan & Harrison, 1990).

Domino & Garbers (1988) and Thomas & Meizel (1989a) were able to detect dramatic increases in Ins(1,4,5)P_3 production at the time of the acrosome reaction in sea urchin and human spermatozoa, respectively. The reactions were induced under essentially physiological conditions. However, in both species InsP_3 production was absolutely dependent on external Ca^{2+} and was inhibited completely by external Ca^{2+}-channel blockers or by external La^{3+}, an ion that competes strongly with Ca^{2+} and blocks its uptake. Thus InsP_3 did not appear to be the mediator of Ca^{2+} entry in either sperm species; rather, it appeared to be produced only as a consequence of Ca^{2+} entry. Although unusual, this is not unknown, because a similar situation, in which Ca^{2+} entry itself is responsible for phospholipase C activation and polyphosphoinositide breakdown, has been observed in several excitable tissues (Eberhard & Holz, 1988).

Diacylglycerol

There is a rapid rise in the level of DAG in spermatozoa following the initiation of Ca^{2+}/ionophore treatment (Table 4), concomitant with polyphosphoinositide breakdown. When treatment is carried out in the presence of the DAG kinase inhibitor R59022 (De Chaffoy de Courcelles et al., 1985), DAG values rise higher whereas the rise in ^{32}P incorporation into PtdOH that accompanies phosphoinositide breakdown is greatly reduced, suggesting strongly that this rise in ^{32}P incorporation is due to the phosphorylation of DAG by DAG kinase. On the other hand, when ionophore treatment is carried out in the presence of the DAG lipase inhibitor RHC80267 (Sutherland & Amin, 1982), values of DAG again rise higher but now there is a large increase in ^{32}P incorporation into PtdOH, probably due to the increased availability of substrate for DAG kinase. Both these inhibitors of DAG metabolism, especially R59022, also enhance the rate of appearance of visible acrosome reactions (Table 5). It is not obvious why R59022 should be more effective than RHC80267 in this respect, but, coupled with the failure of added PtdOH to enhance the onset of acrosome reactions, the finding clearly indicates that PtdOH has no role in the Ca^{2+}/ionophore-induced acrosome reaction. Inclusion of synthetic dioleylglycerol in the ionophore induction system similarly enhances the onset of acrosome reactions (Table 6). Proof that this compound acts 'downstream' of phosphoinositide breakdown is provided by its ability to over-ride the blocking of acrosome reactions by neomycin, coupled with its failure to induce acrosome reactions in the absence of ionophore (Table 6). Taken together, the observations described in this section imply that the critical product of phosphoinositide breakdown necessary for subsequent exocytosis is DAG itself rather than a later metabolite.

As mentioned above, DAG produced from phosphoinositide breakdown exerts a second messenger effect in many cells through stimulation of Ca^{2+}-dependent protein kinase C (see Berridge, 1987; Woodgett et al., 1987). However, we have found no evidence for protein kinase C activity in spermatozoa (Roldan & Harrison, 1988). We could not detect changes in protein phosphorylation pattern in ram sperm extracts during the ionophore-induced acrosome reaction, whether in the presence or absence of phorbol dibutyrate (an activator of protein kinase C). Likewise, phorbol dibutyrate did not perturb the rate of onset of ram sperm acrosome reactions

Table 4. Diacylglycerol (DAG) and phosphatidate (PtdOH) in ram spermatozoa following Ca^{2+}/ionophore treatment in the presence of the DAG kinase inhibitor R59022 or the DAG lipase inhibitor RHC80267

	Lipids 5 min after treatment	
Treatment	DAG ($\mu g/10^8$ spermatozoa)	$[^{32}P]$PtdOH (c.p.m./10^8 spermatozoa)
Control (no treatment)	$1 \cdot 73 \pm 0 \cdot 5$	$49\,043 \pm 4\,825$
Ca^{2+}/A23187	$3 \cdot 27 \pm 0 \cdot 5$	$159\,081 \pm 25\,979$
+ R59022 (100 μM)	$3 \cdot 55 \pm 1 \cdot 1$	$59\,720 \pm 10\,150$
+ RHC80267 (100 μM)	$3 \cdot 66 \pm 0 \cdot 4$	$209\,764 \pm 17\,179$

Spermatozoa were pre-labelled with ^{32}P and treated with 3 mM-Ca^{2+} and 1 μM-A23187 as described by Roldan & Harrison (1989). R59022 (from Janssen Life Sciences, Wantage, Oxon., UK), dissolved in ethanol according to De Chaffoy de Courcelles *et al.* (1985), and RHC80267 (a generous gift from Dr D. R. Morton, The Upjohn Co, Kalamazoo, MI, USA), dissolved in dimethyl sulphoxide, were added to the sperm suspensions at the same time as the ionophore; total final concentrations of solvent (including that of the ionophore) were 3% (v/v) or less. After 5 min of treatment, spermatozoa were precipitated with trichloracetic acid and the lipids extracted according to Roldan & Harrison (1989). PtdOH was isolated and analysed according to Roldan & Harrison (1989), while DAG was isolated and analysed according to Bocckino *et al.* (1987). Values are means $\pm$ s.d. for 3 experiments.

Table 5. Effect of the DAG kinase inhibitor R59022 and the DAG lipase inhibitor RHC80267 on the onset of ionophore-induced acrosome reactions in ram spermatozoa

Treatment	% Acrosome reactions 15 min after treatment
Control (no treatment)	$7 \cdot 4 \pm 2 \cdot 7$
Ca^{2+}/A23187	$58 \cdot 7 \pm 17 \cdot 2$
+ R59022 (100 μM)	$81 \cdot 3 \pm 14 \cdot 0$*
+ RHC80267 (100 μM)	$69 \cdot 0 \pm 10 \cdot 2$

Inhibitors were added at the same time as the ionophore.
Values are means $\pm$ s.d. for 6 experiments.
*$P < 0 \cdot 05$, relative to Ca^{2+}/A23187 alone.

during ionophore induction, even under conditions of limiting Ca^{2+} (phorbol esters lower the Ca^{2+} requirement of protein kinase C). Finally, we could not detect specific phorbol-dibutyrate-binding sites in either ram or boar spermatozoa (such binding sites have been shown to correspond to protein kinase C: Ashendel, 1985). The results are apparently at odds with the findings of Lee *et al.* (1987), who were able to modify the physiological induction of acrosome reactions in mouse spermatozoa with tetradecanoylphorbol acetate. Two points may be made. Firstly, the ready reversibility of the phorbol ester effect noted by Lee *et al.* (1987) does not seem in accord with the generally accepted characteristics of protein kinase C, as phorbol esters are tightly bound and stimulation is protracted (Ashendel, 1985; Woodgett *et al.*, 1987). Secondly, from our studies, there appears to be a relatively high 'resting' level of diacylglycerol in washed ejaculated ram spermatozoa: of the order of 28 nmol per 10^9 spermatozoa, calculated from direct densitometric measurements of Coomassie-stained thin-layer chromatograms and assuming an average molecular weight for DAG of about 620; this compares with a figure of 0·11 nmol per 10^9 platelets (Preiss *et al.*, 1986), cells of dimensions similar to ram sperm heads. The presence of significant levels of DAG in

Table 6. Effect of dioleylglycerol (DOG) and neomycin on the onset of ionophore-induced acrosome reactions in ram spermatozoa

Treatment	% Acrosome reactions 15 min after treatment
Control (no treatment)	$7 \cdot 0 \pm 2 \cdot 9$
Ca^{2+}/A23187	$49 \cdot 0 \pm 10 \cdot 5$
+DOG (100 µM)	$58 \cdot 2 \pm 9 \cdot 3^*$
+neomycin (10 mM)	$14 \cdot 2 \pm 3 \cdot 9^*$
+neomycin (10 mM)+ DOG (100 µM)	$38 \cdot 0 \pm 5 \cdot 2$
DOG (100 µM) alone	$6 \cdot 0 \pm 2 \cdot 6$

DOG (Sigma Chemical Co., Poole, Dorset, UK; dissolved in dimethyl sulphoxide) and/or neomycin sulphate (Sigma) were added at the same time as initiation of ionophore treatment. Values are means $\pm$ s.d. for 4 experiments.
*$P < 0 \cdot 05$, relative to Ca^{2+}/A23187 alone.

untreated spermatozoa can also be deduced from the rapidity with which these cells incorporate $^{32}P_i$ into PtdOH (Roldan & Harrison, 1989). It therefore seems likely that any protein kinase C would already be in an activated state in such cells. Although this might explain our inability to detect the effects or presence of protein kinase C, a concept of reversal of activation during capacitation and then reactivation during induction of the acrosome reaction is difficult to postulate as explanation of the findings of Lee *et al.* (1987). An alternative explanation of phorbol ester effects, not involving protein kinase C, seems more likely (see Woodgett *et al.*, 1987; Sha'afi, 1989; Visconti & Tezon, 1989).

Another possible role of DAG is that of a fusogen (Das & Rand, 1984; Siegel *et al.*, 1989). A direct fusogenic action seems unlikely for two reasons. Firstly, the increase in DAG resulting from breakdown of the polyphosphoinositides is very rapid and reaches a maximum by 5 min, whereas the onset of acrosome reactions begins several minutes later and continues for more than 30 min (Shams-Borhan & Harrison, 1981; Roldan & Harrison, 1989). Secondly, as mentioned above, we have detected two Ca^{2+}-requiring events following phosphoinositide breakdown (and DAG production). Further metabolic processes are therefore indicated. At the same time, the presence of physiological levels of DAG may well enhance the tendency of the membranes to fuse, as suggested by Siegel *et al.* (1989).

Diacylglycerol and phospholipase A$_2$

Our current hypothesis, however, is that the major role of DAG is as a 'second messenger' to stimulate phospholipase A$_2$ activity and inhibit lysophosphatide acyltransferase activity, leading to greatly increased levels of lysophospholipids in the outer acrosomal membrane and overlying plasma membranes (Fig. 5). The presence of these lysophospholipids would lead to fusibility and thence, in the presence of sufficient levels of cytoplasmic Ca^{2+}, to membrane fusion.

The likelihood that lysophospholipids play a role in the acrosome reaction has been indicated by a large number of studies, in particular the detailed investigations by Fleming & Yanagimachi (1981), in which pretreatment of guinea pig spermatozoa with certain lysophospholipids, particularly lysophosphatidylcholine, led to rapid induction of the acrosome reaction after addition of mM concentrations of Ca^{2+}. General theories of membrane fusion have also involved lysophospholipids as fusogens in the presence of Ca^{2+} (Lucy, 1970, 1978). The enzyme phospholipase A$_2$,

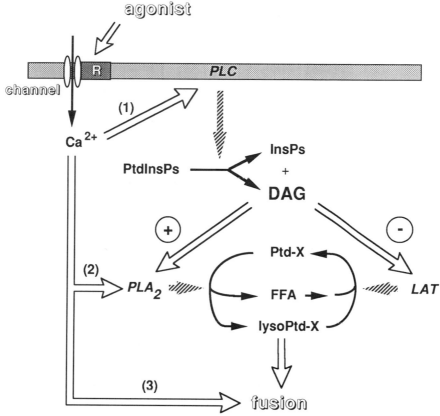

Fig. 5. Possible mechanism leading to membrane fusion during the acrosome reaction. PLC, phospholipase C; PLA_2, phospholipase A_2; LAT, lysophosphatide acyltransferase; Ptd-X phosphatidylcholine, phosphatidylethanolamine or phosphatidylserine; FFA, free fatty acids. Ca^{2+} influx is induced by the action of an agonist (possibly a zona pellucida component) on a receptor-operated channel in the plasma membrane. Resultant enhanced Ca^{2+} levels within the cytoplasm then activate the three sequential processes described in the text. DAG, released through the action of Ca^{2+}-activated PLC, stimulates PLA_2 and inhibits LAT, leading to a build-up of lysoPtd-X which, in the presence of sufficient Ca^{2+}, results in fusion.

responsible for the production of lysophospholipids, has been identified and characterized in spermatozoa (Ono *et al.*, 1982; Thakkar *et al.*, 1983, 1984; Hinkovska *et al.*, 1987), and its release (either soluble or attached to acrosomal membrane remnants) at the time of the acrosome reaction has been demonstrated (Llanos *et al.*, 1982), indicating that at least some of the activity is located in the head region. Several compounds that inhibit phospholipase A_2 also block or delay the onset of the acrosome reaction (Lui & Meizel, 1979; Ono *et al.*, 1982; Drummond & Olds-Clarke, 1986), although there is variation between species, both in the susceptibility of the sperm enzyme to inhibition by a given inhibitor and in the effects on the acrosome reaction. On the other hand, spermatozoa also contain considerable lysophosphatide acyltransferase and acyl CoA synthetase activity, as evidenced by the readiness with which labelled fatty acids are incorporated into phospholipids (Neill & Masters, 1972; Bennet *et al.*, 1987). These enzymes, working in tandem, reacylate lyso-phospholipids produced by phospholipase A_2, often using the fatty acids released by its action; thus, together with phospholipase A_2, they form the basis of a 'futile cycle' (e.g. Kröner *et al.*, 1981; Morash *et al.*, 1989).

   In support of our hypothesis regarding the role of DAG, several recent studies have indicated the ability of this compound to enhance phospholipase A_2 activity in other systems (Dawson *et al.*,

1984; Kramer et al., 1987; Burch, 1988), and Goppelt-Strübe et al. (1987) have shown that DAG will inhibit lysophosphatide acyltransferase. Moreover, phospholipase A_2 from a wide variety of sources (including spermatozoa) has been shown to have a requirement for Ca^{2+} (e.g. Thakkar et al., 1983, 1984; Hinkovska et al., 1987). On present evidence, therefore, we suggest that the second process in the train of Ca^{2+}-requiring events leading to membrane fusion in the acrosome reaction is DAG-stimulated phospholipase A_2 activity, acting in conjunction with DAG inhibition of lysophosphatide acyltransferase, to produce a build-up of fusogenic lysophospholipids. The third process may well be membrane fusion itself, brought about by Ca^{2+} when the levels of these lipids have reached a necessary threshold (Verkleij et al., 1984).

The strong evidence for phospholipase A_2 involvement in the mammalian sperm acrosome reaction has prompted other hypotheses regarding the enzyme's activation, in particular that a zymogen form (Antaki et al., 1989) is activated through proteinase action. Acrosin has been proposed as a possible agent in this respect (see Meizel, 1984); however, the difficulty with this concept is that membrane fusion in the acrosome reaction would appear to require primarily changes in the cytoplasmic leaflets of the acrosomal and plasma membranes (i.e. changes mediated from the sperm head cytoplasm, outside the acrosome), whereas current evidence indicates that acrosin itself remains in the form of an inactive zymogen within the acrosome until the acrosome reaction takes place (Huneau et al., 1984). The possible involvement of metalloproteinases in the acrosome reaction has been reported for both sea urchin (Farach et al., 1987) and man (Thomas & Meizel, 1989b), but the ability of Ca^{2+} to satisfy all ionic requirements in our ionophore-induced reaction militates against a metalloproteinase role in this system.

Relevance of ionophore-induced membrane fusion mechanisms to the physiological situation

The major difference between the ionophore induction system and other systems in which the acrosome reaction can be induced is the need for prior capacitation in the latter, to 'prime' the spermatozoon to respond. The detailed processes that result in capacitation are not yet known. It is clear that major changes take place in the sperm surface (see Yanagimachi, 1988); among other consequences, these changes may result in the unmasking of receptor sites such that agonists can act (see Harrison, 1983; Florman & First, 1988). There is also very little doubt now that stimulated Ca^{2+} influx is a very early event in the triggering of acrosome reactions in capacitated sperm populations (Thomas & Meizel, 1988; Florman et al., 1989). The relevance of our results, gained from ionophore triggering, to studies using other means of induction therefore depends to a large degree on the question as to whether the sudden increase in internal Ca^{2+} activates the same event in the different induction systems. Hitherto, evidence has suggested that one of the consequences of capacitation is an increased steady-state concentration of intracellular (probably cytoplasmic) Ca^{2+} (Singh et al., 1978; Coronel & Lardy, 1987; Fraser, 1987; Handrow et al., 1989); this conclusion has been strengthened by the link between expression of hyperactivated motility and capacitation (see Fraser, 1987; Neill & Olds-Clarke, 1987), together with the demonstration that hyperactivated motility reflects enhanced internal Ca^{2+} levels (Shams-Borhan & Harrison, 1981; Suarez et al., 1987). Because two of the processes we have identified in the acrosome reaction sequence require only low levels of Ca^{2+}, the possibility must be considered that these processes would be set in train by such increased Ca^{2+} levels during capacitation, and that 'physiological' triggering of the acrosome reaction might involve stimulation only of events late in the sequence. However, Florman et al. (1989), measuring Ca^{2+} levels directly in individual bull spermatozoa undergoing zona-induced acrosome reactions, were unable to detect an increase in internal Ca^{2+} in the heads of such cells (previously shown to be capacitated: Florman & First, 1988) until the acrosome reaction itself was triggered by the zona pellucida agonist; similar conclusions regarding stability of internal Ca^{2+} concentrations during capacitation have been drawn from direct measurements of free Ca^{2+} in capacitated rabbit sperm populations (Mahanes *et al.*, 1986). The two opposing groups of results may be reconciled by the consideration that in many experiments completion of capacitation has been assessed essentially by the onset of acrosome reactions in the presence of serum albumin or follicular fluid (containing albumin); we believe such acrosome reactions should be viewed as 'spontaneous' and should be differentiated from those induced by zona-pellucida components. As incubation under capacitating conditions proceeds, spontaneous entry of Ca^{2+} may eventually increase, whence the resultant enhanced internal levels of the ion would initiate early events in the sequence leading to membrane fusion. The effect of albumin would be to remove from the spermatozoa fatty acids released by the phospholipase A_2 action and increase the build-up of lysophospholipids (see results of Lui & Meizel, 1977). This build-up, of itself, would in turn enhance Ca^{2+} entry (Gregson, 1989), and fusion would ensue when lysolipids and internal Ca^{2+} had reached sufficient levels. In our view, the acrosome reaction-inducing effect of albumin would tend to take place further 'down-stream' in the chain of events required for membrane fusion than the Ca^{2+} entry-triggering effect of the zona-pellucida agonist, and the albumin effect would require a prior increase in internal Ca^{2+}.

From the arguments presented above, therefore, we are inclined to believe that events in the ionophore-induced acrosome reaction may reflect rather closely the zona pellucida-induced reaction (which, on current evidence, must be considered the most physiological one). Moreover, the time course of the zona-induced reaction in capacitated sperm populations appears to be similar to that of our ionophore-induced reaction, there being a lag period and then a sigmoid response curve over a period of many minutes (Florman & First, 1988; Lee & Storey, 1989). In human spermatozoa, however, acrosome reactions can occur within a few minutes, even seconds, of stimulation of capacitated populations (Siiteri *et al.*, 1988); similar responses were seen under certain conditions in capacitated guinea-pig spermatozoa (Yanagimachi & Usui, 1974). This very rapid response does not seem to fit with the time period required for the sequence of events we have described, but could be explained if some of the earlier steps had already taken place during capacitation; both the rapidly responding systems had undergone long periods of capacitation in the presence of serum albumin. On the other hand, the observations of Thomas & Meizel (1989a) that Ins(1,4,5)P_3 levels rise sharply on final stimulation is more difficult to explain. One could be forced to conclude that the whole sequence is much more rapid in this system (for reasons which as yet we cannot explain) or that phosphoinositide breakdown may not be a part of the physiological sequence. However, sperm polyphosphoinositides appear to be localized in the acrosomal region: in a cytochemical study of boar spermatozoa, Berruti & Franchi (1986) detected such material only in the outer acrosomal membrane and in the plasma membrane over the anterior part of the head; no polyphosphoinositides were detected in the plasma membrane of the tail.

Of course, there may be several parallel mechanisms in spermatozoa capable of leading to membrane fusion during the acrosome reaction, and, far from being separate, they may be inter-related. For example, egg-jelly fucose sulphate glycoprotein activates both phospholipase C (Domino & Garbers, 1988) and phospholipase D (Domino *et al.*, 1989) in sea urchin spermatozoa, concomitantly with the induction of acrosome reactions; while phospholipase C yields DAG, phospholipase D yields PtdOH. It remains to be proven that either enzyme activity is necessary for the acrosome reaction, but both activities can be expected to lead to increases in DAG and PtdOH, because the data of Domino *et al.* (1989) indicate the presence of DAG kinase and PtdOH phosphohydrolase, enzymes which together interconvert the two compounds. The presence of both DAG and PtdOH that we have observed in unstimulated, non-capacitated ram spermatozoa (see Table 4) suggests that the two enzymes are also present in spermatozoa of mammalian species, forming a 'futile cycling' system in which PtdOH formed by phosphorylation of DAG is rapidly dephosphorylated again (see Fig. 1); any process that fed into this cycle would raise DAG levels, and thence stimulate phospholipase A_2 and inhibit lysophosphatide acyltransferase (if our hypothesis is correct).

Conclusions

From what has been discussed above, it is clear that much of the mechanism of the mammalian sperm acrosome reaction remains to be elucidated. However, our studies have demonstrated that, when the reaction is induced through the use of ionophore, membrane fusion occurs as the result of a train of events that is initiated by Ca^{2+} influx but in which Ca^{2+} also plays further roles. In this system, the first event appears to be polyphosphoinositide breakdown, yielding DAG that acts as an effector for a subsequent process. Relating our data to the findings of others, we have proposed a molecular sequence linking Ca^{2+} entry to membrane fusion. Whether or not our proposed sequence eventually proves to be the same as that occurring in the physiological acrosome reaction, by establishing the biochemical processes that lead to exocytotic membrane fusion in one system, we are providing a framework on which studies of other systems can be based.

We are grateful to the Biochemical Society for permission to reproduce material originally published in the Biochemical Journal (Roldan & Harrison, 1989). We thank Journals of Reproduction & Fertility Ltd, The Wellcome Trust, and The Lalor Foundation for major financial grants supporting our studies described in this review.

References

Aguas, A.P. & Pinto Da Silva, P. (1989) Bimodal redistribution of surface transmembrane glycoproteins during Ca^{2+}-dependent secretion (acrosome reaction) in boar spermatozoa. *J. Cell Sci.* **93**, 467–479.

Allison, A.C. & Hartree, E.F. (1970) Lysosomal enzymes in the acrosome and their possible role in fertilization. *J. Reprod. Fert.* **21**, 501–515.

Antaki, P., Guérette, P., Chapdelaine, A. & Roberts, D.D. (1989) Detection of prophospholipase A_2 in human spermatozoa. *Biol. Reprod.* **41**, 241–246.

Ashendel, C.L. (1985) The phorbol ester receptor: a phospholipid-regulated protein kinase. *Biochim. Biophys. Acta* **822**, 219–242.

Austin, C.R. & Bishop, M.W.H. (1958) Role of the rodent acrosome and perforatorium in fertilization. *Proc. R. Soc. Lond. B* **149**, 241–248.

Baldassare, J.J., Henderson, P.A. & Fisher, G.J. (1989) Isolation and characterization of one soluble and two membrane-associated forms of phosphoinositide-specific phospholipase C from human platelets. *Biochemistry, NY* **28**, 6010–6016.

Barros, C. (1974) Capacitation of mammalian spermatozoa. In *Physiology and Genetics of Reproduction* Part B, pp. 3–24. Eds E. M. Coutinho & F. Fuchs. Plenum Press, New York.

Bennet, P.J., Moatti, J.-P., Mansat, A., Ribbes, H., Cayrac, J.-C., Pontonnier, F., Chap, J. & Douste-Blazy, L. (1987) Evidence for the activation of phospholipases during acrosome reaction of human sperm elicited by calcium ionophore A23187. *Biochim. Biophys. Acta* **919**, 255–265.

Berridge, M.J. (1987) Inositol trisphosphate and diacylglycerol: two interacting second messengers. *Ann. Rev. Biochem.* **56**, 159–193.

Berridge, M.J. & Irvine, R.F. (1989) Inositol phosphates and cell signalling. *Nature, Lond.* **341**, 197–205.

Berruti, G. & Franchi, E. (1986) Calcium and polyphosphoinositides: their distribution in relation to the membrane changes occurring in the head of boar spermatozoa. *Eur. J. Cell Biol.* **41**, 238–245.

Berruti, G., Franchi, E. & Camatini, M. (1986) Ca^{++} localization in boar spermatozoa by the pyroantimonate technique and X-ray microanalysis. *J. exp. Zool.* **237**, 257–262.

Bocckino, S.B., Blackmore, P.F., Wilson, P.B. & Exton, J.H. (1987) Phosphatidate accumulation in hormone-treated hepatocytes via a phospholipase D mechanism. *J. biol. Chem.* **262**, 15309–15315.

Bowen, R.H. (1922) On the idiosome, Golgi apparatus, and acrosome in the male germ cells. *Anat. Rec.* **24**, 159–180.

Burch, R.M. (1988) Diacylglycerol stimulates phospholipase A_2 from Swiss 3T3 fibroblasts. *FEBS Lett.* **234**, 283–286.

Chandler, J.A. & Battersby, S. (1976) X-ray microanalysis of zinc and calcium in ultrathin sections of human sperm cells using the pyroantimonate technique. *J. Histochem. Cytochem.* **24**, 740–748.

Cockcroft, S. & Gomperts, B.D. (1985) Role of guanine nucleotide binding protein in the activation of polyphosphoinositide phosphodiesterase. *Nature, Lond.* **314**, 534–536.

Colwin, L.H. & Colwin, A.L. (1967) Membrane fusion in relation to sperm-egg association. In *Fertilization, Comparative Morphology, Biochemistry, and Immunology*, vol. 1, pp. 295–367. Eds C. B. Metz & A. Monroy. Academic Press, New York.

Coronel, C.E. & Lardy, H.A. (1987) Characterization of Ca^{2+} uptake by guinea pig epididymal spermatozoa. *Biol. Reprod.* **37**, 1097–1107.

Dan, J.C. (1967) Acrosome reaction and lysins. In *Fertilization, Comparative Morphology, Biochemistry, and Immunology*, vol. 1, pp. 237–293. Eds C. B. Metz & A. Monroy. Academic Press, New York.

Das, S. & Rand, R.P. (1984) Diacylglycerol causes major structural transitions in phospholipid bilayer membranes. *Biochem. Biophys. Res. Commun.* **124**, 491–496.

Davis, B.K. (1981) Timing of fertilization in mammals: sperm cholesterol/phospholipid ratio as a determinant of the capacitation interval. *Proc. natn. Acad. Sci. USA* **78**, 7560–7564.

Dawson, R.M.C., Irvine, R.F., Bray, J. & Quinn, P.J. (1984) Long-chain unsaturated diacylglycerols cause a perturbation in the structure of phospholipid bilayers rendering them susceptible to phospholipase attack. *Biochem. Biophys. Res. Commun.* **125**, 836–842.

De Chaffoy de Courcelles, D., Roevens, P. & Van Belle, H. (1985) R59 022, a diacylglycerol kinase inhibitor. Its effect on diacylglycerol and thrombin-induced C kinase activation in the intact platelet. *J. biol. Chem.* **260**, 15762–15770.

De Lisle, R.C. & Williams, J.A. (1986) Regulation of membrane fusion in secretory exocytosis. *Ann. Rev. Physiol.* **48**, 225–238.

Domino, S.E. & Garbers, D.L. (1988) The fucose-sulphate glycoconjugate that induces an acrosome reaction in spermatozoa stimulates inositol 1,4,5-trisphosphate accumulation. *J. biol. Chem.* **263**, 690–695.

Domino, S.E., Bocckino, S.B. & Garbers, D.L. (1989) Activation of phospholipase D by the fucose-sulphate glycoconjugate that induces an acrosome reaction in spermatozoa. *J. biol. Chem.* **264**, 9412–9419.

Downes, C.P. & Michell, R.H. (1981) The polyphosphoinositide phosphodiesterase of erythrocyte membranes. *Biochem. J.* **198**, 133–140.

Drummond, E. & Olds-Clarke, P. (1986) Mouse sperm capacitation involves phospholipase A_2 activity, but not cyclooxygenase activity. *Biol. Reprod.* **34**, (Suppl. 1), 65, abstr.

Eberhard, D.A. & Holz, R.W. (1988) Intracellular Ca^{2+} activates phospholipase C. *Trends in Neurosci.* **11**, 517–520.

Farach, H.A., Mundy, D.I., Strittmatter, W.J. & Lennarz, W.J. (1987) Evidence for the involvement of metalloendoproteases in the acrosome reaction in sea urchin sperm. *J. biol. Chem.* **262**, 5483–5487.

Fléchon, J.-E., Harrison, R.A.P., Fléchon, B. & Escaig, J. (1986) Membrane fusion events in the $Ca^{2+}/$ ionophore-induced acrosome reaction of ram spermatozoa. *J. Cell Sci.* **81**, 43–63.

Fleming, A.D. & Yanagimachi, R. (1981) Effects of various lipids on the acrosome reaction and fertilizing capacity of guinea pig spermatozoa with special reference to the possible involvement of lysophospholipids in the acrosome reaction. *Gamete Res.* **4**, 253–273.

Florman, H.M. & First, N.L. (1988) The regulation of acrosomal exocytosis. I. Sperm capacitation is required for the induction of acrosome reactions by the bovine *zona pellucida in vitro*. *Devl Biol.* **128**, 453–463.

Florman, H.M. & Storey, B.T. (1982) Mouse gamete interactions: the zona pellucida is the site of the acrosome reaction leading to fertilization *in vitro*. *Devl Biol.* **91**, 121–130.

Florman, H.M., Tombes, R.M., First, N.L. & Babcock, D.F. (1989) An adhesion-associated agonist from the zona pellucida activates G protein-promoted elevations of internal Ca^{2+} and pH that mediate mammalian sperm acrosomal exocytosis. *Devl Biol.* **135**, 133–146.

Fraser, L.R. (1987) Minimum and maximum extracellular Ca^{2+} requirements during mouse sperm capacitation and fertilization *in vitro*. *J. Reprod. Fert.* **81**, 77–89.

Fraser, L.R. & Ahuja, K.K. (1988) Metabolic and surface events in fertilization. *Gamete Res.* **20**, 491–519.

Friend, D.S. (1977) The organization of the spermatozoal membrane. In *Immunobiology of Gametes*, pp. 5–30. Eds M. Edidin & M. H. Johnson. Cambridge University Press.

Go, K.J. & Wolf, D.P. (1983) The role of sterols in sperm capacitation. *Adv. Lipid Res.* **20**, 317–330.

Goppelt-Strübe, M., Pfannkuche, H.-J., Gemsa, D. & Resch, K. (1987) The diacylglycerols dioctanoylglycerol and oleoylacetylglycerol enhance prostaglandin synthesis by inhibition of the lysophosphatide acyltransferase. *Biochem. J.* **147**, 773–777.

Green, D.P.L. (1978) The mechanism of the acrosome reaction. In *Development in Mammals*, vol. 3, pp. 65–81. Ed. M. H. Johnson. North-Holland, Amsterdam.

Gregson, N.A. 1989) Lysolipids and membrane damage: lysolecithin and its interaction with myelin. *Biochem. Soc. Trans.* **17**, 280–283.

Handrow, R.R., First, N.L. & Parrish, J.J. (1989) Calcium requirement and increased association with bovine sperm during capacitation by heparin. *J. exp. Zool.* **252**, 174–182.

Harrison, R.A.P. (1983) The acrosome, its hydrolases, and egg penetration. In *The Sperm Cell*, pp. 259–273. Ed. J. André. Martinus Nijhoff, The Hague.

Harrison, R.A.P., Roldan, E.R.S., Lander, D.J. & Irvine, R.F. (1990) Ram spermatozoa produce inositol 1,4,5-trisphosphate but not inositol 1,3,4,5-tetrakisphosphate during the Ca^{2+}/ionophore-induced acrosome reaction. *Cellular Signalling* **2**, 277–284.

Hinkovska, V.Tz., Momchilova, A.B., Petkova, D.H. & Koumanov, K.S. (1987) Phospholipase A2 activity in ram spermatozoa plasma membranes. *Int. J. Biochem.* **19**, 569–572.

Homma, Y., Imaki, J., Nakanishi, O. & Takenawa, T. (1988) Isolation and characterization of two different forms of inositol phospholipid-specific phospholipase C from rat brain. *J. biol. Chem.* **263**, 6592–6598.

Huneau, D., Harrison, R.A.P & Fléchon, J.E. (1984) Ultrastructural localization of proacrosin and acrosin in ram spermatozoa. *Gamete Res.* **9**, 425–440.

Kramer, R.M., Checani, G.C. & Deykin, D. (1987) Stimulation of Ca^{2+}-activated human platelet phospholipase A_2 by diacylglycerol. *Biochem. J.* **248**, 779–783.

Kröner, E.E., Peskar, B.A., Fischer, H. & Ferber, E. (1981) Control of arachidonic acid accumulation in bone marrow-derived macrophages by acyltransferases. *J. biol. Chem.* **256**, 3690–3697.

Langlais, J. & Roberts, K.D. (1985) A molecular membrane model of sperm capacitation and the acrosome reaction of mammalian spermatozoa. *Gamete Res.* **12**, 183–224.

Lee, M.A. & Storey, B.T. (1989) Endpoint of first stage of zona pellucida-induced acrosome reaction in mouse spermatozoa characterized by acrosomal H^+ and Ca^{2+} permeability: population and single cell kinetics. *Gamete Res.* **24**, 303–326.

Lee, M.A., Kopf, G.S. & Storey, B.T. (1987) Effects of phorbol esters and a diacylglycerol on the mouse sperm acrosome reaction induced by the zona pellucida. *Biol. Reprod.* **36**, 617–627.

Llanos, M.N., Lui, C.W. & Meizel, S. (1982) Studies of phospholipase A$_2$ related to the hamster sperm acrosome reaction. *J. exp. Zool.* **221**, 107–117.

Lucy, J.A. (1970) The fusion of biological membranes. *Nature, Lond.* **227**, 814–817.

Lucy, J.A. (1978) Mechanisms of chemically induced cell fusion. In *Membrane Fusion*, pp. 267–304. Eds G. Poste & G. L. Nicolson. Elsevier North-Holland Biomedical Press, Amsterdam.

Lui, C.W. & Meizel, S. (1977) Biochemical studies of the in vitro acrosome reaction inducing activity of bovine serum albumin. *Differentiation* **9**, 59–66.

Lui, C.W. & Meizel, S. (1979) Further evidence in support of a role for hamster sperm hydrolytic enzymes in the acrosome reaction. *J. exp. Zool.* **297**, 173–185.

Mahanes, M.S., Ochs, D.L. & Eng, L.A. (1986) Cell calcium of ejaculated rabbit spermatozoa before and following *in vitro* capacitation. *Biochem. Biophys. Res. Commun.* **134**, 664–670.

Meizel, S. (1984) The importance of hydrolytic enzymes to an exocytotic event, the mammalian sperm acrosome reaction. *Biol. Rev.* **59**, 125–157.

Morash, S.C., Cook, H.W. & Spence, M.W. (1989) Lyso-phosphatidylcholine as an intermediate in phosphatidylcholine metabolism and glycerophosphocholine synthesis in cultured cells: an evaluation of the roles of 1-acyl- and 2-acyl-lysophosphatidylcholine. *Biochim. Biophys. Acta* **1004**, 221–229.

Neill, A.R. & Masters, C.J. (1972) Metabolism of fatty acids by bovine spermatozoa. *Biochem. J.* **127**, 375–385.

Neill, J.M. & Olds-Clarke, P. (1987) A computer-assisted assay for mouse sperm hyperactivation demonstrates that bicarbonate but not bovine serum albumin is required. *Gamete Res.* **18**, 121–140.

Ono, K., Yanagimachi, R. & Huang, T.T.F. (1982) Phospholipase A of guinea pig spermatozoa: its preliminary characterization and possible involvement in the acrosome reaction. *Develop. Growth Differentiation* **24**, 305–310.

Preiss, J., Loomis, C.R., Bishop, W.R., Stein, R., Niedel, J.E. & Bell, R.M. (1986) Quantitative measurement of sn-1,2-diacylglycerols present in platelets, hepatocytes, and ras- and sis-transformed normal rat kidney cells. *J. biol. Chem.* **261**, 8597–8600.

Ribbes, H., Plantavid, M., Bennet, P.J., Chap, H. & Douste-Blazy, L. (1987) Phospholipase C from human sperm specific for phosphoinositides. *Biochim. Biophys. Acta* **919**, 245–254.

Roldan, E.R.S. & Harrison, R.A.P. (1988) Absence of active protein kinase C in ram spermatozoa. *Biochem. Biophys. Res. Commun.* **155**, 901–906.

Roldan, E.R.S. & Harrison, R.A.P. (1989) Polyphosphoinositide breakdown and subsequent exocytosis in the Ca^{2+}/ionophore-induced acrosome reaction of mammalian spermatozoa. *Biochem. J.* **259**, 397–406.

Roldan, E.R.S. & Harrison, R.A.P. (1990) Molecular mechanisms leading to exocytosis during the sperm acrosome reaction. In *Fertilization in Mammals*, 179–196. Eds B. D. Bavister, J. M. Cummins & E. R. S. Roldan. Plenum Press, New York.

Ruknudin, A. (1989) Cytochemical study of intracellular calcium in hamster spermatozoa during the acrosome reaction. *Gamete Res.* **22**, 375–384.

Sha'afi, R.I. (1989) Some effects of phorbol ester are not mediated by protein kinase C. *Biochem. J.* **261**, 688.

Shams-Borhan, G. & Harrison, R.A.P. (1981) Production, characterization, and use of ionophore-induced, calcium-dependent acrosome reaction in ram spermatozoa. *Gamete Res.* **4**, 407–432.

Siegel, D.P., Banschbach, J., Alford, D., Ellens, H., Lis, L.J., Quinn, P.J., Yeagle, P.L. & Bentz, J. (1989) Physiological levels of diacylglycerols in phospholipid membranes induce membrane fusion and stabilize inverted phases. *Biochemistry, NY* **28**, 3703–3709.

Siiteri, J.E., Gottlieb, W. & Meizel, S. (1988) Partial characterization of a fraction from human follicular fluid that initiates the human sperm acrosome reaction in vitro. *Gamete Res.* **20**, 25–42.

Simpson, A.M. & White, I.G. (1988) Measurement and manipulation of cytoplasmic free calcium of ram and boar spermatozoa using quin 2. *Cell Calcium* **9**, 45–56.

Singh, J.P., Babcock, D.F. & Lardy, H.A. (1978) Increased calcium-ion influx is a component of capacitation of spermatozoa. *Biochem. J.* **172**, 549–556.

Suarez, S.S., Vincenti, L. & Ceglia, M.W. (1987) Hyperactivated motility induced in mouse sperm by calcium ionophore A23187 is reversible. *J. exp. Zool.* **244**, 331–336.

Sutherland, C.A. & Amin, D. (1982) Relative activities of rat and dog platelet phospholipase A$_2$ and diglyceride lipase. Selective inhibition of diglyceride lipase by RHC 80267. *J. biol. Chem.* **257**, 14006–14010.

Taylor, S.J. & Exton, J.H. (1987) Guanine-nucleotide and hormone regulation of polyphosphoinositide phospholipase C activity of rat liver plasma membranes. Bivalent-cation and phospholipid requirements. *Biochem. J.* **248**, 791–799.

Thakkar, J.K., East, J., Seyler, D. & Franson, R.C. (1983) Surface-active phospholipase A$_2$ in mouse spermatozoa. *Biochim. Biophys. Acta* **754**, 44–50.

Thakkar, J.K., East, J. & Franson, R.C. (1984) Modulation of phospholipase A$_2$ activity associated with human sperm membranes by divalent cations and calcium antagonists. *Biol. Reprod.* **30**, 679–686.

Thomas, P. & Meizel, S. (1988) An influx of extracellular calcium is required for initiation of the human sperm acrosome reaction induced by human follicular fluid. *Gamete Res.* **20**, 397–411.

Thomas, P. & Meizel, S. (1989a) Phosphatidylinositol 4,5-bisphosphate hydrolysis in human sperm stimulated with follicular fluid or progesterone is dependent upon Ca^{2+} influx. *Biochem. J.* **264**, 539–546.

Thomas, P. & Meizel, S. (1989b) Effects of metalloendoprotease substrates on the human sperm acrosome reaction. *J. Reprod. Fert.* **85**, 241–249.

Vanha-Perttula, T. & Kasurinen, J. (1989) Purification and characterization of phosphatidylinositol-specific phospholipase C from bovine spermatozoa. *Int. J. Biochem.* **21**, 997–1007.

Verkleij, A.J., Leunissen-Bijvelt, J., de Kruijff, B., Hope, M. & Cullis, P.R. (1984) Non-bilayer structures in membrane fusion. In *Cell Fusion* (Ciba Fdn Symp. No. 60), pp. 45–59. Pitman, London.

Visconti, P.E. & Tezon, J.G. (1989) Phorbol esters stimulate cyclic adenosine 3′,5′-monophosphate accumulation in hamster spermatozoa during *in vitro* capacitation. *Biol. Reprod.* **40,** 223–231.

Watson, P.F. & Plummer, J.M. (1986) Relationship between calcium binding sites and membrane fusion during the acrosome reaction induced by ionophore in ram spermatozoa. *J. exp. Zool.* **238,** 113–118.

Whitaker, M. & Aitchison, M. (1985) Calcium-dependent polyphosphoinositide hydrolysis is associated with exocytosis in vitro. *FEBS Lett.* **182,** 119–124.

Woodgett, J.R., Hunter, T. & Gould, K.L. (1987) Protein kinase C and its role in cell growth. In *Cell Membranes, Methods and Reviews*, vol. 3, pp. 215–340. Eds E. Elson, W. Frazier & L. Glaser. Plenum Press, New York.

Yanagimachi, R. (1988) Mammalian fertilization. In *The Physiology of Reproduction*, pp. 135–185. Eds E. Knobil & J. D. Neill. Raven Press, New York.

Yanagimachi, R. & Usui, N. (1974) Calcium dependence of the acrosome reaction and activation of guinea pig spermatozoa. *Expl Cell Res.* **89,** 161–174.

INTERACTION AND FUSION
OF
SPERMATOZOON AND EGG

Chairman
M. Hoshi

J. Reprod. Fert., Suppl. **42** (1990), 71–78

Development of sperm–egg recognition processes in mammals

H. D. M. Moore

*MRC/AFRC Comparative Physiology Research Group, Institute of Zoology,
Zoological Society of London, Regent's Park, London NW1 4RY, UK*

Keywords: mammal; spermatozoa; maturation; fertilizing capacity

Introduction

To understand the nature of recognition processes between the spermatozoon and egg, it is important to consider how and when relevant surface determinants are expressed and the sequential changes they undergo in the male and female genital tract (or *in vitro*). The oocyte contains essential receptors (for spermatozoa) at the zona and oolemma surfaces and these components are in general expressed early in development and thereafter remain functional and relatively stable (Dunbar, 1983). By contrast, the acquisition by mammalian spermatozoa of the ability to fertilize an egg may be viewed as the endpoint of a complex series of morphogenic and developmental processes occurring in the testis and epididymis. The starting point is debatable because interference with germ cell production at any stage may have a downstream effect on sperm fertility. However, it is during haploid development (spermiogenesis), as round undifferentiated germ cells are transformed into testicular spermatozoa, that highly specialized organelles (e.g. acrosome, flagellum) and spatially distinct membrane domains (e.g. equatorial region) are produced that are essential for fertilization (Bellve & O'Brien, 1983). When they leave the testis spermatozoa are usually morphologically complete but are functionally immature and they must undergo further modifications in the epididymis. This sperm maturation culminates in changes to movement characteristics so that full progressive motility is acquired and in subtle alterations to the cell surface which allow spermatozoa to recognize, bind to and penetrate the zona pellucida and then fuse with the oolemma. It may be argued that mixing with seminal plasma proteins at ejaculation and subsequent capacitation in the female tract or *in vitro* constitute additional changes that spermatozoa must endure before they can fertilize. But the full *potential* of a spermatozoon is attained during its post-meiotic development in the testis and epididymis and this article will address these stages.

The region of the epididymis where sperm fertilizing capacity first develops has been defined for a number of species and gross morphological and biochemical changes to spermatozoa during spermiogenesis and epididymal transit have been extensively investigated (see reviews by Eddy *et al.*, 1985; Moore, 1990). There is cogent evidence that in the normal fertile male the final phase of development of sperm fertilizing ability is dependent on factors secreted from the epididymal epithelium under androgen control. However, it has proved difficult to establish the molecular basis for many alterations to spermatozoa due to the apparent complexity of the processes involved and the underlying difficulties of probing *in situ* the testicular and epididymal environments. The definitive studies of Bedford (1967) and Orgebin-Crist (1967) used the endpoint of fertilization to determine causal relationships between modifications to spermatozoa in the epididymis and fertilizing capacity. Retaining this approach it has been possible to dissect out aspects of sperm development and maturation related to sperm recognition of the egg by using immunological probes and cell culture techniques. In my laboratory, the Syrian hamster is the animal of choice since the testis and epididymis are relatively large and in-vitro fertilization techniques are robust.

Although species differences exist it is likely that the mechanisms underlying the development of sperm fertility are common to all eutherian mammals. However, it cannot be assumed that all the features of this process in the hamster are typical and comparative investigations in other species including the human have been undertaken when appropriate.

Spermiogenesis

The final morphology of the spermatozoon is largely generated during spermiogenesis (see Bellve & O'Brien, 1983) and a variety of changes to the germ cell membranes at this time may have a bearing on subsequent sperm–egg interactions. It is clear that spermatids exhibit many membrane determinants not detectable on pre-meiotic cells (O'Rand & Romrell, 1980; Fenderson *et al.*, 1984). As a result of the expression of novel mRNA (Fujimoto & Erickson, 1982; Distel *et al.*, 1984; Zakeri & Wolgemuth, 1986; Hecht, 1987) and post-translational modifications, such as fucosylation (Millette *et al.*, 1987), protein and lipid domains arise in the plasma membrane and underlying acrosomal membranes, producing a mosaic of distinct regions.

In the hamster, monoclonal antibodies recognizing epitopes on acrosomal membranes were generated by immunizing mice with epididymal spermatozoa (Moore *et al.*, 1985; Ellis *et al.*, 1985). The exquisite immunofluorescent localization clearly illustrated the restricted regional and temporal expression of antigens. Monoclonal antibodies marked the formation of the acrosomic granule and the flattening and spreading of the developing acrosome over the anterior nucleus. A variety of different patterns was observed (Fig. 1), presumably reflecting the sequence of membrane modifications concomitant with cell morphogenesis. In some cases, immunofluorescent localization was diminished as spermatozoa passed into the epididymis, possibly indicating a loss or masking of determinants. These results and those of others demonstrate the regional differentiation of germ cell membranes during spermiogenesis but as such are not indicative of changes related to the development of fertilizing capacity. However, germ cell specific antibodies that recognize acrosomal determinants first expressed in the spermatid can also specifically inhibit fertilization. Monoclonal antibody 97·5 inhibited sperm penetration of intact hamster oocytes (*in vivo* and *in vitro*) by preventing the binding of spermatozoa to the zona surface (Moore *et al.*, 1985). Sperm movement and the penetration of zona-free hamster eggs were unaffected, suggesting that the antibody was interfering with sperm–egg interaction rather than sperm motility or the acrosome reaction (Table 1). Moreover this antibody cross-reacted with human spermatozoa and specifically inhibited their binding to salt-stored human oocytes (Moore *et al.*, 1987). Although indirect evidence, these results raise the possibility that novel epitopes first expressed during spermatid development may play a significant role in subsequent recognition events between the spermatozoon and egg.

Changes to the sperm surface during epididymal passage

Numerous studies have demonstrated that there is a modification in the distribution and density of sperm membrane components during epididymal transit (for reviews see Moore, 1983, 1990; Eddy *et al.*, 1985). Some of these changes may be due to intrinsic alterations in the cholesterol/lipid composition of sperm membranes affecting the lateral mobility of intramembranous particles (see Holt, 1982). The appearance of other surface determinants can be accounted for by specific antigens, secreted by the epididymal epithelium in the proximal region of the duct, which attach to the sperm surface. Our studies, first with specific antisera (Moore, 1980, 1981) and then with monoclonal antibodies (Moore & Hartman, 1984; Ellis *et al.*, 1985), showed that expression of such antigens was often associated with the development of sperm fertilizing capacity. Furthermore, antibodies prevented fertilization *in vitro* at titres which did not cause agglutination or alter sperm

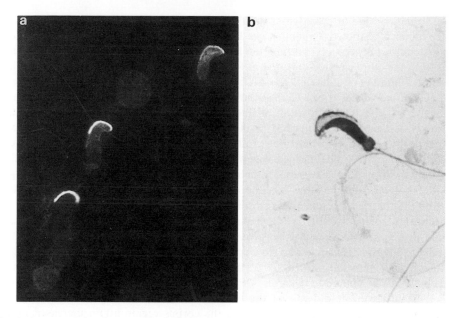

Fig. 1. Acrosome development in the hamster. **(a)** Immunolocalization of monoclonal antibody 97·5 on isolated spermatids and testicular spermatozoa. Fluorescence was localized to the rim of the anterior acrosome. × 580. **(b)** Immunoperoxidase staining of testicular spermatozoa was restricted to the plasma membrane overlying the acrosome and equatorial segment. × 960.

Table 1. In-vitro sperm penetration of intact and zona-free hamster oocytes in the presence of monoclonal antibody 97·5

Titre of hybridoma supernatant	Proportion of oocytes penetrated	
	Intact	Zona-free
1:10	0/42	26/30
1:50	7/32	25/25
1:100	12/47	22/22
1:500	31/34	28/31

motility. These results therefore implicate determinants of epididymal origin in having a role during acquisition of sperm fertilizing ability.

Although studies with Fab fragments would suggest a masking of specific sites on the sperm surface (Tzartos, 1979; Moore, 1981), it remains uncertain whether the effect of antibodies on fertilization could be due to a steric hindrance phenomenon. More direct investigations were therefore undertaken using in-vitro culture of epididymal epithelium as described below.

In-vitro sperm maturation

Organ and tissue culture methods have been attempted to mimic epididymal function. Principal cells cultured *in vitro* show normal morphological features for several days (Klinefelter *et al.*, 1982).

In addition, organ culture of epididymal tubules will induce limited sperm maturation although access to the lumen is restricted (Orgebin-Crist & Jahad, 1979; Cuasnicu *et al.*, 1984). We adopted a simplified system to study epididymal function by using fragmented tubules of hamster epididymal epithelium from the corpus region cultured in RPMI medium supplemented with fetal calf serum, androgens and a number of epithelial growth factors (Moore *et al.*, 1986). This procedure formed plaques of epithelium which, after 24 h in culture, everted to form spheres of tissue with epithelium facing outwards. The secretory function of this epithelial culture was assessed by using a monoclonal antibody C5 against a protein of M_r 34 000 first synthesized and secreted by principal cells in the proximal corpus epididymidis but not produced by epithelium in the initial segment or caput region (Smith *et al.*, 1986). The antigen was observed on the apical surface of principal cells in epithelium culture for at least 4 days and sometimes up to 7 days. In the absence of androgens, the antigen could not be detected after the 2nd day of culture, suggesting that its synthesis and secretion (and that of other proteins) was curtailed.

In the hamster, spermatozoa from the distal corpus region have yet to acquire full fertilizing capacity and display low fertility *in vivo* or *in vitro* (5–15% fertilization rates) due to a reduced ability to bind to the zona pellucida and slow progressive motility. The incubation of such spermatozoa with 3-day-old epithelial cultures for 6 h resulted in a pronounced increase in sperm binding to the zona pellucida compared to controls, although sperm penetration and fertilization were not enhanced. By ligating the epididymis at the junction of the distal corpus and proximal cauda regions for 3 days, spermatozoa recovered from the corpus region attain increased progressive motility but remain immature (Moore & Hartman, 1986). The incubation of these spermatozoa with cultures of epididymal epithelium for 6 h led to a significant increase in fertilizing capacity (50% fertilization rate in recent experiments) both *in vitro* and *in vivo* compared with controls of similar spermatozoa incubated in cultures without androgens or with fibroblasts (Table 2). Since all the sperm samples maintained their motility and underwent similar capacitation and fertilization conditions, the conclusion from this work was that a factor(s) present in the culture of proximal cauda epithelium (with androgens) promoted the final stages of maturation related to the acquisition of functional sperm receptors for the zona pellucida.

Table 2. Fertilizing ability *in vitro* of spermatozoa from the ligated distal corpus epididymidis of hamsters after incubation with epithelial culture (with and without androgen) or in the absence of epithelial culture

Proportion of oocytes fertilized†			
Distal corpus spermatozoa*			Cauda spermatozoa (controls)
Epithelial culture with androgen	Epithelial culture without androgen	Without culture	Without culture
93/240 (39%)†	21/226 (9%)	5/124 (4%)	69/78 (88%)

*Significantly different from controls, $P \leq 0.005$.
†Means of 8 experiments (unpublished results).

Conditioned medium recovered from epithelial cultures can also promote sperm maturation but not to the same extent (22% fertilization rate) as when principal cells are present (H. D. M. Moore, unpublished observation), suggesting that the factor(s) involved may be labile. Studies with C5 monoclonal antibody indicated that epitopes can be specifically transferred from the epididymal epithelium to spermatozoa *in vitro* since immature spermatozoa from the caput region incubated with corpus epithelial cultures acquired antigen on their post-acrosomal region and annulus (Fig. 2).

This transfer of a moiety to restricted regions of the sperm plasmalemma might be expected of a specific coupling mechanism. The membrane changes were accompanied by the induction of progressive motility in a proportion of the spermatozoa and it is tempting to speculate that such specific binding to the annulus by C5 could induce changes in flagellum movement (Smith *et al.*, 1986). However, the molecular weight of M_r 34 000 would indicate that C5 is not Forward Motility Protein as reported by Hoskins *et al.* (1979).

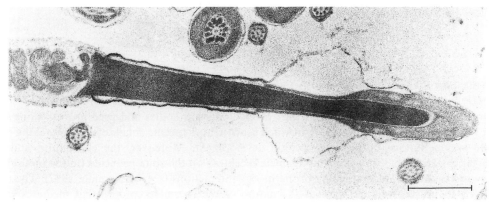

Fig. 2. Electron micrograph of a section of a hamster spermatozoon from the corpus epididymidis after immunolocalization with C5 monoclonal antibody. Staining was restricted to the plasmalemma over the post-acrosomal region and the annulus (not shown). Bar = 1 μm.

Acquisition of human sperm fertilizing capacity

Studies involving the recovery of epididymal spermatozoa from fertile men undergoing vasectomy (Moore *et al.*, 1983) or from patients with cancer (Hinrichsen & Blaquier, 1982) or in a coma (Dacheux *et al.*, 1987) all indicate that the ability of spermatozoa to display sustainable progressive motility, to penetrate zona-free hamster eggs, and to bind to salt-stored human oocytes (H. D. M. Moore, unpublished observation) increases as they pass into the corpus and cauda epididymidis. In contrast to rodents, this process is gradual in men and there is considerable individual variation. The results of surgical re-anastomosis procedures (epididymovasostomy) to bypass a blockage in the epididymis have supported the experimental findings and it is generally recognized that the likelihood of producing competent spermatozoa is low if the vas deferens is anastomosed to the proximal 7–10 mm of excurrent duct (Schoysman & Bedford, 1986). Recently, however, Silber (1989) has reported that anastomosis to the very proximal region of the caput epididymidis may enable fertile spermatozoa to be ejaculated and samples of spermatozoa aspirated by microsurgical technique from the efferent ducts and proximal caput epididymidis of men with blocked excurrent ducts can be used to fertilize oocytes *in vitro* and establish pregnancies. At first sight, it seems difficult to equate these results with the need for human sperm maturation. However, while most spermatozoa remain immature in the proximal duct a small proportion do display some progressive motility and if selected (by swim-up methods and Percoll gradients) may be capable of fertilization. It will be important to establish the exact origin of this small population of spermatozoa. Have they been transported by a reflux action from a more distal epididymal site and therefore undergone a maturation process? Or do they come directly from the testis, in which case is their in-vitro fertilizing capacity complete on entering the epididymis? For normal fertile men, however, passage through at least the proximal epididymis is required to produce a fertile ejaculate.

To investigate the role of human epididymal epithelium during sperm maturation we have established short-term cultures of epididymal epithelium by using tissue from patients undergoing epididymovasostomy or vasectomy under general anaesthesia and who have volunteered a portion of epididymis. The culture technique is similar to that used for the hamster epididymis although longer preincubation with collagenase is required to remove the large amount of connective tissue surrounding the epididymal tubule. Pulse-labelling techniques with [^{35}S]methionine indicate that these cultures actively synthesize and secrete proteins at M_r 20–22 000.

Conclusions

Over the past 20 years the general features of sperm development and maturation have been characterized extensively, but the molecular mechanisms involved in the development of sperm recognition of the egg still remain unclear. Monoclonal antibodies and gene probes, along with improved co-culture techniques, have provided us with more specific details of changes taking place on the sperm surface during post-meiotic development. Moreover, the elucidation and full characterization of the complementary gamete receptors on the zona pellucida (in the mouse) has greatly increased our understanding of sperm–egg interactions (see Wassarman, 1987). The main questions to be resolved are: what is the nature of the sperm receptor(s) that mediates initial binding between the spermatozoon and egg? And when does this receptor become expressed and functional?

There are several candidates for the role of sperm receptor for the zona pellucida. In the mouse, galactosyl transferase may mediate sperm–egg binding and other glycosyl transferases have been implicated in a variety of species (see Macek & Shur, 1988). Sperm surface proteases may also function as receptors (Benau & Storey, 1987). Alternatively, pro-acrosin has been shown in the boar to be a zona pellucida binding protein (Jones *et al.*, 1988). Lastly, studies in our own laboratory and by other groups have implicated a number of membrane antigens identified with specific monoclonal and polyclonal antibodies (see Moore & Hartman, 1984; Primakoff *et al.*, 1985; Moore *et al.*, 1987; O'Rand *et al.*, 1988). Leyton & Saling (1989a) have reported that a protein of M_r 95 000 in the mouse plasmalemma serves as a receptor for the ZP3 molecule of the zona pellucida and also acts as a substrate for tyrosine kinase. The binding of spermatozoa to the zona is thought to aggregate this M_r 95 000 protein and thereby trigger the acrosome reaction (Leyton & Saling, 1989b). In this regard, it is of interest that the monoclonal antibody 97·5 also recognizes an antigen of M_r 95 000 and specifically blocked attachment of hamster and human spermatozoa to the zona pellucida (Moore *et al.*, 1987).

The final expression of a functional sperm receptor requires the presence of androgen-dependent factors from epididymal principal cells. Since fertilization is blocked by antibodies recognizing antigens first detected on spermatids, sperm maturation may involve the modification of an existing membrane determinant synthesized during spermiogenesis. Alternatively, an additional epididymal secretory moiety could be incorporated into the sperm plasmalemma to promote sperm–egg recognition.

It is encouraging that some of the steps involved in sperm maturation, at least in the hamster, can now be carried out *in vitro*. It is anticipated that such co-culture methods with testicular and epididymal tissue along with the use of appropriate gene cloning techniques should lead to the complete elucidation of mechanisms involved in the development of sperm fertilizing capacity.

Aspects of this work are supported by a programme grant from the Medical Research Council and the Agriculture and Food Research Council, and by project grants from the World Health Organization and the Wellcome Trust.

References

Bedford, J.M. (1967) Effect of duct ligation on the fertilising capacity of spermatozoa in the epididymis of the rabbit. *J. exp. Zool.* **166**, 271–281.

Benau, D.A. & Storey, B. T. (1987) Characterization of the mouse sperm plasma membrane zona-binding site sensitive to trypsin inhibitors. *Biol. Reprod.* **36**, 282–292.

Bellve, A.R. & O'Brien, D.A. (1983) The mammalian spermatozoon: structure and temporal assembly. In *Mechanisms and Control of Animal Fertilisation*, pp. 55–137. Ed. J. F. Hartmann. Academic Press, New York.

Cuasnicu, P.S., Gonzalez-Echeverria, F., Piazza, A. & Blaquier, J.A. (1984) Addition of androgens to cultured hamster epididymis increases zona recognition by immature spermatozoa. *J. Reprod. Fert.* **70**, 541–547.

Dacheux, J.L., Chevier, C. & Lanson, Y. (1987) Motility and surface transformations of human spermatozoa during epididymal transit. *Ann. N.Y. Acad. Sci.* **513**, 560–563.

Distel, R.J., Kleene, K.C. & Hecht, N.B. (1984) Haploid expression of a mouse testis A—tubulin gene. *Science, NY* **224**, 68–70.

Dunbar, B.S. (1983) Morphological, biochemical and immunochemical characterization of the mammalian zona pellucida. In *Mechanism and Control of Animal Fertilization*, pp. 139–175. Ed. J. F. Hartmann. Academic Press, New York.

Eddy, E.M., Vernon, R.B., Muller, C.H., Hahnel, A.C. & Fenderson, B.A. (1985) Immunodissection of sperm surface modifications during epididymal maturation. *Am. J. Anat.* **174**, 225–237.

Ellis, D.H., Hartman, T.D. & Moore, H.D.M. (1985) Maturation and function of the hamster spermatozoon probed with monoclonal antibodies. *J. Reprod. Immunol.* **7**, 229–314.

Fenderson, B.A., O'Brien, D.A., Millette, C.F. & Eddy, E.M. (1984) Stage specific expression of three cell surface carbohydrate antigens during murine spermatogenesis detected with monoclonal antibodies. *Devl Biol.* **103**, 117–128.

Fujimoto, H. & Erickson, R.P. (1982) Functional assays for mRNA detect many new messages after male meiosis in mice. *Biochem. Biophys. Res. Commun.* **108**, 1369–1375.

Hecht, N.B. (1987) Gene expression during spermatogenesis. *Ann. N.Y. Acad. Sci.* **513**, 90–101.

Hinrichsen, M.J. & Blaquier, J.A. (1982) Evidence supporting sperm maturation in human epididymis. *J. Reprod. Fert.* **60**, 291–294.

Holt, W.V. (1982) Functional development of the mammalian sperm plasma membrane. *Oxford Rev. Reprod. Biol.* **4**, 195–240.

Hoskins, D.D., Johnson, D., Brandt, H. & Acott, T.S. (1979) Evidence for a role for a forward motility protein in the epididymal development of sperm motility. In *The Spermatozoon*, pp. 43–53. Eds D. W. Fawcett & J. M. Bedford. Urban and Schwarzenberg, Baltimore.

Jones, R., Brown, C.R. & Lancaster, R.T. (1988) Carbohydrate-binding properties of boar sperm acrosin and assessment of its role in sperm–egg recog-nition and adhesion during fertilization. *Development* **102**, 781–792.

Klinefelter, G. T., Amann, R.P. & Hammerstedt, R.H. (1982) Culture of principal cells from the rat caput epididymidis. *Biol. Reprod.* **26**, 885–901.

Leyton, L. & Saling, P. (1989a) 95 kd sperm proteins bind ZP3 and serve as tyrosine kinase substrates in response to zona binding. *Cell* **57**, 1123–1130.

Leyton, L. & Saling, P. (1989b) Evidence that aggregation of mouse sperm receptors by ZP3 triggers the acrosome reaction. *J. Cell Biol.* **108**, 2163–2168.

Macek, M.B. & Shur, B.D. (1988) Protein-carbohydrate complementarity in mammalian gamete recognition. *Gamete Res.* **20**, 93–109.

Millette, C.F., Cardullo, R.A., Armant, D.R. & Gerton, G.L. (1987) Fucosylation events during mammalian spermatogenesis. *Annls N.Y. Acad. Sci.* **513**, 58–73.

Moore, H.D.M. (1980) Localization of specific glycoproteins secreted by the rabbit and hamster epididymis. *Biol. Reprod.* **22**, 705–718.

Moore, H.D.M. (1981) Glycoprotein secretion of the epididymis in the rabbit and hamster: Localization on epididymal spermatozoa and the effect of specific antibodies on fertilization in vivo. *J. exp. Zool.* **215**, 77–85.

Moore, H.D.M. (1983) Physiological and in vitro models of sperm maturation. In *In Vitro Fertilisation and Embryo Transfer*, pp. 9–38. Eds. P. G. Crosignani & B. L. Rubin. Academic Press, London.

Moore, H.D.M. (1990) The epididymis. In *Scientific Foundation of Urology*, 3rd edn, pp. 399–410. Eds G. D. Chisholm & W. R. Fair, Heinemann, London.

Moore, H.D.M. & Hartman, T.D. (1984) Localization by monoclonal antibodies of various surface antigens of hamster spermatozoa and the effect of antibodies on fertilization in vitro. *J. Reprod. Fert.* **70**, 175–183.

Moore, H.D.M. & Hartman, T.D. (1986) In-vitro development of the fertilizing ability of hamster epididymal spermatozoa after co-culture with epithelium from the proximal cauda epididymidis. *J. Reprod. Fert.* **78**, 347–352.

Moore, H.D.M., Hartman, T.D. & Pryor, J.P. (1983) Development of the oocyte penetrating capacity of the spermatozoa in the human epididymis. *Int. J. Androl.* **6**, 310–318.

Moore, H.D.M., Hartman, T.D., Brown, A.C., Smith, C.A. & Ellis, D.H. (1985) Expression of sperm antigens during spermatogenesis and maturation detected with monoclonal antibodies. *Expl Clin. Immunogenet.* **2**, 84–96.

Moore, H.D.M., Hartman, T.D. & Smith, C.A. (1986) In-vitro culture of hamster epididymal epithelium and induction of sperm motility. *J. Reprod. Fert.* **78**, 327–326.

Moore, H.D.M., Hartman, T.D., Bye, A.P., Lutjen, P., De Witt, M. & Trounson, A.O. (1987) Monoclonal antibody against a sperm antigen Mr 95 000 inhibits attachment of human spermatozoa to the zona pellucida. *J. Reprod. Immunol.* **11**, 157–166.

O'Rand, M.G. & Romrell, L.J. (1980) Appearance of regional surface autoantigens during spermatogenesis: comparison of anti-testis and anti-sperm autoantisera. *Devl Biol.* **75**, 431–441.

O'Rand, M.G., Widgren, E.E. & Fisher, S.J. (1988) Characterisation of the rabbit sperm membrane autoantigen, RSA, as a lectin-like zona binding protein. *Devl Biol.* **129**, 231–240.

Orgebin-Crist, M.-C. (1967) Maturation of spermatozoa in the rabbit epididymis. Fertilising ability and embryonic mortality in does inseminated with epididymal spermatozoa. *Annls Biol. Anim. Biochim. Biophys.* **7**, 373–379.

Orgebin-Crist, M.-C. & Jahad, N. (1979) The maturation of rabbit epididymal spermatozoa in organ culture: stimulation by epididymal cytoplasmic extracts. *Biol. Reprod.* **21**, 511–516.

Primakoff, D., Hyatt, H. & Myles, D.G. (1985) A role for the migrating sperm surface antigen pH 20 in guinea-pig sperm binding to the egg zona pellucida. *J. Cell Biol.* **101**, 2239–2244.

Schoysman, R.J. & Bedford, J.M. (1986) The role of the human epididymis in sperm maturation and sperm storage as reflected in the consequences of epididymovasostomy. *Fert. Steril.* **46**, 293–299.

Silber, S.J. (1989) Results of microsurgical vasoepididymostomy: role of epididymis in sperm maturation. *Human Reprod.* **4**, 298–303.

Smith, C.A., Hartman, T.D. & Moore, H.D.M. (1986) A determinant of M_r 34 000 expressed by hamster epididymal epithelium binds specifically to spermatozoa in co-culture. *J. Reprod. Fert.* **78**, 337–345.

Tzartos, S.J. (1979) Inhibition of in-vitro fertilization of intact and denuded hamster eggs by univalent antisperm antibodies. *J. Reprod. Fert.* **55**, 447–455.

Wassarman, P.M. (1987) The biology and chemistry of fertilization. *Science, NY* **235**, 554–560.

Zakeri, Z.F. & Wolgemuth, D.J. (1986) Developmental stage-specific expression of HSP 70 gene family during differentiation of the mammalian male germ line. *Molec. cell. Biol.* **7**, 1791–1796.

J. Reprod. Fert., Suppl. **42** (1990), 79–87

Regulation of mammalian fertilization by zona pellucida glycoproteins

P. M. Wassarman

Department of Cell and Developmental Biology, Roche Institute of Molecular Biology, Roche Research Center, Nutley, New Jersey 07110, USA

Keywords: mammalian fertilization; zona pellucida; sperm receptor; acrosome reaction; zona reaction

Introductory remarks

This report focusses on our efforts to identify and characterize macromolecules located at the surface of mammalian eggs that support gamete recognition and adhesion during the process of fertilization. In particular, during the past 10 years or so we have investigated the role of egg zona pellucida (ZP) glycoproteins as regulators of gamete interactions in mice. The ZP is a relatively thick extracellular coat that completely surrounds all mammalian eggs and is thought to be responsible for species-specific gamete adhesion that ultimately leads to formation of a zygote. Our research has considered the synthesis and structure of ZP glycoproteins, as well as the functions of these glycoproteins before, during, and after fertilization. Although much of this research has been carried out with mice, accumulating evidence suggests that our conclusions about the regulation of fertilization by ZP glycoproteins may also apply to many other eutherian mammals.

In retrospect, the research path we followed to examine the molecular basis of fertilization in mice has provided several key pieces of information along the way. Among these are: (1) ZP glycoproteins are synthesized by growing oocytes, not by follicle cells; (2) the ZP is constructed of only a few glycoprotein species; (3) a single ZP glycoprotein, ZP3, serves as both 'primary' sperm receptor and acrosome reaction (exocytosis)-inducer; (4) sperm receptor oligosaccharide, not protein, is recognized by spermatozoa during gamete adhesion; (5) a single ZP glycoprotein, ZP2, serves as a 'secondary' sperm receptor during gamete adhesion; (6) after fertilization or activation of mouse eggs, modification of ZP2 and ZP3 by cortical granule enzymes establishes a secondary block to polyspermy. These and other findings are reviewed below.

Fertilization in mice

The fertilization pathway in mice consists of many steps that occur in a compulsory order when eggs and spermatozoa are incubated together *in vitro* (Gwatkin, 1977; Wassarman, 1987a, b, 1990; Yanagimachi, 1988).

Attachment. The initial loose association between eggs and spermatozoa does not exhibit species specificity and is termed attachment. Operationally, attached spermatozoa can be removed easily from the egg ZP surface by gentle pipetting with mouth-operated, broad-bore micropipettes. Spermatozoa attach to the ZP of the unfertilized egg and the embryo.

Primary binding. The subsequent tight association between eggs and spermatozoa does exhibit species specificity and is termed primary binding. Operationally, bound spermatozoa cannot be removed easily from the egg ZP surface by gentle pipetting with mouth-operated, broad-bore micropipettes or by other physical methods. Spermatozoa bind to unfertilized egg ZP, but not to embryo ZP. The egg ZP component to which acrosome-intact spermatozoa bind in a species-specific manner is termed the primary *sperm receptor*.

Acrosome reaction. Spermatozoa undergo exocytosis (acrosome reaction) while bound to the egg ZP surface. The acrosome is a large, lysosome-like organelle that overlies the sperm nucleus and contains enzymes that enable bound spermatozoa to penetrate the ZP, and to reach and fuse with egg plasma membrane. The acrosome reaction involves multiple point fusions of sperm plasma and outer acrosomal membrane, formation of hybrid vesicles, and exposure of inner acrosomal membrane with its associated acrosomal contents.

Secondary binding. Spermatozoa that undergo the acrosome reaction after binding to the ZP must remain bound in order to penetrate the extracellular coat. Presumably, secondary binding of acrosome-reacted spermatozoa involves components of the sperm inner acrosomal membrane (exposed as a result of the acrosome reaction) and secondary 'sperm receptors' in the ZP.

Penetration. Bound, acrosome-reacted spermatozoa penetrate the ZP by making a narrow path (about the width of the sperm head) through the extracellular coat. Penetration probably involves digestion of one or more ZP glycoproteins by a proteinase (perhaps, acrosin) associated with sperm inner acrosomal membrane.

Fusion. Upon reaching the perivitelline space, a spermatozoon can fuse with egg plasma membrane to form a zygote. Plasma membrane that remains at the posterior portion of the sperm head, not inner acrosomal membrane, participates in the fusion of male and female gametes.

Primary block to polyspermy. Following fusion of gametes, supernumerary spermatozoa in the perivitelline space are prevented from fusing with fertilized eggs and, thereby, polyspermy is avoided. This primary block to polyspermy may be attributable to depolarization of egg plasma membrane within seconds of gamete fusion.

Cortical reaction. Underlying the egg plasma membrane are several thousand lysosome-like organelles, called cortical granules, that fuse with the egg plasma membrane (cortical reaction) after fusion of a spermatozoon and the egg. Cortical granule contents, which include a variety of lytic enzymes, are deposited into the perivitelline space, enter the ZP, and modify ZP glycoproteins.

Zona reaction. Modification of ZP glycoproteins by cortical granule enzymes leads to changes in the properties of the ZP (zona reaction) following fertilization. These changes constitute a secondary block to polyspermy at the level of the ZP.

General characteristics of the mouse zona pellucida

Several features of the ZP are worthy of note at the outset (Gwatkin, 1977; Wassarman, 1988a; Dietl, 1989). (1) The ZP varies in thickness, from less than 2 μm to more than 25 μm, for eggs from different mammals, and the thickness of the ZP apparently is correlated directly with protein content. The mouse egg ZP is about 7 μm thick and contains 3–4 ng protein. (2) The ZP is a loose meshwork of fibrillogranular strands (filaments) that is permeable to enzymes, immunoglobulins, and small viruses and, consequently, the ZP does not serve as a significant barrier to macromolecules. (3) The ZP first appears during oogenesis, as non-growing oocytes (arrested in the dictyate stage of first meiotic prophase) enter their growth phase, and increases in thickness as oocytes increase in diameter. In mice, growth of oocytes, from about 12 μm to about 80 μm in diameter, takes 2–3 weeks. (4) The ZP is composed of glycoproteins, with a ratio of protein to carbohydrate of about 3–5 to 1 for eggs from different mammals. The mouse ZP is composed of 3 glycoproteins, called ZP1, ZP2 and ZP3. (5) The ZP is solubilized by a variety of agents that disrupt either covalent (e.g. proteases and dithiothreitol) or non-covalent (e.g. low pH and high temperature) bonds. (6) The ZP is largely responsible for the species specificity observed during in-vitro fertilization and is the site of the secondary block to polyspermy following fertilization. (7) The ZP of fertilized eggs is considerably more insoluble ('harder') than the ZP of oocytes and unfertilized (ovulated) eggs. (8) The ZP remains around cleaving embryos throughout preimplantation development, until hatching occurs at the expanded blastocyst stage, just before implantation; in mice this is at about Day 4·5 of development (100–120 cells).

Characteristics of mouse zona pellucida glycoproteins

Typical of many other secreted glycoproteins, mouse ZP glycoproteins ZP1 (average apparent $M_r = 200\,000$), ZP2 (average apparent $M_r = 120\,000$), and ZP3 (averge apparent $M_r = 83\,000$) exhibit considerable heterogeneity on SDS-PAGE (Bleil & Wassarman, 1980a; Wassarman, 1988a). Their migration on isoelectric focussing gels indicates that ZP1 (average pI $= 4\cdot1$, monomer), ZP2 (average pI $= 5\cdot2$), and ZP3 (average pI $= 4\cdot7$) are all relatively acidic glycoproteins. However, the amino acid compositions of the ZP glycoproteins do not account for their relatively low pI values, but are consistent with the pI values of their polypeptide chains (ZP1, pI $= 6\cdot6$; ZP2, pI $= 6\cdot5$; ZP3, pI $= 6\cdot5$). The polypeptide chains of ZP2 and ZP3 have average apparent M_r values of 81 000 and 44 000, respectively (Greve *et al.*, 1982; Salzmann *et al.*, 1983; Wassarman, 1988a). In the presence of detergents, ZP2 and ZP3 are monomers, whereas ZP1 is a dimer of polypeptide chains held together by intermolecular disulphide bonds. The 2 disulphide-linked polypeptide chains of ZP1 each have an average apparent M_r of 75 000. There is some evidence that all 3 glycoproteins are sulphated, probably on their oligosaccharides (Shimizu *et al.*, 1983), and that ZP2 and ZP3 contain intramolecular disulphides. All 3 glycoproteins contain asparagine-linked (N-linked), complex-type oligosaccharides (6 chains on ZP2 and 3 or 4 chains on ZP3), and at least ZP2 and ZP3 contain serine/threonine-linked (O-linked) oligosaccharides (Greve *et al.*, 1982; Salzmann *et al.*, 1983; Wassarman, 1988a). Terminal sialic acid (sensitive to neuraminidase digestion) on oligosaccharides of ZP glycoproteins contributes significantly to their acidic nature. The heterogeneity of ZP glycoproteins exhibited on SDS-PAGE is due to the oligosaccharides of the glycoproteins, not to their polypeptide chains. ZP1, ZP2 and ZP3 associate with one another via non-covalent bonds to assemble the ZP.

Biosynthesis of mouse zona pellucida glycoproteins

Mouse ZP glycoproteins are synthesized and secreted by growing oocytes, not by their surrounding follicle cells (Bleil & Wassarman, 1980b; Greve *et al.*, 1982; Roller & Wassarman, 1983; Salzmann *et al.*, 1983; Shimizu *et al.*, 1983; Wassarman, 1988a). Apparently, all 3 glycoproteins are synthesized and secreted concomitantly by oocytes, with ZP glycoprotein synthesis representing as much as 7–8% of the total protein synthesis in growing oocytes. The nascent polypeptide chains of ZP1, ZP2 and ZP3 are N-glycosylated co-translationally, in the endoplasmic reticulum, with high-mannose-type oligosaccharides, giving rise to 160 000 (dimer), 91 000, and 53 000/56 000 M_r precursors, respectively. These precursors move to the Golgi apparatus where N-linked oligosaccharides are processed to complex-type and, at about the same time, O-linked oligosaccharides are added (at least to ZP2 and ZP3), giving rise to the mature forms of the glycoproteins that are secreted by oocytes. Thus, overall, the biosynthetic pathways for ZP1, ZP2 and ZP3 resemble those described for other glycoproteins secreted by eukaryotic cells (Kornfeld & Kornfeld, 1985; Pfeffer & Rothman, 1987).

Molecular probes have been used to examine ZP3 gene expression by in-situ hybridization (Philpott *et al.*, 1987; Kinloch *et al.*, 1989; Roller *et al.*, 1989), Northern gel hybridization (Ringuette *et al.*, 1986; Roller *et al.*, 1989), and RNAse protection analysis (Roller *et al.*, 1989; Kinloch *et al.*, 1989). All 3 types of analysis demonstrate that ZP3 mRNA (about 1·5 kb) is present exclusively in growing and fully-grown oocytes, and that the levels of ZP3 mRNA in these cells apparently accounts for all ZP3 transcripts in ovarian RNA preparations. During oocyte growth, the amount of ZP3 mRNA increases from undetectable levels in non-growing oocytes (12–15 μm in diameter) to about 300 000 copies in 65 μm oocytes, and then undergoes a modest decline to about 240 000 copies in fully-grown (80–85 μm) oocytes (Roller *et al.*, 1989; Kinloch *et al.*, 1989). During ovulation, when fully-grown oocytes undergo meiotic maturation and become unfertilized eggs (during a 10–12-h period), the level of ZP3 mRNA falls dramatically to about 2% (about 5000 copies per egg) the amount present in fully-grown oocytes. ZP3 mRNA is not detectable in mouse brain, heart, kidney, liver, muscle, testis, uterus, follicle cells, fertilized eggs, or 13-day post-implantation embryos. Consequently, ZP3 is an example of oocyte-specific and, therefore, sex-specific gene expression in mammals.

The availability of ZP3 molecular probes has also made it possible to determine various structural features of the glycoprotein (Kinloch *et al.*, 1988, 1989; Ringuette *et al.*, 1988). (For a review of ZP3 gene organization see Kinloch & Wassarman, 1989.) ZP3 is synthesized as a 424 amino acid polypeptide chain (M_r 46 300), of which the amino terminal 22 amino acids are predicted to constitute a signal sequence that is cleaved from the mature protein (M_r 43 900). The entire primary structure of the polypeptide chain has been determined and it exhibits a number of interesting features. (1) Compared with the average vertebrate protein (Doolittle, 1986), ZP3 contains an unusually high number of proline and serine plus threonine residues. (2) Many of the proline residues are clustered in one region of the polypeptide chain. (3) The polypeptide is neither strongly hydrophobic nor hydrophilic, except for the signal sequence and 2 small domains near the carboxy-terminus that are probably sequestered from an aqueous environment. (4) The polypeptide chain contains very little α-helix-forming potential. Rather it consists of stretches of 5–29 residues in an extended chain conformation, interrupted by stretches of 4–10 residues in reverse turn or coil conformations. (5) There are 6 potential N-linked glycosylation sites, having the consensus sequence (Struck & Lennarz, 1980) Asn-Xaa-Ser/Thr (only 3 or 4 of these sites are actually glycosylated). To date, no specific polypeptide structural requirements have been established for O-linked glycosylation of glycoproteins.

Functions of mouse zona pellucida glycoproteins

ZP glycoproteins play several roles during mouse development (Wassarman, 1987a, b, 1988a, b, 1990). (1) ZP1, ZP2 and ZP3 are structural glycoproteins involved in assembly of the ZP during oogenesis. (2) ZP3 serves as a primary receptor for spermatozoa during initial gamete interactions. (3) ZP3 serves as an acrosome-reaction inducer after binding of acrosome-intact spermatozoa to the ZP. (4) ZP2 serves as a secondary receptor for bound spermatozoa after the acrosome reaction. (5) Finally, modifications of ZP2 and ZP3 following fertilization enable them to play a role in the slow block to polyspermy. Each of these functions for ZP glycoproteins is discussed briefly below.

Role of ZP1–3 as structural glycoproteins

The mouse ZP is composed of very long filaments (several μm in length) that are interconnected and so produce an extremely porous extracellular matrix (Greve & Wassarman, 1985; Wassarman, 1988a). Each filament is a polymer constructed of ZP2–ZP3 dimers (M_r 180 000), with each dimer located every 15 nm or so (periodically) along the filaments. Filaments are interconnected by ZP1, which is a minor component of the ZP as compared with ZP2 and ZP3 (ZP2 and ZP3 are present in approximately equimolar amounts). Selective proteolytic degradation of ZP1 or reduction of ZP1 intermolecular disulphides results in disruption of interconnections between filaments (Greve & Wassarman, 1985). All 3 glycoproteins therefore play a structural role during assembly of the ZP around growing oocytes.

Role of ZP3 as primary sperm receptor

Based on the fertilization pathway outlined above, a sperm receptor would be expected to fulfil several requirements *in vitro*. (1) Receptor from egg ZP should bind to spermatozoa and prevent the spermatozoa from binding to ovulated eggs. (2) Receptor from embryo ZP should not bind to spermatozoa and not prevent the spermatozoa from binding to ovulated eggs. (3) Receptor from egg ZP should bind to the head of an acrosome-intact spermatozoon but not to the head of an acrosome-reacted spermatozoon. (4) Receptor from egg ZP should not bind to a wide variety of cell types. (5) Finally, receptor from egg ZP should exhibit a certain degree of species specificity in binding to spermatozoa.

Of the many purified glycoproteins tested *in vitro*, including all 3 mouse ZP glycoproteins, only ZP3 exhibits the characteristics expected for a bona-fide sperm receptor (Bleil & Wassarman, 1980c, 1986; Vazquez *et al.*, 1989; Wassarman *et al.*, 1985; Wassarman, 1987a, b). Each acrosome-intact spermatozoon binds to tens-of-thousands of ZP3 molecules located at the surface of the ZP (every 15 nm along ZP filaments). Spermatozoa recognize and bind to a particular class of ZP3 O-linked oligosaccharides (about M_r 3900) which represents a relatively small fraction of the total O-linked oligosaccharides of the glycoprotein (Florman *et al.*, 1984; Florman & Wassarman, 1985; Wassarman, 1989). The purified oligosaccharides, at nanomolar concentrations, prevent binding of spermatozoa to eggs and, consequently, prevent fertilization. A galactose residue, located in α-linkage at the non-reducing terminus of the oligosaccharides, serves as an essential determinant for binding of spermatozoa to ZP3 (Bleil & Wassarman, 1988; Wassarman, 1989). Removal of this galactose by treatment with α-galactosidase or conversion of the sugar's C-6 alcohol to an aldehyde by treatment with galactose oxidase inactivates ZP3 (or its oligosaccharides) as a sperm receptor. In the latter case, subsequent treatment with sodium borohydride (restoring a C-6 alcohol) restores the glycoprotein's ability to serve as a sperm receptor.

In mice, therefore, gamete adhesion is supported by ZP glycoprotein ZP3 which serves as a primary sperm receptor. Adhesion is attributable to certain of the glycoprotein's O-linked oligosaccharides which, perhaps, are also responsible for the species specificity of gamete adhesion. In this context, carbohydrates have been implicated in cellular recognition and adhesion in a variety of other biological systems (Bock & Harnett, 1989; Jaworski & Weply, 1989).

Role of ZP3 as acrosome-reaction inducer

After binding to the egg ZP, mouse spermatozoa undergo the acrosome reaction, a form of exocytosis. It is essential for bound spermatozoa to undergo the acrosome reaction in order for them to penetrate the ZP and fuse with the egg plasma membrane. The acrosome reaction has an absolute requirement for Ca^{2+}, involves a Ca^{2+}-dependent phospholipase, guanine nucleotide-binding proteins (G proteins), and altered cyclic nucleotide metabolism, and is characterized by Na^+ and Ca^{2+} influx and H^+ efflux through plasma membrane surrounding the sperm head (Kopf & Gerton, 1990; Wassarman, 1990). Many of these properties are characteristic of receptor-mediated signal transduction in somatic cells (Berridge, 1987; Gilman, 1987).

Of the 3 ZP glycoproteins tested, only egg ZP3 induces spermatozoa to undergo the acrosome reaction *in vitro* (Bleil & Wassarman, 1983; Florman *et al.*, 1984; Wassarman *et al.*, 1985; Wassarman, 1987a, b; Endo *et al.*, 1988; Leyton & Saling, 1989). Egg ZP3 is as effective as ionophore A23187 in inducing spermatozoa to undergo the acrosome reaction and this response to ZP3 is inhibited by pertussis toxin (Endo *et al.*, 1987a, 1988; Vazquez *et al.*, 1989), an inhibitor of signal transduction that acts at the level of G proteins. Comparison of the effectiveness of ZP3 as an inhibitor of sperm binding to eggs (sperm receptor function) and as an acrosome-reaction inducer indicates that the latter requires significantly higher concentrations of ZP3 and exhibits sigmoidal behaviour (Bleil & Wassarman, 1983). Furthermore, the ability of ZP3 to serve as an acrosome-reaction inducer depends on the glycoprotein's O-linked oligosaccharides and polypeptide chain (Florman *et al.*, 1984; Leyton & Saling, 1989; Wassarman, 1989). These and other observations suggest that induction of the acrosome reaction by ZP3 depends on multivalent interactions of the glycoprotein with a sperm plasma membrane component, and may result in aggregation ('capping' or 'patching') of the complementary sperm component (Wassarman *et al.*, 1985; Leyton & Saling, 1989).

In mice, therefore, binding of spermatozoa to ZP3 is sufficient to induce spermatozoa to undergo the acrosome reaction. ZP3 apparently acts through a signal transduction system in spermatozoa comparable to that found in a variety of somatic cells. It should be noted that these results are not unique to mice. Spermatozoa from other mammals also undergo a ZP glycoprotein-induced acrosome reaction (Cherr *et al.*, 1986; O'Rand & Fisher, 1987; Cross *et al.*, 1988; Florman & First, 1988; Moller *et al.*, 1990).

Role of ZP2 as secondary sperm receptor

Mouse spermatozoa that undergo the acrosome reaction following binding to ZP3 must remain bound to the ZP in order to penetrate the extracellular coat. In fact, many spermatozoa are released from the ZP after undergoing the acrosome reaction on the ZP. Maintenance of sperm binding is achieved by interaction of acrosome-reacted spermatozoa, via their inner acrosomal membrane, with ZP2 which, like ZP3, is located every 15 nm along ZP filaments (Bleil & Wassarman, 1986; Bleil *et al.*, 1988). Thus, ZP2 serves as a secondary receptor for spermatozoa. Certain evidence suggests that binding of acrosome-reacted spermatozoa to ZP2 is supported by a trypsin-like proteinase associated with the sperm inner acrosomal membrane (Bleil *et al.*, 1988). Compared with primary binding of spermatozoa secondary binding is apparently stabilized by relatively weak interactions. Since bound, acrosome-reacted spermatozoa must penetrate the ZP, relatively weak interactions could be advantageous for progress of a spermatozoon through the extracellular coat. Once spermatozoa begin to penetrate the ZP, their forward swimming motion and location within the extracellular matrix provide additional constraints on the cell.

Role of ZP2 and ZP3 in the secondary block to polyspermy

After fusion of spermatozoon and egg, the ZP becomes refractory (zona reaction) both to the binding of free-swimming spermatozoa and penetration by spermatozoa that had partly penetrated the extracellular coat before fertilization. The former is due to inactivation of ZP3 as a sperm receptor, and the latter apparently is due to modification of ZP2. In both cases, cortical granule enzymes released into the ZP, as a result of the cortical reaction, are responsible for the changes in ZP glycoproteins that constitute a secondary (slow) block to polyspermy.

As indicated above, embryo ZP3 is inactive as a sperm receptor and acrosome-reaction inducer, even though it is indistinguishable from egg ZP3 by SDS-PAGE analysis, as well as by other criteria (Bleil & Wassarman, 1980c; Wassarman *et al.*, 1985; Wassarman, 1987a, b, 1988a). However, recent results suggest that inactivation of ZP3, following either fertilization or artificial activation (by ionophore A23187) of eggs, is due to modification of the glycoprotein's O-linked oligosaccharides (J. Bleil & P. Wassarman, unpublished results). The modified (embryonic) form of ZP3 is called $ZP3_f$ (Bleil & Wassarman, 1980c). The nature and extent of the modification to ZP3 oligosaccharides remain to be determined.

ZP2 undergoes limited proteolysis after fertilization or artificial activation (by ionophore A23187) of eggs (Bleil *et al.*, 1981; Endo *et al.*, 1987b; Moller & Wassarman, 1989). Proteolysis occurs near the amino- or carboxy-terminus of the glycoprotein, producing a glycopeptide of M_r 23 000 that remains attached to ZP2 by intramolecular disulphide bonds (Bleil *et al.*, 1981; Moller & Wassarman, 1989). Therefore, in the presence of reducing agents, ZP2 migrates on gels with an apparent M_r of 90 000, rather than 120 000. The modified (embryonic) form of ZP2 is called $ZP2_f$ (Bleil *et al.*, 1981; Moller & Wassarman, 1989). Proteolysis of ZP2 is catalysed by a cortical granule proteinase that has an apparent M_r between 21 000 and 34 000 and is insensitive to a wide range of proteinase inhibitors (Moller & Wassarman, 1989). Conversion of ZP2 to $ZP2_f$ correlates with the significant decrease in solubility of the ZP ('hardening') following fertilization or artificial activation of eggs. Proteolysis of ZP2 probably causes a structural rearrangement of the ZP that promotes filament–filament interactions and, thereby, makes the ZP more insoluble. In addition, proteolysis of ZP2 may preclude maintenance of binding of acrosome-reacted spermatozoa to the ZP by inactivating ZP2 as a secondary sperm receptor (Bleil *et al.*, 1988; Moller & Wassarman, 1989).

Summary and concluding remarks

The multiple forms and functions of mouse ZP glycoproteins can be summarized as follows.

ZP1 (M_r 200 000) is a ZP filament crosslinker (i.e. structural glycoprotein). It consists of 2 identical polypeptide chains (M_r 75 000 each), held together by intermolecular disulphide bonds, and an undetermined number of N-linked and O-linked oligosaccharides.

ZP2 (M_r 120 000) is a ZP filament structural glycoprotein and secondary sperm receptor. It consists of a polypeptide chain of M_r 81 000, 6 complex-type N-linked oligosaccharides, and an undetermined number of O-linked oligosaccharides.

ZP2$_f$ (M_r 90 000/23 000) is an inactivated form of ZP2, modified by limited proteolysis (by a cortical granule proteinase), that participates in the zona reaction (slow block to polyspermy) following activation of eggs.

ZP3 (M_r 83 000) is a ZP filament structural glycoprotein, primary sperm receptor and acrosome-reaction inducer. It consists of a polypeptide chain of M_r 44 000, 3 or 4 complex-type N-linked oligosaccharides, and an undetermined number of O-linked oligosaccharides.

ZP3$_f$ (M_r 83 000) is an inactivated form of ZP3, apparently containing modified O-linked oligosaccharides (probably modified by cortical granule glycosidases), that participates in the zona reaction (slow block to polyspermy) following activation of eggs.

The ZP is a unique organelle that regulates gamete interactions during fertilization in mammals. Although the ZP is relatively simple in terms of composition, the multifunctional nature of its constituent glycoproteins permits the ZP to perform its various tasks. The fundamental 'functional unit' of the mouse ZP could be thought of as a single protein consisting of 2 non-identical polypeptide chains (ZP2 and ZP3). This functional unit (a dimer of $M_r \sim 180\,000$) regulates gamete interactions, beginning with initial binding of spermatozoa to the ZP and concluding with penetration of the ZP by spermatozoa. After fertilization, inactivation of the functional unit (ZP2 and ZP3) by cortical granule enzymes precludes interactions between spermatozoa and the fertilized egg ZP.

While much of our understanding of the details of ZP involvement in fertilization comes from research carried out with mouse gametes, analogous studies suggest that the knowledge gained will apply to other mammals as well. Such knowledge undoubtedly will open many avenues for research on both basic and clinical aspects of contraception and conception in humans. Hopefully, the fruits of research on mammalian fertilization will continue to be applied in ways that enrich our lives.

I have great pleasure in acknowledging past and present members of my laboratory for their valuable experimental and conceptual contributions to the research summarized here. This research was supported in part by the NICHD, NSF, Rockefeller Foundation, and Hoffmann-La Roche Inc.

References

Berridge, M.J. (1987) Inositol triphosphate and diacylglycerol: two interacting second messengers. *Annu. Rev. Biochem.* **56**, 159–193.

Bleil, J.D. & Wassarman, P.M. (1980a) Structure and function of the zona pellucida: identification and characterization of the mouse oocyte's zona pellucida. *Devl Biol.* **76**, 185–203.

Bleil, J.D. & Wassarman, P. M. (1980b) Synthesis of zona pellucida proteins by denuded and follicle-enclosed mouse oocytes during culture *in vitro*. *Proc. natn. Acad. Sci., USA* **77**, 1029–1033.

Bleil, J.D. & Wassarman, P.M. (1980c) Mammalian sperm-egg interaction: Identification of a glycoprotein in mouse egg zonae pellucidae possessing receptor activity for sperm. *Cell* **20**, 873–882.

Bleil, J.D. & Wassarman, P.M. (1983) Sperm-egg interactions in the mouse: sequence of events and induction of the acrosome reaction by a zona pellucida glycoprotein. *Devl Biol.* **95**, 317–324.

Bleil, J.D. & Wassarman, P.M. (1986) Autoradiographic visualization of the mouse egg's sperm receptor bound to sperm. *J. Cell Biol.* **102**, 1363–1371.

Bleil, J.D. & Wassarman, P.M. (1988) Galactose at the nonreducing terminus of O-linked oligosaccharides of mouse egg zona pellucida glycoprotein ZP3 is essential for the glycoprotein's sperm receptor activity. *Proc. natn. Acad. Sci., USA* **85**, 6778–6782.

Bleil, J.D., Beall, C.F. & Wassarman, P.M. (1981) Mammalian sperm-egg interaction: fertilization of mouse eggs triggers modification of the major zona pellucida glycoprotein. *Devl Biol.* **86**, 189–197.

Bleil, J.D., Greve, J.M. & Wassarman, P.M. (1988) Identification of a secondary sperm receptor in the mouse egg zona pellucida: role in maintenance of binding of acrosome-reacted sperm. *Devl Biol.* **128**, 376–385.

Bock, G. & Harnett, S. (Eds) (1989) *Carbohydrate Function in Cellular Recognition* (Ciba Found. Symp.), No. 145. John Wiley and Sons, Chichester.

Cherr, G.N., Lambert, H., Meizel, S. & Katz, D.F. (1986) *In vitro* studies of the golden hamster sperm acrosome reaction: completion on the zona pellucida and induction by homologous soluble zonae pellucidae. *Devl Biol.* **114**, 119–131.

Cross, N.L., Morales, P., Overstreet, J.W. & Hanson, F.W. (1988) Induction of acrosome reactions by the human zona pellucida. *Biol. Reprod.* **38**, 235–244.

Dietl, J. (Ed.) (1989) *The Mammalian Egg Coat: Structure and Function.* Springer-Verlag, Berlin.

Doolittle, R.F. (1986) *Of Urfs and Orfs.* University Science Books, Mill Valley, CA.

Endo, Y., Lee, M.A. & Kopf, G.S. (1987a) Evidence for the role of a guanine nucleotide-binding regulatory protein in the zona pellucida-induced mouse sperm acrosome reaction. *Devl Biol.* **119**, 210–216.

Endo, Y., Schultz, R.M. & Kopf, G.S. (1987b) Effects of a phorbol ester on mouse eggs: dissociation of sperm receptor activity from acrosome reaction-inducing activity of the mouse zona pellucida glycoprotein, ZP3. *Devl Biol.* **119**, 199–209.

Endo, Y., Lee, M.A. & Kopf, G.S. (1988) Characterization of an islet-activating protein-sensitive site in mouse sperm that is involved in the zona pellucida-induced acrosome reaction. *Devl Biol.* **129**, 12–24.

Florman, H.M. & First, N.L. (1988) I. Sperm capacitation is required for the induction of acrosome reactions by the bovine zona pellucida *in vitro*. *Devl Biol.* **128**, 453–463.

Florman, H.M. & Wassarman, P.M. (1985) O-Linked oligosaccharides of mouse egg ZP3 account for its sperm receptor activity. *Cell* **41**, 313–324.

Florman, H.M., Bechtol, K.B. & Wassarman, P.M. (1984) Enzymatic dissection of the functions of the mouse egg's receptor for sperm. *Devl Biol.* **106**, 243–255.

Gilman, A.G. (1987) G proteins: transducers of receptor-generated signals. *Annu. Rev. Biochem.* **56**, 615–649.

Greve, J.M. & Wassarman, P.M. (1985) Mouse egg extracellular coat is a matrix of interconnected filaments possessing a structural repeat. *J. molec. Biol.* **181**, 253–264.

Greve, J.M., Salzmann, G.S., Roller, R.J. & Wassarman, P.M. (1982) Biosynthesis of the major zona pellucida glycoprotein secreted by oocytes during mammalian oogenesis. *Cell* **31**, 749–759.

Gwatkin, R.B.L. (1977) *Fertilization Mechanisms in Man and Mammals.* Plenum Press, New York.

Jaworski, E.G. & Weply, J.K. (Eds) (1989) *Glycobiology* (UCLA Symp. Mol. Biol.), vol. 111. Alan R. Liss, New York.

Kinloch, R.A. & Wassarman, P.M. (1989) Profile of a mammalian sperm receptor gene. *New Biologist* **1**, 232–238.

Kinloch, R.A., Roller, R.J., Fimiani, C.M., Wassarman, D.A. & Wassarman, P.M. (1988) Primary structure of the mouse sperm receptor's polypeptide chain determined by genomic cloning. *Proc. natn. Acad. Sci., USA* **85**, 6409–6413.

Kinloch, R.A., Roller, R.J. & Wassarman, P.M. (1989) Organization and expression of the mouse sperm receptor gene. In *Developmental Biology* (UCLA Symp. Mol. Biol. No. 125), pp. 9–20. Eds E. Davidson, J. Ruderman & J. Posakony. A.R. Liss, New York.

Kopf, G.S. & Gerton, G.L. (1990) The mammalian sperm acrosome and the acrosome reaction. In: *Elements of Mammalian Fertilization*, (in press). Ed. P. M. Wassarman. CRC Press, Boca Raton.

Kornfeld, R. & Kornfeld, S. (1985) Assembly of asparagine-linked oligosaccharides. *Annu. Rev. Biochem.* **54**, 631–664.

Leyton, L. & Saling, P. (1989) Evidence that aggregation of mouse sperm receptors by ZP3 triggers the acrosome reaction. *J. Cell Biol.* **108**, 2163–2168.

Moller, C.C. & Wassarman, P.M. (1989) Characterization of a proteinase that cleaves zona pellucida glycoprotein ZP2 following activation of mouse eggs. *Devl Biol.* **132**, 103–112.

Moller, C.C., Bleil, J.D., Kinloch, R.A. & Wassarman, P.M. (1990) Structural and functional relationships between mouse and hamster zona pellucida glycoproteins. *Devl Biol.* **137**, 276–286.

O'Rand, M.G. & Fisher, S.J. (1987) Localization of zona pellucida binding sites on rabbit spermatozoa and induction of the acrosome reaction by solubilized zonae. *Devl Biol.* **119**, 551–559.

Pfeffer, S.R. & Rothman, J.E. (1987) Biosynthetic protein transport and sorting by the endoplasmic reticulum and Golgi. *Annu. Rev. Biochem.* **56**, 829–852.

Philpott, C.C., Ringuette, M.J. & Dean, J. (1987) Oocyte-specific expression and developmental regulation of ZP3, the sperm receptor of the mouse zona pellucida. *Devl Biol.* **121**, 568–575.

Ringuette, M.J., Sobieski, D.A., Chamow, S.M. & Dean, J. (1986) Oocyte-specific gene expression: Molecular characterization of a cDNA coding for ZP3, the sperm receptor of the mouse zona pellucida. *Proc. natn. Acad. Sci., USA* **83**, 4341–4345.

Ringuette, M.J., Chamberlin, M.E., Baur, A.W., Sobieski, D.A. & Dean, J. (1988) Molecular analysis of cDNA coding for ZP3, a sperm binding protein of the mouse zona pellucida. *Devl Biol.* **127**, 287–295.

Roller, R.J. & Wassarman, P.M. (1983) Role of asparagine-linked oligosaccharides in secretion of glycoproteins of the mouse egg's extracellular coat. *J. biol. Chem.* **258**, 13243–13249.

Roller, R.J., Kinloch, R.A., Hiraoka, B.Y., Li, S.S.-L. & Wassarman, P.M. (1989) Gene expression during mammalian oogenesis and early embryogenesis: quantification of three messenger RNAs abundant in fully grown mouse oocytes. *Development* **106**, 251–261.

Salzmann, G.S., Greve, J.M., Roller, R.J. & Wassarman, P.M. (1983) Biosynthesis of the sperm receptor during oogenesis in the mouse. *EMBO J.* **2**, 1451–1456.

Shimizu, S., Tsuji, M. & Dean, J. (1983) *In vitro* biosynthesis of three sulfated glycoproteins of murine zonae pellucidae by oocytes grown in culture. *J. biol. Chem.* **258**, 5858–5863.

Struck, D.K. & Lennarz, W.J. (1980) The function of saccharide-lipids in synthesis of glycoproteins. In *The Biochemistry of Glycoproteins and Proteoglycans*, pp. 35–83. Ed. W. J. Lennarz. Plenum Press, New York.

Vazquez, M.H., Phillips, D.M. & Wassarman, P.M. (1989) Interaction of mouse sperm with purified sperm receptors covalently linked to silica beads. *J. Cell Sci.* **92**, 713–722.

Wassarman, P.M. (1987a) The biology and chemistry of fertilization. *Science, NY* **235**, 553–560.

Wassarman, P.M. (1987b) Early events in mammalian fertilization. *Annu. Rev. Cell Biol.* **3**, 109–142.

Wassarman, P.M. (1988a) Zona pellucida glycoproteins. *Annu. Rev. Biochem.* **57**, 415–442.

Wassarman, P.M. (1988b) Fertilization in mammals. *Sci. Am.* **256**, 78–84.

Wassarman, P.M. (1989) Role of carbohydrates in receptor-mediated fertilization in mammals. In *Carbohydrate Recognition in Cellular Function* (Ciba Found. Symp. No. 145), pp. 135–155. Eds G. Bock & S. Harnett. John Wiley and Sons, Chichester.

Wassarman, P.M. (1990) Profile of a mammalian sperm receptor. *Development* **108**, 1–17.

Wassarman, P.M., Bleil, J.D., Florman, H.M., Greve, J.M., Roller, R.J., Salzmann, G.S. & Samuels, F.G. (1985) The mouse egg's receptor for sperm: What is it and how does it work? *Cold Spring Harbor Symp. Quant. Biol.* **50**, 11–19.

Yanagimachi, R. (1988) Mammalian fertilization. In *The Physiology of Reproduction* 1 vol., pp. 135–185. Eds E. Knobil & J. D. Neill. Raven Press, New York.

J. Reprod. Fert., Suppl. **42** (1990), 89–105

Identification and functions of mammalian sperm–egg recognition molecules during fertilization

R. Jones

Department of Molecular Embryology, Institute of Animal Physiology and Genetics Research, Babraham Hall, Cambridge CB2 4AT, UK

Keywords: fertilization; zona pellucida; acrosome; proacrosin; cell adhesion

Introduction

Fertilization in mammals is a unique cell–cell interaction event in which two morphologically disparate gametes, the spermatozoon and egg, recognize and fuse with each other in a highly specific and regulated fashion (Yanagimachi, 1988). Only when all the complementary signals and responses have been successfully completed will syngamy and transfer of genetic information take place. The intricacy of the cascade of events leading from initial recognition to fusion minimizes the possibility that spurious interactions with other cell types will elicit a response. If this should happen, then that particular spermatozoon or egg is directed along a pathway that will lead to its rapid senescence and death.

In this review of fertilization processes in mammals, attention will focus on the very early events during recognition and binding of spermatozoa to the zona pellucida. The developmental stages preceding fertilization (gametogenesis, maturation and capacitation) will not be discussed in detail here (for reviews of these aspects see Bellve, 1979; Eddy, 1988; Fraser & Ahuja, 1988; Jones, 1989a; Saling 1989) except in the context of what they reveal about the identity of sperm–zona adhesion molecules. The nature of the receptors for spermatozoa on the zona pellucida has been reviewed comprehensively by Wassarman (1987, 1990). Therefore, in this article I shall concentrate on what is known about the complementary ligand molecules on spermatozoa, their mechanism of action and how the various candidates suggested so far fit into established knowledge on the biology of fertilization as a whole.

Site of putative zona-binding molecules on spermatozoa

It is generally agreed that in the majority of species the population of 'fertile' spermatozoa that reach the oviduct still have intact acrosomes when they first encounter the cumulus oophorus surrounding the egg. Work in several laboratories has shown that if spermatozoa complete their acrosome reaction before encountering the cumulus they stick to it irreversibly (Talbot, 1985; Cherr *et al.*, 1986; Cummins & Yanagimachi, 1986). Also, in most species (rabbit and guinea-pig may be exceptions; see later) the viability of acrosome-reacted spermatozoa is quite short. The plasma membrane overlying the acrosomal domain must therefore be the site of at least some zona recognition molecules since this is the region that first encounters the zona. This has been demonstrated comprehensively for the mouse (Saling & Storey, 1979; Bleil & Wassarman, 1980; Storey *et al.*, 1984) and also seems to be true for ram (Crozet & Dumont, 1984), bull (Florman & First, 1988), boar (Peterson *et al.*, 1980) and human (Singer *et al.*, 1985) spermatozoa. It is fair to point out, however, that this is still a controversial subject. Interpretations of the exact status of the acrosome become equivocal because of technical difficulties and problems with comparing different

attach to the zona with an intact acrosome (Saling & Storey, 1979). It has not been identified cytochemically but its properties are not unlike those described for a M_r 15 000 plasma membrane protein found on the acrosomal cap of capacitated mouse spermatozoa (Aarons et al., 1984; Poirier et al., 1986; Boettger et al., 1989). This protein is heat-labile, easily solubilized by simply freezing and thawing spermatozoa, and binds a naturally occurring M_r 6400 proteinase inhibitor from the seminal vesicles. The inhibitor is present on ejaculated spermatozoa but dissociates from its acceptor protein if they are incubated in utero or in vitro. Therefore, it has many features of a decapacitation factor. Significantly, pre-exposure of homologous zonae to the purified M_r 15 000 acceptor interferes with sperm binding (Poirer et al., 1986). Further characterization of both the MUGB hydrolysing site and the M_r 15 000 acceptor is required to determine whether they are coincident.

Antigens identified by monoclonal antibodies (McAbs)

Spermatogenic cells are produced behind an immunological barrier in the testis and consequently many antigens on spermatozoa are autoantigens. It has long been known from clinical work that sperm-agglutinating antibodies are frequently found in sera from infertile couples and vasectomized men (Jones, 1980). Although these autoantibodies do not appear to have any ill effects on general health, they pose considerable problems when attempts are made to restore fertility. Not surprisingly therefore, the immunobiology of spermatozoa has received close attention for many years.

A large number of McAbs have now been produced to sperm antigens and seminal plasma proteins from a wide variety of species. They have been used as diagnostic agents (see Gaunt et al., 1983), as probes to map domain organization of surface membrane antigens (see Primakoff & Myles, 1983; and numerous others), as markers for maturation and capacitation of spermatozoa (see Feuchter et al., 1981), and to identify antigens with potential roles in fertilization. In the latter respect, the basic tenet has been to screen McAbs in in-vitro fertilization tests or by passive immunization for their ability to inhibit fertilization. Those that were successful for one reason or another were then selected for further investigation. This has been done with varying degrees of success for the mouse (Saling & Lakoski, 1985; Okabe et al., 1986), hamster (Moore & Hartman, 1984), rabbit (Naz et al., 1984; O'Rand & Irons, 1984), human (Naz, 1988), guinea-pig (Primakoff et al., 1985) and rat (Haneji & Koide, 1988; Shalgi et al., 1990). Unfortunately, not all of these studies have been done in the same way or have been sufficiently rigorous to pinpoint the exact site of inhibition, e.g. zona binding or induction of the acrosome reaction. A notable exception in this respect is the work of Saling et al. (1985) with the mouse. Out of 6 McAbs that bound specifically to the equatorial segment only 2 (M29 and M37) inhibited fertilization. The block was then found to occur at the level of fusion with the oolema. Another inhibitory McAb (M42) that localized on the acrosomal cap was traced to its ability to prevent the zona-induced acrosome reaction (Saling & Lakoski, 1985; Saling, 1986). Latest evidence indicates that M42 McAb blocks a very early step in the cascade of events leading to the acrosome reaction and that the antigen (a high-mass doublet protein at M_r 220 000–240 000) may regulate Ca^{2+} or H^+ fluxes (Leyton & Saling, 1989).

One long-held view is that new antigens that arise during epididymal maturation must have some significance since caput spermatozoa do not bind to eggs whereas cauda spermatozoa have the potential to do so when placed under the appropriate conditions. While there is no doubt that spermatozoa acquire a 'coating' of new glycoproteins secreted by the epididymis, there is growing evidence that antigens that play a key role in fertilization are actually synthesized in the testis. These antigens may then be modified and/or change their domain distribution during subsequent maturation and capacitation. Three examples are PH-20 antigen in the guinea-pig (Myles & Primakoff, 1984), M42 in the mouse (Saling & Lakoski, 1985) and 2B1 antigen in the rat. The case of 2B1 antigen is instructive. This antigen first appears all over the surface of round spermatids in the testis but on fully formed spermatozoa it is restricted principally to the tail where it has a patchy distribution (Gaunt *et al.*, 1983). A McAb to this antigen blocks fertilization *in vitro* in a specific and dose-dependent manner when added to capacitated spermatozoa (Shalgi *et al.*, 1990); half-maximal inhibition is obtained with 1·6 µg purified IgG/ml. The McAb has no detectable adverse effects on sperm motility and blocks fertilization at the level of zona recognition and binding. Its inhibitory effects are specific as 8 other McAbs failed to have a significant influence on fertilization *in vitro*.

At first sight it seemed puzzling that an antigen on the sperm tail should be relevant for fertilization. However, a close examination by indirect immunofluorescence of spermatozoa adhering to the surface of the zona revealed that they all had 2B1 antigen over the acrosomal domain (Shalgi *et al.*, 1990). The question then arose as to how the antigen assumed this new location? Was it being exposed (e.g. by the acrosome reaction) or was it actively migrating there from the tail and could this explain why a McAb to it blocked sperm–zona binding?

Answers to these questions were provided by monitoring the distribution of 2B1 antigen on spermatozoa during capacitation *in vitro*. When freshly washed cauda spermatozoa were incubated in a capacitation medium, RFM (Kaplan & Kraicer, 1978), and then labelled with 2B1 McAb and FITC-conjugated rabbit anti-mouse IgG, fluorescence appeared over the acrosomal domain (Fig. 1). This phenomenon was temperature-dependent and did not take place if spermatozoa were incubated in a non-capacitating medium such as PBS. The same result was obtained if spermatozoa were pre-labelled with FITC-conjugated 2B1 IgG and incubated in RFM in the presence of a 100-fold excess 'cold' 2B1 IgG. This experiment excluded the possibility that the McAb or antigen detached from the membrane on the tail and then re-bound to the acrosome. Furthermore, acute exposure of fresh cauda spermatozoa to dissociating reagents (1 M-NaCl, 5 mM-2-mercaptoethanol) or inducers of the acrosome reaction (A23187 + Ca^{2+}) failed to mimic these effects. On the basis of these experiments it was concluded that 2B1 antigen migrated from the tail domain to the acrosomal domain concomitant with capacitation (Jones *et al.*, 1990). Migration was antigen-selective (other antigens on the sperm tail did not migrate) and Ca^{2+}-dependent but was not inhibited by metabolic poisons. Immunogold labelling studies also showed that the antigen was confined to the plasma membrane and that the McAb did not cross-react with epitopes on intracellular organelles. A quantitative comparison of the intensity of fluorescence (as a reflection of the amount of 2B1 antigen) on different regions of the spermatozoa during capacitation revealed that appearance of the antigen on the acrosome was balanced by its disappearance from the tail (Fig. 2). Significantly, the molecular weight of 2B1 antigen decreased slightly (M_r 300–500) during capacitation, suggesting that processing (e.g. removal of a small peptide) or modification (e.g. phosphorylation) was obligatory for migration. This phenomenon was exacerbated during epididymal maturation when the molecular weight decreased by M_r 3000–4000 from testis to cauda. Unlike capacitation, however, the antigen did not change its domain distribution during passage through the epididymis.

The behaviour of 2B1 antigen as described above is very similar to that reported for PH-20 antigen on guinea-pig spermatozoa (Myles & Primakoff, 1984). Both actively migrate from one domain to another as part of overall physiological changes to the spermatozoon (capacitation or acrosome reaction) and both are processed during epididymal maturation. The net result is that there is re-direction and concentration of an existing membrane protein into a new domain where it was previously excluded. In this new environment it may acquire novel functions by virtue of its association with other proteins and lipids. This has been demonstrated for activation of the catalytic subunit of adenylate cyclase when it makes contact with its receptor protein (Martin, 1983). It would be of great interest to discover some enzymic activity associated with 2B1 antigen. The mechanism that regulates this membrane re-modelling is still an enigma. Possibilities are that intramembranous barriers or submembranous cytoskeletal elements restrain some antigens static and permanently within one domain whilst permitting migration of others. Perhaps it is selective modifications of antigens that is the critical step in directing them to different domains.

spermatozoa bound avidly. Myles *et al.* (1987) have shown that acrosome-intact guinea-pig spermatozoa can bind to the surface of the zona, suggesting that even in this species primary zona
ligands are present on the plasma membrane.

Strong evidence that acrosomal antigens have affinity for the zona pellucida has arisen from
experiments in which solubilized zona glycoproteins have been used as probes to detect complementary ligands on whole spermatozoa or in sperm extracts. This was first explored by Dietl *et al.*
(1983) for the boar and later by Sullivan & Bleau (1985) for the hamster. Sullivan & Bleau (1985)
detected binding of ^{125}I-labelled zona glycoproteins (ZPGPs) to a protein of M_r 26 400 on Western
blots but did not identify its cellular location. O'Rand *et al.* (1985) also reported a variety of low
molecular mass zona binding proteins in extracts of rabbit, mouse, boar and human spermatozoa
and showed that there was some cross-reactivity between species. During our work with pig
spermatozoa, we found that homologous ^{125}I-labelled ZPGPs bound strongly to a component
at M_r 53 000 on Western blots containing sperm proteins (Fig. 4). Weaker binding was detected
to other proteins at M_r 68 000, 38 000 and 18 000–20 000. This profile was highly reproducible
provided proteinase inhibitors (e.g. 1 mM-*p*-aminobenzamidine (pAB) and 1 mM-phenylmethyl-
sulphonylfluoride) were present in the initial detergent extracts. If they were omitted, then the
amount of low molecular mass binding proteins increased noticeably. The M_r 53 000 zona-binding
protein was then identified as proacrosin on the basis of (a) coincidence in molecular mass with boar
proacrosin (Polakoski & Parrish, 1979); (b) cross-reactivity with an antibody to ram acrosin (Jones,
1987; Jones & Brown, 1987); (c) cytochemical distribution within the acrosome (Jones *et al.*, 1988);
(d) *N*-terminal sequence analysis of the purified M_r 53 000 component which gave Arg-
Asp-Asn-Ala-Thr-Cys-Asp-. This is identical with that published by Fock-Nüzel *et al.* (1984) for the
N-terminus of boar acrosin light chain. The M_r 38 000 component represents a form of active acrosin
(probably β-acrosin; Polakoski & Parrish, 1979), the amounts of it increasing considerably under
conditions (pH 8·0) conducive to proacrosin activation. The M_r 18 000–24 000 proteins may represent some of the lower molecular mass forms of acrosin or cleaved fragments from the auto-
activation process. Alternatively, they may be derived partly from the seminal vesicles as seminal
plasma also contains large amounts of low mass zona-binding proteins (Jones *et al.*, 1988). The latter
proteins probably bind to the sperm surface during ejaculation but little further is known about their
behaviour during capacitation or relevance to the ability of a spermatozoon to bind to the zona. The
high molecular mass zona-binding protein at M_r 67 000 may be a form of 'pre-proacrosin' as described by Berruti (1985). In the guinea-pig proacrosin is synthesized post-meiotically in round
spermatids in the testis and is then processed during late spermiogenesis to a lower molecular
mass form (Hardy *et al.*, 1987). This processing may even continue during epididymal maturation
(Arboleda & Gerton, 1988). Whatever its identity, the cytochemical evidence indicates that the
M_r 67 000 antigen must be intra-acrosomal as intact spermatozoa do not stain with FITC–ZPGPs.
However, if boar spermatozoa are permeabilized by cold shock under conditions that reduce loss of
the acrosomal matrix (e.g. in low ionic strength media or in the presence of 2 mM-pAB), then
fluorescence is restricted to the acrosomal region.

These results parallel to a considerable extent reports of a fucose-binding protein in boar
spermatozoa (Töpfer-Petersen *et al.*, 1985; Friess *et al.*, 1987; Töpfer-Petersen & Henshen, 1987).
Originally, this protein was detected on the plasma membrane overlying the acrosome and found
to have an M_r 53 000 when a neoglycoprotein (horseradish peroxidase conjugated with fucose)
was used as a probe. Later, *N*-terminal sequencing identified it unequivocally as proacrosin
(Töpfer-Petersen & Henshen, 1987). It has been referred to as a lectin although this terminology may
be premature. Strictly speaking, a lectin should not have enzymic activity, should not be an
immunoglobulin, should be polyvalent and should have haemagglutinating activity (Barondes, 1981).
Proacrosin does not fulfil at least two of these requirements nor is it specific for fucose residues. We
have no evidence using Western blots on solid-phase assay systems that any monosaccharide (0·2 M-
L(−)-fucose or D(+)-fucose or D(+)-mannose or D(+)-galactose or D(+)-glucose), disaccharide
(0·25 M-lactose or -sucrose), trisaccharide (80 mM-fucosyllactose or 0·25 M-raffinose) or aminosugars

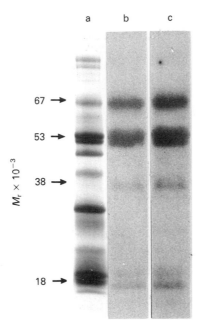

Fig. 4. SDS-PAGE proteins extracted at pH 3 from washed, ejaculated boar spermatozoa stained with **(a)** Coomassie blue, and autoradiographs from parallel blots probed with **(b)** ^{125}I-labelled zona pellucida glycoproteins, or **(c)** ^{125}I-labelled fucoidan. Arrows indicate the molecular masses (M_r) of major zona- and fucoidan-binding components. The M_r 53 000 protein represents proacrosin and the M_r 38 000 protein β-acrosin. The identities of the M_r 67 000 and M_r 18 000 proteins are not known (see text).

(0·20 M-glucosamine or galactosamine) will block binding of ^{125}I-labelled ZPGPs to boar proacrosin (Fig. 5). Only sulphated polymers have this capacity and with varying potency: dextran sulphate (M_r 500 000) > fucoidan > polyvinylsulphate > dextran sulphate (M_r 5000) > galactan > mannan > xylan. Non-sulphated polymers such as dextran (M_r 500 000) have no inhibitory ability (Fig. 5), nor does hyaluronic acid or chondroitin sulphates A or C at 2 mg/ml or 0·25 M-glucose 6-sulphate or 0·25 M-glucosamine-1,3-disulphate. The overall conclusions to be drawn from these experiments are as follows. (a) It is the presence of sulphate ester groups on zona glycoproteins that regulate interaction with basic residues on proacrosin. Thus, polyvinylsulphate is almost as good a competitor as dextran sulphate or fucoidan. (b) The density and orientation of sulphate groups along the polymer backbone are critical factors. This would explain why the chrondroitin sulphates are not inhibitory despite having a charge density similar to fucoidan or dextran sulphate M_r 500 000). (e) Binding of ^{125}I-labelled ZPGPs to proacrosin is sensitive to ionic strength of the buffer, being inhibited by 50% at 0·495 M-NaCl. The interaction therefore involves an electrostatic component although other forces must also be involved to stabilize the binding. Pig zona pellucida glycoproteins contain approximately 2% sulphate (Dunbar *et al.*, 1980).

These conclusions are very close to those drawn by DeAngelis & Glabe (1987, 1988) for the mechanism of interaction between bindin from sea-urchin spermatozoa and fucose-rich proteoglycans on the surface of homologous eggs. Bindin is species specific, is found within the acrosomal granule, and has high affinity ($K_d = 1 \times 10^{-8}$ M) for sulphated polysaccharides on the vitelline layer (roughly equivalent to the zona pellucida in mammals). Egg jelly fucans and fucoidan (a fucose-rich polysaccharide from *Fucus vesiculosis*) bind avidly to sperm bindin and sulphate ester groups are important since solvolytic desulphation inactivates the probes. Resulphation, however, restores their activity. The spatial orientation of these sulphates is critical because other

a   b   c   d   e   f   g   h   i   j   k   l   m   n

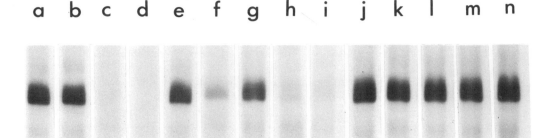

Fig. 5. Autoradiographs from Western blots containing pH 3 extracted proteins from boar spermatozoa that had been pre-blocked with the following compounds before addition of the ^{125}I-labelled zona probe. Only the region with proacrosin (M_r 53 000) is shown. (a) PBS (control). (b) 5 mM-p-aminobenzamidine. (c) 2 mg fucoidan/ml. (d) 2 mg dextran sulphate/ml (M_r 500 000). (e) 2 mg mannan/ml. (f) 2 mg galactan/ml. (g) 2 mg chondroitin sulphate A/ml. (h) 5 mg heparin/ml. (i) 2 mg dextran sulphate/ml (M_r 5000). (j) 2 mg dextran/ml (M_r 500 000). (k) 0·25 mM-lactose. (l) 0·25 mM-L($-$)fucose. (m) 0·25 mM-D($+$)galactose. (n) 0·25 mM-D($+$) mannose.

sulphated polymers such as heparin and chondroitin sulphates have binding affinities many times lower than the resulphated fucans. DeAngelis & Glabe (1988) have proposed that basic residues (arginines, lysines and histidines) in bindin form cyclic resonating structures with sulphate groups and that it is this complementarity that determines binding. We suggest that a similar situation holds for interaction of proacrosin and ^{125}I-labelled ZPGPs and that functionally proacrosin is analogous to bindin. It might be more accurate, therefore, to refer to proacrosin as a polysulphate binding protein rather than a lectin.

One prediction from the above hypothesis is that basic residues on bindin and mammalian proacrosin should lie on the exterior surface of the molecule in order to be available for interaction with projecting sulphates on the polysaccharide. The gene for bindin has been sequenced (Gao et al., 1986) but unfortunately its 3-dimensional structure is not yet known. Human and boar proacrosins have also been sequenced (Adham et al., 1989; Baba et al., 1989) and the high degree of homology with pancreatic trypsinogen has allowed computer-aided predictions to be made of their tertiary structure (Fig. 3). Such models show that all basic residues in boar proacrosin (25 arginines, 15 lysines and 7 histidines) lie on the surface of the molecule and not in internal domains.

Do other proteinases also bind sulphated polysaccharides? From a survey of 8 proteinases (chymotrypsinogen, trypsinogen, elastase, pepsinogen, plaminogen, thrombin, bacterial trypsin and Staphylococcus aureus proteinase) only chymotrypsinogen and trypsinogen bound significant amounts of ^{125}I-labelled fucoidan, albeit with lower affinities than did boar proacrosin (Jones, 1989c). Again this can be related to the high pI ($>9·0$) of the proteins in question. It is conceivable that this 'secondary' property of proacrosin, chymotrypsinogen and trypsinogen might influence the ability of the proteinases to interact with naturally occurring glycoprotein substrates and in some cases, it may even usurp the original function of the enzyme. A case in point here may be sperm proacrosin.

As mentioned above, guinea-pig spermatozoa are considered to be an extreme example of acrosome-reacted spermatozoa binding to the zona. It was therefore of interest to examine this species in detail. In the early work Huang et al. (1981, 1982) and Huang & Yanagimachi (1984) used fucoidan as a probe to investigate the cytochemical distribution of putative zona-binding proteins before and after the acrosome reaction. The validity of using fucoidan as a probe is based on three premises. First, it displays selective affinity for adhesion molecules in a variety of cell types (DeAngelis & Glabe, 1987). Second, it has a strong inhibitory effect on sperm–egg recognition in vitro (Huang et al., 1982; Boldt et al., 1989). Third, it binds to the same sperm proteins as do

[125]I-labelled ZPGPs (pig; Jones *et al.*, 1988). There are therefore good reasons to believe that fucoidan mimics homologous zona glycoproteins in its mechanism of binding to mammalian spermatozoa.

Huang & Yanagimachi (1984) observed that a FITC–avidin–biotin–fucoidan probe did not bind to intact, motile guinea-pig spermatozoa but if spermatozoa were acrosome-reacted then fluorescence was localized over the anterior head and equatorial segment. We have found a similar situation using fluoresceinamine–fucoidan (Jones & Williams, 1990). Intact spermatozoa remained unstained whereas permeabilized or acrosome-reacted spermatozoa were fluorescent over the head (Fig. 6). We have identified the fucoidan-binding proteins on Western blots and found them to have M_r values of 95 000, 60 000, 48 000, 34 000, 30 000 and 18 000–20 000. The M_r 48 000 component was shown to be proacrosin and the M_r 34 000 and 30 000 proteins probably represent active forms of acrosin on the basis of their cross-reactivity with an antibody to boar proacrosin and having proteinase activity on gelatin-containing gels. The M_r 95 000, 60 000 and 18 000–20 000 components were not identified but were considered to be intra-acrosomal. Like boar proacrosin, only certin kinds of sulphated polymers such as polyvinylsulphate, dextran sulphate (M_r 500 000) and galactan could compete with fucoidan binding to guinea-pig proacrosin/acrosin, leading to the conclusion once again that it is not simply the presence or absence of sulphate groups that is important (chrondroitin sulphates A and C, mannan and glucose 6-sulphate were not inhibitory) but their spatial orientation and alignment along the backbone of the polymer that determines the avidity of binding.

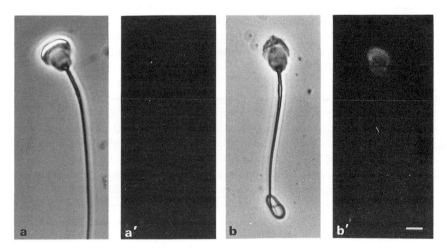

Fig. 6. Paired phase-contrast (a and b) and fluorescence (a′ and b′) photographs of guinea-pig spermatozoa stained with fluoresceinamine-fucoidan. (a) and (a′) acrosome-intact spermatozoon. (b) and (b′) spermatozoon permeabilized by cold shock in the presence of 1 mM-*p*-aminobenzamidine (this proteinase inhibitor prevents loss of acrosomal contents). Note staining of the acrosome in (b′) but not in (a′). Bar = 4 μm.

Collectively, therefore, these results demonstrate that acrosomal matrix components and/or acrosomal membranes have affinity for egg vestments. Since proacrosin is present in all mammalian spermatozoa investigated so far, it has merits as the universal 'sticky' molecule for secondary or firm binding to the zona pellucida. The fact that it is contained within the acrosome means that it is protected from spurious interactions with other cells and targetted to its site of action. Species specificity may be determined by subtle differences in the density and arrangement of polysulphate groups on zona glycoproteins and by complementarity in the 3-dimensional structure of the homologous proacrosin. Cross-activity or 'leakiness' in the system (e.g. mouse spermatozoa will bind to hamster, guinea-pig and rat eggs; Yanagimachi, 1981) would be due to similarities in proacrosins or zona glycoproteins between closely related species.

PH-20 antigen

Passing reference has already been made in this review to PH-20 antigen on guinea-pig spermatozoa in terms of its capacity to migrate from one regional domain to another and in the ability of a McAb to it to block sperm–zona binding (Primakoff & Myles, 1983). However, it is relevant at this stage to describe it in more detail as it is one of the few well characterized antigens shown to be present on the inner acrosomal membrane.

PH-20 antigen is synthesized in the Golgi complex during spermiogenesis when acrosomal membrances are being formed (Phelps & Myles, 1987). On fully formed testicular spermatozoa it has 2 locations; approximately 70% of the total is on the inner acrosomal membranes (PH-20_{AM}) while 30% is on the plasma membrane overlying the head and tail (PH-20_{PM}) (Cowan et al., 1986). During epididymal maturation PH-20_{PM} molecules are thought to concentrate on to the post-acrosomal domain. However, it is during the acrosome reaction that the dynamic properties of PH-20 antigen became apparent. During or after loss of the acrosomal cap PH-20_{PM} activity migrates on to the inner acrosomal membrane vacating the postacrosomal region altogether. Thus, the inner acrosomal membrane now contains a mixture of PH-20_{AM} and PH-20_{PM}. It is not clear at present whether migration per se is Ca^{2+}-dependent or whether it is simply a consequence of the acrosome reaction. Commensurate with this behaviour are the very high diffusion constants measured for PH-20_{PM}; 1.8×10^{-10} cm^2/sec on the postacrosomal and 4.9×10^{-9} cm^2/sec on the inner acrosomal membrane (Phelps et al., 1988). These high values are probably due to the protein having a phosphatidylinositol (PI) 'anchor' into the membrane. They also hint at significant differences in the composition and arrangements of lipids between the plasma membrane and inner acrosomal membrane.

A revealing finding about the mechanism of PH-20_{PM} movement is that the molecule undergoes site-specific endoproteolysis before or during migration (Primakoff et al., 1988a). The parent protein has been shown to have an M_r of 64 000 with a minor form at M_r 56 000. However, if the acrosome is induced to react in the absence of proteinase inhibitors, then almost all the recovered PH-20 protein is in the form of 2 disulphide-linked fragments of M_r 41 000–48 000 and 27 000. This suggests that one aspect of capacitation of guinea-pig spermatozoa involves site-specific endoproteolysis of PH-20_{pm}. Alternatively, if proteolysis does not take place until after the acrosome reaction has been initiated, then acrosomal hydrolases (acrosin?) may be responsible. If the latter suggestion is correct, then it suggests a hitherto unsuspected connection between the acrosome reaction and behaviour of a surface membrane antigen with a putative role in fertilization. The PH-20 antigen has been shown to have potential as a contraceptive immunogen in male and female guinea-pigs (Primakoff et al., 1988b). Once the full sequence of the protein is known it may be possible to refine this approach using synthetic peptides, as has been demonstrated with fragments of ZP3 from mouse zonae (Millar et al., 1989).

Conclusions

The foregoing discussion has highlighted some of the candidates for zona recognition and binding molecules on mammalian spermatozoa. One conclusion to be drawn is that there seems to be more than one type of ligand and that they function at different times and different stages. The time window for activity of one may be very short depending on the species and experimental circumstances, with the result that one level may by-pass or override the other, thereby appearing as the dominant mechanism. A case in point here is the guinea-pig. Notwithstanding the above, and the likelihood that different antigens are required for different facets of fertilization, it is still perplexing that so many different antigens should have been found on spermatozoa with zona-binding activity, even allowing for species differences. It would have been expected that such a fundamental and important biological process as fertilization would have been regulated by highly conserved molecules throughout evolution. So far, with the exception of proacrosin, this expectation is not readily apparent. Only when all the diverse candidates listed above have been fully characterized will it be possible to discern underlying trends and common properties.

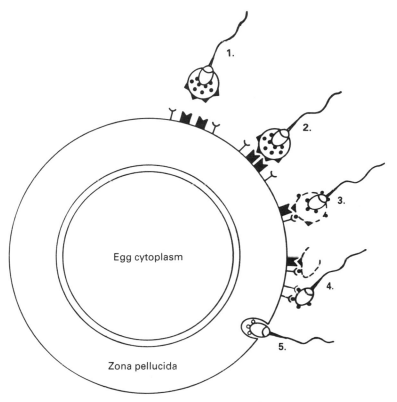

Fig. 7. Diagram of possible sequence of events during attachment and binding of the fertilizing spermatozoon to the zona pellucida (see text). ⋈ = primary sperm receptor on the zona. Υ = secondary sperm receptor on the zona. ▲ = primary zona ligand on the spermatozoon (e.g. GalTase, MUGB site, RSAs, 2B1 antigen). ● = secondary zona ligand (e.g. proacrosin/acrosin, PH 20).

Several models to explain sperm–zona binding have been proposed in recent years (Shur, 1986; Jones *et al.*, 1988; Yanagimachi, 1988; Saling, 1989). The scheme shown in Fig. 7 is an extension of these models in an attempt to incorporate some of the latest data and concepts into a working hypothesis. It is thought that there are two kinds of receptors for spermatozoa on the zona, primary and secondary. Based on information from the mouse (Wassarman, 1987), the primary receptor is envisaged as a carbohydrate residue on one zona glycoprotein (ZP3). The situation in other species is not known but it is reasonable to presume that the mouse pattern is a useful basis. This receptor is then recognized specifically by complementary (primary) ligands on the plasma membrane overlying the acrosomal domain of the fertilizing spermatozoon. These ligands may be molecules like GalTase, MUGB site, RSAs or 2B1 antigen. The result is low affinity attachment of the sperm head to the zona but with sufficient strength to resist lateral displacement forces generated by the motile tail. Apparently, very few bonds are actually required to tether a spermatozoon to the zona (Baltz & Cardullo, 1989). This initial attachment also has the immediate effect of inducing the acrosome reaction (step 3), possibly due to aggregation of ligand complexes into functional units as described in detail by Saling (1989). Once fenestration of the acrosome has been initiated, acrosomal contents begin to disperse. Some, like proacrosin/acrosin, have the property of re-locating on to external membranes overlying the acrosomal cap, equatorial segment and postacrosomal regions. At this stage a second phase of high affinity binding takes place. In the mouse the secondary zona receptor appears to be associated with ZP2 which is modified in the process (Bleil et al., 1988). We speculate that proacrosin/acrosin is a secondary ligand on spermatozoa and that it interacts with sulphated carbohydrate residues on ZP2 (or its equivalent in other species). Interestingly, mouse ZP2 is fairly heavily sulphated whereas ZP3 is poorly sulphated (Shirnizu et al., 1983). The secondary binding phase is enhanced by localized proteolysis of the zona by acrosin, thereby increasing the avidity of the protein–carbohydrate interaction. This has been shown experimentally; zona glycoproteins pre-digested with active acrosin have higher affinity for proacrosin on Western blots (Jones et al., 1988). A mechanism of this sort is also well known from haemagglutination studies in which the efficiency of agglutination of red cells by lectins is increased (in some cases it is obligatory, e.g. galaptin; Harrison et al., 1984) by trypsinization. In a simplistic sense, spermatozoa could be said to 'agglutinate' to the zona. Guinea-pig and rabbit spermatozoa may provide an example whereby steps 1 and 2 are very transitory and steps 3 and 4 dominant. The sequence of events following secondary binding then becomes problematic. Clearly, the spermatozoon must not bind so strongly that it cannot initiate penetration of the zona; some change in binding affinity must take place. Perhaps some proacrosin activates completely to low molecular mass fragments that have weaker polysulphate binding properties (represented as open circles in step 5). This would release the spermatozoon sufficiently to begin penetrating the zona by forward shearing forces. Hedrick et al. (1988) have described zona penetration as alternating cycles of proteolysis and binding. The important observation by Urch & Hedrick (1988) that sulphated polysaccharides inhibit acrosin amidase activity lends weight to this concept. The acrosomal cap or 'ghost' would remain behind on the surface of the zona, apparently immobilized by the high affinity secondary binding components (step 4). Such ghosts have been observed on fertilized hamster and rat eggs (Yanagimachi & Phillips, 1984; Shalgi et al., 1989).

This hypothesis explains some, but not all, of the biological 'facts' about fertilization outlined at the beginning of this review. It will be important in future work to 'fine-tune' many of the details of the process so that established concepts can be continuously refined. None the less, there is cause for optimism that our perception of fertilization will expand rapidly as more details of this particular jig-saw puzzle are pieced together.

I thank Mrs Dianne Styles and Mrs Linda Notton for preparation of the typescript; Mr J. Coadwell for computer graphics and preparation of Fig. 3; and Ms Rachel Williams for helpful comments on the manuscript.

References

Aarons, D., Speake, J.L. & Poirer, G.R. (1984) Evidence for a proteinase inhibitor binding component associated with murine spermatozoa. Biol. Reprod. 31, 811–817.

Adham, I.M., Klemm, U., Maier, W-M., Hoyer-Fender, S., Tsaousidou, S. & Engel, W. (1989) Molecular cloning of preproacrosin and analysis of its expression pattern in spermatogenesis. Eur. J. Biochem. 182, 563–568.

Arboleda, C.E. & Gerton, G.L. (1988) Studies of three major proteases associated with guinea-pig sperm acrosomes. J. exp. Zool. 244, 277–287.

Baba, T., Watanabe, K., Kashiwabara, S. & Arai, Y. (1989) Primary structure of human proacrosin deduced from its cDNA sequence. FEBS Lett. 244, 296–300.

Baltz, J.M. & Cardullo, R.A. (1989) On the number and rate of formation of sperm-zona bonds in the mouse. Gamete Res. 24, 1–8.

Barondes, S.H. (1981) Lectins: their multiple endogenous cellular functions. Ann. Rev. Biochem. 50, 207–231.

Bellve, A.R. (1979) The molecular biology of mammalian spermatogenesis. In Oxford Reviews of Reproductive

Biology, vol. 1, pp. 159–261. Ed. C. A. Finn. Clarendon Press, Oxford.

Benau, D.A. & Storey, B.T. (1987) Charaterization of the mouse sperm plasma membrane zona-binding site sensitive to trypsin inhibitors. *Biol. Reprod.* **36**, 282–292.

Berruti, G. (1985) Evidence of a high molecular weight form of acrosin in boar acrosomal extract. *Int. J. Biochem.* **17**, 87–94.

Bleil, J.D. & Wassarman, P.M. (1980) Mammalian sperm-egg interaction: identification of a glyco-protein in mouse egg zonae pellucidae possessing receptor activity for sperm. *Cell* **20**, 873–882.

Bleil, J.D., Greve, J.M. & Wassarman, P.M. (1988) Identification of a secondary sperm receptor in the mouse egg zona pellucida: role in maintenance of binding the acrosome-reacted sperm to eggs. *Devl Biol.* **128**, 376–385.

Boettger, H., Richardson, R., Free, D., Rushing, S. & Poirier, G.R. (1989) Effects of *in vitro* incubation on a zona binding site found on murine spermatozoa. *J. exp. Zool.* **249**, 90–98.

Boldt, J., Howe, A.M., Parkenson, J.B., Gunter, L.E. & Kuehn, E. (1989) Carbohydrate involvement in sperm-egg fusion in mice. *Biol. Reprod.* **40**, 887–896.

Cherr, G.N., Lambert, H., Meizel, S. & Katz, D.F. (1986) *In vitro* studies of the golden hamster sperm acrosome reaction: completion on the zona pellucida and induction by homologous soluble zonae pellucidae. *Devl Biol.* **114**, 119–131.

Cowan, A.E., Primakoff, P. & Myles, D.G. (1986) Sperm exocytosis increases the amount of PH-20 antigen on the surface of guinea-pig sperm. *J. Cell Biol.* **103**, 1289–1297.

Crozet, N. & Dumont, M. (1984) The site of the acrosome reaction during *in vivo* penetration of the sheep oocyte. *Gamete Res.* **10**, 97–105.

Cummins, J.M. & Yanagimachi, R. (1986) Development of ability to penetrate the cumulus oophorus by hamster spermatozoa capacitated *in vitro*, in relation to the timing of the acrosome reaction. *Gamete Res.* **15**, 187–212.

DeAngelis, P.L. & Glabe, C.G. (1987) Polysaccharide structural features that are critical for the binding of sulphated fucans to bindin, the adhesive protein from sea urchin sperm. *J. biol. Chem.* **262**, 13946–13952.

DeAngelis, P.L. & Glabe, C.G. (1988) Role of basic amino acids in the interaction with sul-phated fucans. *Biochemistry, NY* **27**, 8189–8194.

Dietl, J., Czuppon, A., Weichert, K. & Mettler, L. (1983) Identification of a sperm receptor-glycoprotein from the porcine zona pellucida. *Hoppe-Seyler's Z. Physiol. Chem.* **364**, 261–267.

Dunbar, B.S., Wardrip, N.J. & Hedrick, J.L. (1980) Iso-lation, physiochemical properties, and macromolecu-lar composition of the zona pellucida from porcine oocytes. *Devl Biol.* **121**, 478–488.

Eddy, M. (1988) The spermatozoon. In *The Physiology of Reproduction*, vol. 1, pp. 27–68. Eds E. Knobil & J. Neill. Raven Press, New York.

Esaguy, N., Welch, J.E. & O'Rand, M. (1988) Ultrastruc-tural mapping of a sperm plasma membrane auto-antigen before and after the acrosome reaction. *Gamete Res.* **19**, 387–399.

Feuchter, F.A., Vernon, R.B. & Eddy, E.M. (1981) Analy-sis of the sperm surface with monoclonal antibodies: topographically restricted antigens appearing in the epididymis. *Biol. Reprod.* **24**, 1099–1110.

Florman, H.M. & First, N.L. (1988) The regulation of acrosomal exocytosis: sperm capacitation is required for the induction of acrosome reactions by the bovine zona pellucida *in vitro*. *Devl Biol.* **128**, 453–463.

Fock-Nüzel, R., Lottspeich, F., Henshen, A. & Müller-Esterl, W. (1984) Boar acrosin is a two-chain molecule. Isolation and primary structure of the light chain; homology with the pro-part of other serine proteinases. *Eur. J. Biochem.* **141**. 441–446.

Fraser, L.R. & Ahuja, K.K. (1988) Metabolic and surface events in fertilization. *Gamete Res.* **20**, 491–519.

Friess, A.E., Töpfer-Petersen, E., Nguyen, H. & Schill, W.B. (1987) Electron microscope localization of a fucose-binding protein in acrosome reacted boar spermatozoa by the fucosylperoxidase-gold method. *Histochemistry* **86**, 297–303.

Gao, B., Klein, L.E., Britten, R.J. & Davidson, E.H. (1986) Sequence of mRNA coding for bindin, a species-specific sea urchin sperm protein required for fertiliz-ation. *Proc. natn. Acad. Sci. USA* **83**, 8634–8638.

Gaunt, S.J., Brown, C.R. & Jones, R. (1983) Identifi-cation of mobile and fixed antigens on the plasma membrane of rat spermatozoa using monoclonal antibodies. *Expl Cell Res.* **144**, 275–284.

Haneji, T. & Koide, S.S. (1988) An immunoreactive human sperm antigen in rat spermatogenic cells. In *Contraception Research for Today and the Nineties*, vol. 1, pp. 315–322. Ed. G. P. Talwar. Springer-Verlag, Berlin.

Hardy, D.M., Wild, G.C. & Tung, K.S.K. (1987) Purifi-cation and initial characterization of proacrosins from guinea pig testes and epididymal spermatozoa. *Biol. Reprod.* **37**, 189–199.

Harrison, F.L., Fitzgerald, J.E. & Catt, J.W. (1984) Endogenous β-galactoside-specific lectins in rabbit tissues. *J. Cell Sci.* **72**, 147–162.

Hartmann, J.F. & Hutchinson, C.F. (1974) Nature of the prepenetration contact interactions between hamster gametes *in vitro*. *J. Reprod. Fert.* **36**, 49–57.

Hathaway, H.J. & Shur, B.D. (1988) Novel cell surface receptors during mammalian fertilization and develop-ment. *Bioessays* **9**, 153–158.

Hedrick, J.L., Urch, U.A. & Hardy, D.M. (1988) The structure-function properties of the sperm enzyme acrosin. In *Enzymes in Agricultural Biotechnology*, pp. 55–73. Eds S. Shoemaker, P. Sonnet & J. Whitaker. ACS Books, Washington.

Huang, T.T.F. & Yanagimachi, R. (1984) Fucoidin inhibits attachment of guinea pig spermatozoa to the zona pellucida through binding to the inner acro-somal membrane and equatorial domains. *Expl. Cell Res.* **153**, 363–373.

Huang, T.T.F., Fleming, A.D. & Yanagimachi, R. (1981) Only acrosome-reacted spermatozoa can bind to and penetrate zona pellucida: a study using the guinea pig. *J. exp. Zool.* **217**, 287–290.

Huang, T.T.F., Ohzu, E. & Yanagimachi, R. (1982) Evidence suggesting that L-fucose is part of a recog-nition signal for sperm-zona pellucida attachment in mammals. *Gamete Res.* **5**, 355–361.

Jones, R. (1987) Evidence for boar sperm proacrosin as a carbohydrate binding protein. *Cell Biol. Int. Rep.* **11**, 833.

Jones, R. (1989a) Membrane remodelling during sperm maturation in the epididymis. *Oxford Rev. Reprod. Biol.* **11**, 285–337.

Jones, R. (1989b) Identification of carbohydrate-binding proteins in mammalian spermatozoa (human, bull, boar, ram, stallion and hamster) using [^{125}-I]fucoidin and [^{125}-I]neoglycoprotein probes. *Human Reprod.* **4**, 550–557.

Jones, R. (1989c) Unusual fucoidin-binding properties of chymotrypsinogen and trypsinogen. *Biochim. Biophys. Acta* **1037**, 227–232.

Jones, R. & Brown, C.R. (1987) Identification of a zona-binding protein from boar spermatozoa as proacrosin. *Expl Cell Res.* **171**, 505–508.

Jones, R., Brown, C.R. & Lancaster, R.T. (1988) Carbohydrate-binding properties of boar sperm pro-acrosin and assessment of its role in sperm-egg recognition and adhesion during fertilization. *Development* **102**, 781–792.

Jones, R., Shalgi, R., Hoyland, J. & Phillips, D.M. (1990) Topographical rearrangement of a plasma membrane antigen during capacitation of rat spermatozoa *in vitro*. *Devl Biol.* **139**, 349–362.

Jones, R. & Williams, R.M. (1990) Fucoidan-binding proteins in guinea-pig spermatozoa: identification of proacrosin/acrosin as major receptors and mechanism of recognition. *Development* **109**, 41–50.

Jones, W.R. (1980) Immunologic infertility: fact or fiction. *Fert. Steril.* **33**, 577–586.

Kaplan, R. & Kraicer, P.F. (1978) Effect of elevated calcium concentration on fertilization of rat oocytes *in vitro*. *Gamete Res.* **1**, 281–285.

Kusan, F.B., Fleming, A.D. & Seidel, G.E. (1984) Successful fertilization *in vitro* of fresh intact oocytes by perivitelline (acrosome-reacted) spermatozoa of the rabbit. *Fert. Steril.* **41**, 766–770.

Lancaster, R.T., Brown, C.R. & Jones, R. (1988) Factors influencing sperm-egg recognition and binding in the pig. *Proc. 11th Int. Congr. Anim. Reprod. & AI, Dublin*, vol. 3, **337**, abstr.

Leyton, L. & Saling, P.M. (1989) 95 kd sperm proteins bind ZP3 and serve as tyrosine kinase substrates in response to zona binding. *Cell* **57**, 1123–1130.

Martin, B.R. (1983) Hormone receptors and the adenylate cyclase system: historical overview. In *Current Topics in Membranes and Transport*, vol. 18, pp. 3–9. Eds A. Kleinzeller & B. R. Martin. Academic Press, New York.

Millar, S.E., Charnow, S.M., Baur, A.W., Oliver, C., Robey, F. & Dean, J. (1989) Vaccination with a synthetic zona pellucida peptide produces long-term contraception in female mice. *Science, NY* **246**, 935–938.

Moore, H.D.M. & Hartman, T.D. (1984) Localization by monoclonal antibodies of various surface antigens of hamster spermatozoa and the effect of antibody on fertilization *in vitro*. *J. Reprod. Fert.* **70**, 175–183.

Myles, D.G. & Primakoff, P. (1984) Localized surface antigens of guinea-pig sperm migrate to new regions prior to fertilization. *J. Cell Biol.* **99**, 1634–1641.

Myles, D.G., Hyatt, H. & Primakoff, P. (1987) Binding of both acrosome-intact and acrosome-reacted guinea-pig sperm to the zona pellucida during *in vitro* fertilization. *Devl Biol.* **121**, 559–567.

Naz, R.K. (1988) Role of the fertilization antigen (FA-1) in immunoregulation of fertility and involuntary infertility in humans. In *Progress in Vaccinology*, vol. 1, pp. 323–339. Ed G. P. Talwar. Springer-Verlag, Berlin.

Naz, R.J., Rosenblum, B.B. & Menge, A.C. (1984) Characterization of a membrane antigen from rabbit testis and sperm isolated by using monoclonal antibodies and effect of its antiserum on fertility. *Proc. natl. Acad. Sci. USA* **81**, 857–861.

Okabe, M., Takada, K., Adachi, T., Kohama, Y. & Mimura, T. (1986) Inconsistant reactivity of an anti-sperm monoclonal antibody and its relationship to sperm capacitation. *J. Reprod. Immunol.* **9**, 67–70.

O'Rand, M.G. & Irons, G.P. (1984) Monoclonal antibodies to rabbit sperm autoantigens. II. Inhibition of human sperm penetration of zona-free hamster eggs. *Biol. Reprod.* **30**, 731–736.

O'Rand, M.G., Widgren, E.E. & Fisher, S.J. (1988) Characterization of the rabbit sperm membrane autoantigen, RSA, as a lectin-like zona-binding protein. *Devl Biol.* **129**, 231–240.

O'Rand, M.G., Matthews, J.E., Welch, J.E. & Fisher, S.J. (1985) Identification of zona binding proteins of rabbit, pig, human, and mouse spermatozoa on nitrocellulose blots. *J. exp. Zool.* **235**, 423–428.

Peterson, R.N., Russell, L.D., Bundman, D. & Freund, M. (1980) Sperm-egg interaction: evidence for boar sperm plasma membrane receptors for porcine zona pellucida. *Science, NY* **207**, 73–74.

Phelps, B.M. & Myles, D.G. (1987) The guinea-pig sperm plasma membrane protein, PH-20, reaches the surface via two transport pathways and becomes localized to a domain after an initial uniform distribution. *Devl Biol.* **123**, 63–72.

Phelps, B.M., Primakoff, P., Koppel, D.E., Low, M.G. & Myles, D.G. (1988) Restricted lateral diffusion of PH-20, a PI-anchored sperm membrane protein. *Science, NY* **240**, 1780–1782.

Poirier, G.R., Robinson, R., Richardson, R., Hinds, K. & Clayton, D. (1986) Evidence for a binding site on the sperm plasma membrane which recognizes the murine zona pellucida: a binding site on the sperm plasma membrane. *Gamete Res.* **14**, 235–243.

Polakoski, K.L. & Parrish, R.F. (1979) Boar proacrosin. Purification and preliminary activation studies of proacrosin isolated from ejaculated boar sperm. *J. biol. Chem.* **252**, 1888–1894.

Primakoff, P. & Myles, D.G. (1983) A map of the guinea-pig sperm surface constructed with monoclonal antibodies. *Devl Biol.* **98**, 417–428.

Primakoff, P., Hyatt, H. & Myles, D.G. (1985) A role for the migrating sperm surface antigen PH-20 in guinea-pig sperm binding to the egg zona pellucida. *J. Cell Biol.* **101**, 2239–2244.

Primakoff, P., Cowan, A., Hyatt, H., Tredick-Kline, J. & Myles, D.G. (1988a) Purification of the guinea-pig sperm PH-20 antigen and detection of a site specific endoproteolytic activity that cleaves the antigen into two disulphide linked fragments. *Biol. Reprod.* **38**, 921–934.

Primakoff, P., Lathrop, W., Woolman, L., Cowan, A. & Myles, D. (1988b) Fully effective contraception in male and female guinea-pigs immunized with the sperm protein PH-20. *Nature, Lond.* **335**, 543–546.

Saling, P.M. (1981) Involvement of trypsin-like activity in binding of mouse spermatozoa to zonae pellucidae. *Proc. natn. Acad. Sci. USA* **78**, 6231–6235.

Saling, P.M. (1986) Mouse sperm antigens that participate in fertilization. A monoclonal antibody prevents zona penetration by inhibition of the acrosome reaction. *Devl Biol.* **117**, 511–519.

Saling, P.M. (1989) Mammalian sperm interaction with extracellular matrices of the egg. *Oxford Rev. Reprod. Biol.* **11**, 339–388.

Saling, P.M. & Lakoski, K.A. (1985) Mouse sperm antigens that participate in fertilization. II. Inhibition of sperm penetration through the zona pellucida using monoclonal antibodies. *Biol. Reprod.* **33**, 527–536.

Saling, P.M. & Storey, B.T. (1979) Mouse gamete interactions during fertilization *in vitro*: chlortetracycline as a fluorescent probe for the mouse sperm acrosome reaction. *J. Cell Biol.* **83**, 544–555.

Saling, P.M., Irons, G. & Waibel, R. (1985) Mouse sperm antigens that participate in fertilization. I. Inhibition of sperm fusion with the egg plasma membrane using monoclonal antibodies. *Biol. Reprod.* **33**, 515–526.

Shalgi, R., Phillips, D.M. & Jones, R. (1989) Status of the rat acrosome during sperm-zona pellucida interactions. *Gamete Res.* **22**, 1–13.

Shalgi, R., Matityahu, A., Gaunt, S.J. & Jones, R. (1990) Identification of antigens on rat spermatozoa with a potential role in fertilization. *Molec. Reprod. & Dev.* **25**, 286–296.

Shimizu, S., Tsuji, M. & Dean, J. (1983) *In vitro* biosynthesis of three sulphated glycoproteins of murine zonae pellucidae by oocytes grown in follicle culture. *J. biol. Chem.* **258**, 5858–5863.

Shur, B.D. (1986) The receptor function of galactosyltransferase during mammalian fertilization. In *The Molecular and Cellular Biology of Fertilization*, pp. 79–93. Ed. J. L. Hedrick. Plenum Press, New York.

Singer, S.L. Lambert, H., Overstreet, J.W., Harrison, F.W. & Yanagimachi, R. (1985) The kinetics of human sperm binding to the human zona pellucida and zona-free hamster oocyte *in vitro*. *Gamete Res.* **12**, 29–39.

Storey, B.T., Lee, M.A., Muller, C., Ward, C.R. & Wirtshafter, D.G. (1984) Binding of mouse spermatozoa to the zonae pellucidae of mouse eggs in cumulus: evidence that the acrosomes remain substantially intact. *Biol. Reprod.* **31**, 1119–1128.

Sullivan, R. & Bleau, G. (1985) Interaction of isolated compounds from mammalian sperm and egg. *Gamete Res.* **12**, 101–116.

Talbot, P. (1985) Sperm penetration through oocyte investments in mammals. *Am. J. Anat.* **174**. 331–346.

Töpfer-Petersen, E. & Henshen, A. (1987) Acrosin shows zona and fucose binding, novel properties for a serine proteinase. *FEBS Lett.*, **226**, 68–42.

Töpfer-Petersen, E., Friess, A.E., Nguyen, H. & Schill, W.B. (1985) Evidence for a fucose-binding protein in boar spermatozoa. *J. Histochem.* **83**, 139–145.

Urch, U.A. & Hedrick, J.L. (1988) The inhibition of boar acrosin amidase activity by sulphated polysaccharides. *Biol. Chem. Hoppe-Seyler*, **369**, 727–732.

Wassarman, P.M. (1987) The biology and chemistry of fertilization. *Science, NY* **235**, 554–560.

Wassarman, P.M. (1990) Regulation of mammalian fertilization by zona pellucida glycoproteins. *J. Reprod. Fert.*, *Suppl.* **42**, 79–87.

Yanagimachi, R. (1981) Mechanisms of fertilization in mammals. In *Fertilization and Embryonic Development In Vitro*, pp. 81–182. Eds L. Mastroianni & J. D. Biggers. Plenum Press, New York.

Yanagimachi, R. (1988) Mammalian fertilization. In *The Physiology of Reproduction*, Vol. 1, pp. 135–185. Eds E. Knobil & J. Neill. Raven Press, New York.

Yanagimachi, R. & Phillips, D.M. (1984) The status of acrosomal caps of hamster spermatozoa immediately before fertilization *in vitro*. *Gamete Res.* **9**, 1–19.

J. Reprod. Fert., Suppl. **42** (1990), 107–116

First messengers at fertilization

Laurinda A. Jaffe

Physiology Department, Univ. of Connecticut Health Center, Farmington, CT 06032, USA

Summary. To investigate the 'first messengers' that pass between the spermatozoon and egg to initiate development, the function of G-proteins and membrane potential at fertilization have been examined. G-proteins are present in eggs, and activating them with GTP-γ-S, cholera toxin, or receptors for serotonin or acetylcholine (expressed following mRNA injection) causes activation responses in eggs similar to those occurring at fertilization. ADP-ribosylation of most of the pertussis-sensitive G-proteins in *Xenopus* eggs does not block the responses to spermatozoa or serotonin. These results suggest that activation of a pertussis-insensitive G-protein may initiate activation responses in the egg at fertilization. In many species, one of these responses is a change in the egg's membrane potential, which prevents entry of additional spermatozoa. Results of cross-species fertilizations between voltage-sensitive and voltage-insensitive species indicate that the voltage-dependence of fertilization is due to the presence of a voltage-sensitive component in the sperm membrane, suggesting that the 'first messenger' is a positively charged component of the sperm membrane that inserts into the egg membrane to initiate sperm–egg fusion and egg activation.

Keywords: fertilization; G-proteins; sperm–egg fusion; egg activation; membrane potential

The nature of the 'first messengers' that pass between the spermatozoon and egg causing the initiation of development has remained elusive since early observations first raised the question. One early idea was that the energy apparent in the sperm tail's motion was somehow transferred to the egg at fertilization, thus initiating development (see Newport, 1853). Over the years, as 'second messengers' such as calcium, pH and inositol trisphosphate (IP_3) have been discovered, our understanding has moved closer to the initial events, and our models have become more specific. However, the first messengers are only beginning to be identified (Gould *et al.*, 1986; Gould & Stephano, 1987). One approach to looking for the first messengers has been to examine how the egg is specialized to receive the messages; this paper will consider the possible function of G-proteins in this process. Another approach has been to ask how the messengers are stopped by polyspermy-preventing mechanisms; this paper will review the function of the egg's membrane potential in polyspermy prevention, and what this may indicate about the first messengers.

G-proteins and egg activation

G-proteins are a class of membrane proteins that function in many cells to couple membrane receptors to membrane effector enzymes (Stryer & Bourne, 1986; Gilman, 1987; Dohlman *et al.*, 1987; Lochrie & Simon, 1988). The possible functions of G-proteins in eggs, oocytes and spermatozoa have been recently reviewed (Turner & Jaffe, 1989), and the present paper will focus on the particular question of egg activation by spermatozoa. The model proposed is that the spermatozoon activates a receptor in the egg plasma membrane, which in turn activates a G-protein, thus stimulating IP_3 production and Ca release, leading to opening of ion channels, exocytosis of cortical vesicles, and perhaps later events as well.

G-proteins have been identified in sea urchin and frog eggs by use of cholera and pertussis toxins, which catalyse ADP-ribosylation of certain G-proteins. In sea urchin eggs, both a cholera toxin substrate (M_r 47 000) and a pertussis toxin substrate (M_r 39–40 000) are present (Oinuma *et al.*, 1986; Turner *et al.*, 1987). Frog eggs contain a pertussis toxin substrate of M_r 40 000 (D. Kline, G. S. Kopf, L. F. Muncy & L. A. Jaffe, unpublished observations); we have not detected a cholera toxin substrate in mature frog eggs, although such substrates have been reported in immature frog oocytes (see Turner & Jaffe, 1989). Use of G-protein-specific antibodies has also indicated the presence of G-proteins in mammalian oocytes (Garty *et al.*, 1988).

Experiments with GTP-γ-S, cholera toxin, and exogenously introduced G-protein-coupled receptors

Early evidence that G-proteins may function at fertilization came from experiments showing that guanosine-5′-0-3-(thiotriphosphate) (GTP-γ-S) injection into sea urchin eggs caused cortical vesicle exocytosis (Turner *et al.*, 1986) and calcium release (Swann *et al.*, 1987). Likewise in hamster eggs, GTP-γ-S caused ion channel opening and calcium release similar to the responses at fertilization (Miyazaki, 1988). However, since GTP-γ-S could potentially affect a variety of GTP-dependent processes, it was important to use more specific G-protein activators. As one such activator, we injected cholera toxin, which caused exocytosis in sea urchin eggs (Turner *et al.*, 1987), but did not activate hamster (Miyazaki, 1988) or frog eggs (D. Kline, G. S. Kopf, L. F. Muncy & L. A. Jaffe, unpublished observations).

As another class of specific G-protein activators, we used certain neurotransmitter receptors known to act by way of G-proteins. In a series of experiments with both amphibian (Kline *et al.*, 1988; D. Kline, G. S. Kopf, L. F. Muncy & L. A. Jaffe, unpublished observations) and echinoderm eggs (Shilling *et al.*, 1990), we found that eggs into which we introduced these neurotransmitter receptors could be activated by application of the corresponding agonists. We introduced serotonin 1c receptors (Julius *et al.*, 1988) and muscarinic acetylcholine m1 receptors (Bonner *et al.*, 1987), both known to act by way of G-proteins to stimulate IP_3 production, by injection of specific mRNA into frog (*Xenopus laevis*) and starfish (*Asterina miniata*) oocytes. (DNA for the serotonin 1c and acetylcholine m1 receptors was generously provided by D. Julius and T. Bonner, respectively.) The oocytes were cultured for 1–3 days to allow expression of the receptors, then matured to eggs by addition of progesterone (frog) or 1-methyladenine (starfish).

Application of serotonin (1 nM) or acetylcholine (10 μM) to frog eggs expressing these receptors caused four fertilization-like responses: an activation potential, cortical vesicle exocytosis, endocytosis and cortical contraction. Application of serotonin (100 nM) to starfish eggs expressing serotonin 1c receptors caused cortical vesicle exocytosis. Eggs that had not been injected with mRNA for these receptors did not activate in response to acetylcholine or serotonin. These results indicate that stimulation of egg G-proteins, using activated neurotransmitter receptors as highly specific activators of G-proteins, can produce responses very much like those occurring at fertilization.

Experiments with GDP-β-S

The next question has been to determine whether the spermatozoon acts by this pathway. This problem has been approached experimentally by using inhibitors of G-protein function. In initial studies, guanosine 5′-0-(2-thiodiphosphate) (GDP-β-S) was used as an inhibitor (Turner *et al.*, 1986).

We reported the following results concerning the effects of injecting GDP-β-S into sea urchin eggs on the subsequent occurrence of cortical vesicle exocytosis in response to spermatozoa or IP_3:

    (a) 3 mM-GDP-β-S→spermatozoa→no exocytosis

    (b) 3 mM-GDP-β-S→IP_3→exocytosis

    (c) 3 mM-GDP-β-S→spermatozoa→no exocytosis→IP_3→no exocytosis.

Table 1. Effects of GDP-β-S injection (mM) on fertilization envelope elevation in response to spermatozoa

[GDP-β-S]*	Time between injection and insemination† (min)	Fraction of eggs with fertilization envelopes‡
3–4	2–30	20/21
3–4	45–110	4/17
7–8	3–60	1/11
0 (24 mM-LiCl)	30–130	8/8

*Li$_3$ GDP-β-S (guanosine-5′-0-2-thiodiphosphate) (Boehringer-Mannheim) was dissolved at 0·5 M in a buffer of 100 mM-potassium aspartate, 10 mM-Hepes, pH 7·0. Injections of 4–12 pl were made as described by Hiramoto (1962), in a chamber as described by Kiehart (1982), filled with natural sea water at 20°C. The average egg diameter was 110 µm, corresponding to an intracellular volume of 700 pl, which was used to calculate intracellular concentration.

†Spermatozoa were diluted ∼1:200 in natural sea water and applied to the edge of the chamber within 1 min after dilution. Many spermatozoa bound to each egg, and almost all non-injected eggs in the chamber formed fertilization envelopes within a few minutes after insemination.

‡Fertilization envelope elevation was scored by observation with a ×16 objective, using differential interference contrast optics. In most cases the envelope was either fully elevated or not elevated. Intermediate cases were occasionally seen, and were scored as positive if the elevation was visible on >1/8 of the egg's circumference. In particular, the 5 envelopes which formed on eggs inseminated >45 min after injection of 3–4 mM-GDP-β-S, or after injection of 7–8 mM-GDP-β-S were all only partly elevated, whereas only one partial elevation was seen in the series of eggs inseminated <30 min after injection of 3–4 mM-GDP-β-S. Each set of results represents data from 2–4 female sea urchins.

From these results, we concluded that although sperm-induced exocytosis was blocked by GDP-β-S (result a), IP$_3$-induced exocytosis was not (result b). For reasons that we did not understand at the time, eggs injected with GDP-β-S, then inseminated, and then injected with IP$_3$, did not undergo exocytosis (result c).

Because of the peculiar result of Exp. C, and because of several questions raised recently about the validity of using GDP-β-S as a specific blocker of G-protein function (Authi et al., 1988: Krishnamurthi et al., 1988; Limor et al., 1989; Whitaker et al., 1989), the effects of injecting GDP-β-S into sea urchin eggs were reinvestigated.

Eggs of *Lytechinus variegatus* were injected with GDP-β-S and subsequently either inseminated or injected with IP$_3$ (Tables 1 and 2). Although 7–8 mM-GDP-β-S always blocked both spermatozoa and IP$_3$ responses, 3–4 mM-GDP-β-S only blocked these responses if there was a delay between injection of GDP-β-S and injection of IP$_3$ or application of spermatozoa. In the series of eggs tested with spermatozoa, those eggs inseminated <30 min after injection of GDP-β-S underwent exocytosis, while those inseminated >45 min after injection of GDP-β-S did not (Table 1). In the series of eggs tested with IP$_3$, those eggs injected with IP$_3$ <6 min after injection of GDP-β-S underwent exocytosis, while those injected with IP$_3$ >50 min after injection of GDP-β-S did not (Table 2) (in this series, delays intermediate between 6 and 50 min were not examined systematically).

Although the timing of our original experiments is not known precisely, in retrospect it seems likely that the delay between GDP-β-S injection and sperm application was systematically larger

Laurinda A. Jaffe

Table 2. Effects of GDP-β-S injection (mM) on fertilization envelope elevation in response to IP_3 injection

[GDP-β-S]*	Time between injections (min)†	Fraction of eggs with fertilization envelopes‡
3–4	2–5	10/12
3–4	50–80	0/12
7–8	1–50	0/16
0 (24 mM-LiCl)	3–65	8/8

*See Table 1.
†Eggs were injected first with GDP-β-S (see Table 1), and then, after the indicated delay, they were injected with IP_3 (inositol 1,4,5-trisphosphate) (Amersham). IP_3 was dissolved at 10 μM in a buffer of 100 mM-potassium aspartate, 10 mM-Hepes, pH 7·0. Then 3–6 pl of this stock were injected to give a final concentration in the egg of 40–80 nM.
‡See Table 1.

than the delay between GDP-β-S injection and IP_3 injection. This could explain the observed differences between the GDP-β-S effects on sperm and IP_3 responses. Another factor that could have been important was that the experiments of Turner *et al.* (1986) involving spermatozoa were performed on different days and with different females (3 females, 20 eggs) than were the experiments involving IP_3 injection (2 females, 12 eggs); in the present study, the same females were used on the same days for each type of experiment.

Why GDP-β-S inhibits exocytosis in response to IP_3 injection is not known. The results of Whitaker *et al.* (1989) indicate that the inhibition occurs after the rise in calcium. The inhibition is not due to the lithium ions introduced by injection of the trilithium salt of GDP-β-S, since injection of 24 mM-LiCl does not inhibit stimulation of exocytosis by spermatozoa (Table 1) or IP_3 (Table 2). Impurities in the commercial GDP-β-S preparations do not appear to be the cause of the inhibition since similar concentrations of repurified GDP-β-S (triethylammonium salt, 98% pure) also inhibited IP_3-induced exocytosis (data not shown; such experiments were difficult to interpret definitively because of possible effects of the triethylammonium counterion). The surface of eggs injected with 8 mM-GDP-β-S often seems less elastic; that is a micropipette enters such eggs without distending the membrane. This suggests a possible effect of GDP-β-S on GTP-dependent polymerization of cytoskeletal proteins such as tubulin (see Carlier, 1988). Since GDP-β-S could inhibit any GTP-dependent reaction, many targets are possible.

The present findings invalidate one piece of evidence in support of the hypothesis that spermatozoa activate sea urchin eggs by way of a G-protein, but do not argue against this hypothesis. Interestingly, GDP-β-S does show a differential effect on sperm- and IP_3-induced responses in hamster eggs (Miyazaki, 1988).

Experiments with pertussis toxin

We next used a more specific inhibitor of G-protein function, pertussis toxin. Pertussis toxin ADP-ribosylates G-proteins if their sequence includes a cysteine residue at the site 4 amino acids from the carboxy terminus of the α subunit (Gilman, 1987). Of currently known G-proteins, $α_i$, $α_o$ and $α_t$ have this cysteine, while $α_s$, $α_y$ and $α_z$ do not (Lochrie & Simon, 1988). ADP-ribosylating those G-proteins that are pertussis toxin substrates functionally uncouples them from the receptors that normally activate them.

In studies of sea urchin, starfish, and hamster, pertussis toxin does not inhibit egg activation at fertilization (Turner *et al.*, 1987; Miyazaki, 1988; Shilling *et al.*, 1989). One uncertainty in such experiments has been the extent to which pertussis toxin application is effective in ADP-ribosylating the egg's G-proteins; recent work with frog eggs has, however, shown that under conditions in which most of the pertussis toxin substrates were modified, activation responses at fertilization occurred normally (D. Kline, G. S. Kopf, L. F. Muncy & L. A. Jaffe, unpublished observations). These experiments were done by incubating *Xenopus* oocytes in a solution containing $4 \mu g$ pertussis toxin/ml for 3 days. After the incubation, the oocytes were matured to eggs by applying progesterone and insulin, and the vitelline envelopes were removed to allow fertilization and to ensure that the preparation was not contaminated by follicle cells. One group of these eggs was used to prepare membranes for subsequent pertussis toxin treatment in the presence of ^{32}P-NAD. The other group of eggs was used to test electrical and morphological responses to insemination.

Egg membranes which were made from cells pretreated with pertussis toxin incorporated much less of the ^{32}P label incorporated by membranes from control-pretreated cells (as determined by densitometry of autoradiographs). This indicated that most of the pertussis toxin substrate had been modified during the initial pertussis toxin incubation. Nevertheless, eggs pretreated with pertussis toxin under these conditions showed normal responses to fertilization. The peak amplitude and rise time of the fertilization potential, as well as the interval between insemination and the fertilization potential rise, were the same as in control-treated eggs. These results indicated that the pertussis toxin substrate present in *Xenopus* eggs is probably not involved in signal transduction at fertilization, although it will be useful to try to find conditions where the ribosylation of the pertussis toxin substrate is more complete.

Whether the pertussis toxin substrate in *Xenopus* oocytes functions in mediating the hormonal stimulation of meiotic maturation remains uncertain. The results described above do not indicate such a function, and the findings of several previous studies are variable (Pellaz & Schorderet-Slatkine, 1989; Turner & Jaffe, 1989). In starfish oocytes, hormonal stimulation of meiotic maturation is inhibited by injection of pertussis toxin, suggesting that the pertussis toxin substrate in starfish oocytes mediates the hormonal response (Shilling *et al.*, 1989).

Although the pertussis toxin substrates in *Xenopus* and other eggs do not seem to mediate fertilization responses, there may be other G-proteins present in the egg membrane that serve this function. Evidence suggesting this comes from experiments examining the pertussis toxin sensitivity of the serotonin response in *Xenopus* eggs expressing the serotonin 1c receptor (D. Kline, G. S. Kopf, L. F. Muncy & L. A. Jaffe, unpublished observations). Oocytes injected with serotonin 1c receptor mRNA were incubated with $4 \mu g$ pertussis toxin/ml for 3 days and then matured; conditions were identical to those described above, in which we have shown that most of the pertussis toxin substrates are ADP-ribosylated and thus inactivated. Nevertheless, these eggs showed responses to serotonin indistinguishable from control responses in peak amplitude and rise time of the activation potential, as well as the interval between serotonin addition and the rise of the activation potential. The eggs were activated with 1 nM-serotonin, a concentration selected because it was the lowest concentration of serotonin that produced activation in all of the eggs. Because serotonin 1c receptors belong to the family of receptors that have no known functions other than activation of G-proteins (Julius *et al.*, 1988), we assume that activation of eggs by serotonin is by way of a G-protein, and with the reservation that a small fraction of the pertussis toxin-sensitive G-proteins in the eggs was not modified under our pertussis toxin incubation conditions, we interpret our experiments to suggest that the *Xenopus* egg membrane contains a non-pertussis toxin-sensitive G-protein that can couple to pathways producing responses in the egg very much like those occurring at fertilization. Identification and functional testing of pertussis toxin-insensitive G-proteins in eggs, by use of antibodies (Simonds *et al.*, 1989) or guanine nucleotide binding (Devary *et al.*, 1987), may help to answer the question of the function of G-proteins in egg activation at fertilization.

Voltage-dependence of initial sperm–egg interactions

Another set of experimental evidence that contributes to understanding of first messengers at fertilization comes from studies of the voltage dependence of initial sperm–egg interactions. This subject has been reviewed by Jaffe & Cross (1986) (see also Lynn & Chambers, 1984; McCulloh *et al.*, 1987; Lynn *et al.*, 1988). This article will consider only one aspect of the work: the inhibition of fertilization in some but not all animal species, by a positive potential across the egg membrane. The potential needed to inhibit fertilization varies from about 0 mV to about $+40$ mV, depending on the species and the concentration of spermatozoa. At potentials approaching this level, the probability of fertilization approaches zero. This inhibition of fertilization by positive membrane potential serves the function, in a variety of species, of preventing polyspermy, since the fertilizing spermatozoon causes a rapid shift in the egg's membrane potential to a positive level.

Evidence that the positive potential blocks sperm–egg *fusion*, as opposed to some subsequent event in the sperm entry process, comes from direct observations with the light microscope, during voltage clamping of sea urchin eggs (Lynn & Chambers, 1984). Spermatozoa do not enter the egg cytoplasm, sperm tail motility does not change, and no fertilization cone is seen at the site of contact. These observations are supported by electron microscopic observations of fertilization in the echiuroid worm *Urechis caupo*, which show that, during the period of positive membrane potential, supernumerary spermatozoa and egg plasma membranes are in contact, but not fused (Paul & Gould-Somero, 1976; Gould-Somero *et al.*, 1979). With the reservation that a small or transient fusion site might not have been detected with the microscopic methods that have been used, we consider that the positive potential blocks sperm–egg fusion. This conclusion is also supported by measurements of membrane capacitance (McCulloh & Chambers, 1986).

In addition to inhibiting sperm–egg fusion, the positive potential inhibits egg activation. In sea urchins, frogs, toads, and the primitive salamander, *Hynobius*, the activation responses of ion channel opening and/or cortical vesicle exocytosis are prevented by the same level of positive potential that inhibits sperm–egg fusion (see especially Lynn & Chambers, 1984: Iwao, 1989). *Urechis* may be an exception to this conclusion (Gould-Somero *et al.*, 1979; Gould & Stephano, 1987), although further investigation of this apparent exception is needed. The correlated effects of positive potential on sperm–egg fusion and egg activation provide evidence that the two events are regulated by related mechanisms. In principle, this could result if fusion is necessary for activation, or if an activation event is necessary for fusion, or if one molecular component mediates both activation and fusion. Available evidence does not distinguish between these possibilities, but the similar inhibition of activation and fusion by positive membrane potential may provide a useful key. With this in mind, we are interested in identifying the molecular components that account for the voltage-dependence of fertilization.

Two general models have been proposed to account for the voltage dependence of fertilization (see Jaffe & Cross, 1986). One model proposes that the egg membrane contains a 'sperm receptor', the conformation of which depends on membrane potential; at a negative potential, the receptor would be available to interact with spermatozoa, while at a positive potential it would not. An alternative model proposes that the potential-sensitive component is contributed by the sperm membrane; specifically the spermatozoa might contain a positively charged 'fusion protein' that must insert in the egg membrane to initiate the fusion process. The insertion of a charged protein into the lipid bilayer could be regulated by the electric field across the bilayer.

Cross-species fertilization experiments

By making cross-species fertilizations between species with voltage-sensitive and voltage-insensitive fertilization, we tested whether the voltage-sensitive characteristic is determined by the sperm species or the egg species. Our most conclusive study involved an investigation of fertilization between two salamander species, *Cynops pyrrhogaster* and *Hynobius nebulosus* (Iwao & Jaffe,

1989). Like most salamanders, *Cynops* allows many spermatozoa to enter the egg cytoplasm, but only one sperm nucleus fuses with the egg nucleus; extra sperm nuclei disintegrate in the egg cytoplasm. Correspondingly, *Cynops* has voltage-insensitive fertilization; *Cynops* sperm entry into *Cynops* eggs occurs with equal probability at 0 mV and +40 mV. *Hynobius* is unique among known salamanders in having monospermic fertilization; the egg produces a fertilization potential like that of frogs and toads, and entry of *Hynobius* spermatozoa into the *Hynobius* egg cytoplasm is voltage-dependent. A membrane potential of $\geq +40$ mV inhibits fertilization in *Hynobius*.

When *Cynops* eggs were inseminated with *Hynobius* spermatozoa, fertilization was voltage-sensitive. *Hynobius* spermatozoa entered the *Cynops* egg cytoplasm at a clamp potential of 0 mV, but not at +40 mV. This indicated that, the sperm species determined whether fertilization was voltage-sensitive.

It was not possible to investigate the voltage-sensitivity of the converse cross-fertilization, that is *Hynobius* eggs with *Cynops* spermatozoa, due to the technical difficulty that *Cynops* spermatozoa could not pass through the *Hynobius* egg jelly coat. However, analogous experiments were performed with other species: a voltage-sensitive egg species, *Xenopus laevis* or *Rana pipiens*, and a voltage-insensitive sperm species, *Notophthalamus viridescens* (Jaffe *et al.*, 1983). These cross-fertilizations were voltage-insensitive, indicating that as with the converse type of cross, voltage-sensitivity is a property determined by the sperm species.

This conclusion is supported by results of additional crosses (*Strongylocentrotus* × *Urechis*, Jaffe *et al.*, 1982; *Bufo* × *Hynobius*, Iwao & Jaffe, 1989) in which both sperm and egg species had voltage-dependent fertilization, but in which the voltage required to block fertilization differed. In both cases, the voltage required to block fertilization was that characteristic of the sperm species.

The results of this series of cross-fertilization experiments argue that the voltage-sensitive component in the fertilization reaction is not a receptor in the egg membrane, but rather a component contributed by the spermatozoon. Particularly conclusive is the evidence that an egg of a species that has no voltage sensitivity in homologous fertilization can show voltage sensitivity when cross-fertilized with spermatozoa of a voltage-sensitive species.

A model of the first messengers at fertilization

To account for the results of our cross-species fertilization experiments, and to incorporate various other findings that have been described in this paper, a model like that shown in Fig. 1 could be imagined (see Jaffe & Cross, 1986; Iwao & Jaffe, 1989). According to such a model, the sperm membrane might contain 'fusion proteins' analogous to viral fusion proteins (White *et al.* 1983); like the viral fusion proteins, the sperm fusion proteins might have hydrophobic segments that insert into the target cell (egg cell) membrane to initiate fusion. In species in which a positive membrane potential inhibits sperm–egg fusion, a positive charge might be present on the region of the fusion protein that inserts into the egg plasma membrane. Insertion of such a positively charged peptide would be inhibited by a positive membrane potential across the egg plasma membrane, based on evidence that insertion of other charged proteins into lipid bilayers depends on membrane potential (Kempf *et al.*, 1982).

In species in which membrane potential does not inhibit sperm–egg fusion, the region of the fusion protein that inserts into the egg membrane might not have a positive charge. Among species in which the level of positive membrane potential required to inhibit sperm–egg fusion varies, the amount of positive charge on the fusion protein might vary.

This model does not provide an explanation for the absence of sperm entry into sea urchin eggs clamped at negative membrane potentials (Lynn & Chambers, 1984), but it remains to be determined whether the inhibition at negative potentials is an inhibition of sperm–egg fusion or of a later step in the process of sperm entry into the egg cytoplasm. The 'negative block' differs from the 'positive block' in that negative potentials do not prevent the egg activation events of cortical

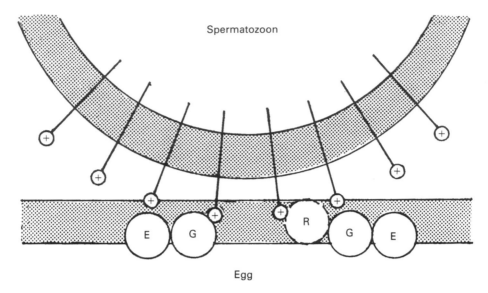

Fig. 1. A possible model of the first messengers at fertilization. The initial interaction between sperm and egg plasma membranes might involve the insertion into the egg membrane of a sperm 'fusion protein' that might also function as an 'agonist'. The fusion protein is depicted as having a positive charge on the region inserting into the egg membrane; this charge could account for the voltage-dependence of sperm–egg fusion. Contact of this sperm protein with a receptor (R) in the membrane could lead to egg activation by way of a G-protein (G) and effector enzyme (E) (right hand side of the figure). Alternatively, the sperm protein might cause egg activation by direct contact with the G-protein (left hand side of the figure).

vesicle exocytosis and ion channel opening; another difference is that, at negative clamp potentials, fertilization cones form, while at positive clamp potentials, they do not. How the 'negative block' might fit into a model like that in Fig. 1 depends on whether the negative potential inhibits fusion itself or a later step in sperm entry.

Figure 1 also suggests a possible way in which a positive membrane potential could inhibit both sperm–egg fusion and egg activation. Perhaps the region of the fusion protein that inserts into the egg membrane also functions as an 'agonist' to activate a receptor in the egg membrane. Sperm 'agonists' have not been identified with certainty in any species, but a protein isolated from *Urechis* spermatozoa is a likely candidate (Gould *et al.*, 1986; Gould & Stephano, 1987). Consistent with the idea that a sperm agonist might need to insert into the egg membrane in order to bind to its receptor, G-protein-related receptors of other cells have agonist binding sites that appear to be located in the membrane-spanning region of the molecule (Dohlman *et al.*, 1988; Wong *et al.*, 1988). Alternatively, the sperm 'agonist' might be a component that interacts directly with the egg G-protein. In such a case, the agonist might approach the G-protein by insertion into the egg membrane, as occurs when the wasp venom mastoporan activates G-proteins (Higashijima *et al.*, 1988). Another way the sperm agonist molecule could approach the egg G-protein could be as a consequence of sperm–egg fusion, which could allow a membrane-associated agonist to diffuse into the egg bilayer or a cytoplasmic agonist to pass into the egg cytoplasm by way of the fusion bridge. Investigation of the common 'voltage sensor' involved in membrane potential regulation of sperm–egg fusion and egg activation may contribute to an understanding of both of these processes and their interrelationship.

Support for this work was provided by grants from the NIH and from the University of Connecticut Health Center.

References

Authi, R., Rao, G.H., Evenden, B.J. & Crawford, N. (1988) Action of guanosine 5'-(beta-thio) diphosphate on thrombin-induced activation and Ca^{2+} mobilization in saponin-permeabilized and intact human platelets. *Biochem. J.* **255**, 885–893.

Bonner, T.I., Buckley, N.J., Young, A.C. & Brann, M.R. (1987) Identification of a family of muscarinic acetylcholine receptor genes. *Science, NY* **237**, 527–532.

Carlier, M.-F. (1988) Role of nucleotide hydrolysis in the polymerization of actin and tubulin. *Cell Biophys.* **12**, 105–117.

Devary, O., Heichal, O., Blumenfeld, A., Cassel, D., Suss, E., Barash, S., Rubinstein, C.T., Minke, B. & Selinger, Z. (1987) Coupling of photoexcited rhodopsin to inositol phospholipid hydrolysis in fly photoreceptors. *Proc. natn. Acad. Sci. USA* **84**, 6939–6943.

Dohlman, H.G., Caron, M.G. & Lefkowitz, R.J. (1987) A family of receptors coupled to guanine nucleotide regulatory proteins. *Biochemistry, NY* **26**, 2657–2664.

Dohlman, H.G., Caron, M.G., Strader, C.D., Amlaiky, N. & Lefkowitz, R.J. (1988) Identification and sequence of a binding site peptide of the β_2-adrenergic receptors. *Biochemistry, NY* **27**, 1813–1817.

Garty, N.B., Galiani, D., Aharonheim, A., Ho, Y.-K., Phillips, D.M., Dekel, M. & Salomon, Y. (1988) G-proteins in mammalian gametes: an immunocytochemical study. *J. Cell Sci.* **91**, 21–31.

Gilman, A.G. (1987) G Proteins: transducers of receptor-generated signals. *Ann. Rev. Biochem.* **56**, 615–649.

Gould, M. & Stephano, J.L. (1987) Electrical responses of eggs to acrosomal protein similar to those induced by sperm. *Science, NY* **235**, 1654–1656.

Gould, M., Stephano, J.L. & Holland, L.Z. (1986) Isolation of protein from *Urechis* sperm acrosomal granules that binds sperm to eggs and initiates development. *Devl Biol.* **117**, 306–318.

Gould-Somero, M., Jaffe, L.A. & Holland, L.Z. (1979) Electrically mediated fast polyspermy block in eggs of the marine worm *Urechis caupo*. *J. Cell Biol.* **82**, 426–440.

Higashijima, T., Uzu, S., Nakajima, T. & Ross, E.M. (1988) Mastoporan, a peptide toxin from wasp venom, mimics receptors by activating GTP-binding regulatory proteins (G-proteins). *J. biol. Chem.* **263**, 6491–6494.

Hiramoto, Y. (1962) Microinjection of the live spermatozoa into sea urchin eggs. *Expl Cell Res.* **27**, 416–426.

Iwao, Y. (1989) An electrically mediated block to polyspermy in the primitive urodele *Hynobius nebulosus* and phylogenetic comparison with other amphibians. *Devl Biol.* **134**, 438–445.

Iwao, Y. & Jaffe, L.A. (1989) Evidence that the voltage-dependent component in the fertilization process is contributed by the sperm. *Devl Biol.* **134**, 446–451.

Jaffe, L.A. & Cross, N.L. (1986) Electrical regulation of sperm-egg fusion. *Ann. Rev. Physiol.* **48**, 191–200.

Jaffe, L.A., Gould-Somero, M. & Holland, L.Z. (1982) Studies of the mechanism of the electrical polyspermy block during cross-species fertilization. *J. Cell Biol.* **92**, 616–621.

Jaffe, L.A., Cross, N.L. & Picheral, B. (1983) Studies of the voltage-dependent polyspermy block using cross-species fertilization of amphibians. *Devl Biol.* **98**, 319–326.

Julius, D., MacDermott, A.B., Axel, R. & Jessell, T.M. (1988) Molecular characterization of a functional cDNA encoding the serotonin lc receptor. *Science, NY* **241**, 558–564.

Kempf, C., Klausner, R.D., Weinstein, J.N., Van Renswoude, J., Pincus, M. & Blumenthal, R. (1982) Voltage-dependent transbilayer orientation of melittin. *J. biol. Chem.* **257**, 2469–2476.

Kiehart, D.P. (1982) Microinjection of echinoderm eggs: apparatus and procedures. *Methods Cell Biol.* **25**, 13–31.

Kline, D., Simoncini, L., Mandel, G., Maue, R.A., Kado, R.T. & Jaffe, L.A. (1988) Fertilization events induced by neurotransmitters after injection of mRNA in *Xenopus* eggs. *Science, NY* **241**, 464–467.

Krishnamurthi, S., Patel, Y. & Kakkar, V.V. (1988) Inhibition of agonist-induced platelet aggregation, Ca^{2+} mobilization and granule secretion by guanosine 5'-[β-thio]diphosphate and GDP in intact platelets. *Biochem. J.* **250**, 209–214.

Limor, R., Schvartz, I., Hazum, E., Ayalon, D. & Naor, Z. (1989) Effect of guanine nucleotides on phospholipase C activity in permeabilized pituitary cells: possible involvement of an inhibitory GTP-binding protein. *Biochem. Biophys. Res. Commun.* **159**, 209–215.

Lochrie, M.A. & Simon, M.I. (1988) G protein multiplicity in eukaryotic signal transduction systems. *Biochemistry, NY* **27**, 4957–4965.

Lynn, J.W. & Chambers, E.L. (1984) Voltage clamp studies of fertilization in sea urchin eggs. I. Effect of clamped membrane potential on sperm entry, activation, and development. *Devl Biol.* **102**, 98–109.

Lynn, J.W., McCulloh, D.H. & Chambers, E.L. (1988) Voltage clamp studies of fertilization in sea urchin eggs. II. Current patterns in relation to sperm entry, nonentry, and activation. *Devl Biol.* **128**, 305–323.

McCulloh, D.H. & Chambers, E.L. (1986) Fusion and "unfusion" of sperm and egg are voltage dependent in the sea urchin, *Lytechinus variegatus*. *J. Cell Biol.* **103**, 236a, abstr.

McCulloh, D.H., Lynn, J.W. & Chambers, E.L. (1987) Membrane depolarization facilitates sperm entry, large fertilization cone formation, and prolonged current responses in sea urchin oocytes. *Devl Biol.* **124**, 177–190.

Miyazaki, S. (1988) Inositol 1,4,5-trisphosphate-induced calcium release and guanine nucleotide-binding protein-mediated periodic calcium rises in golden hamster eggs. *J. Cell Biol.* **106**, 345–353.

Newport, G. (1853) On the impregnation of the ovum in the amphibia. And on the direct agency of the spermatozoan. *Phil. Trans. R. Soc. Lond.* **143**, 233–290.

Oinuma, M., Katada, T., Yokosawa, H. & Ui, M. (1986) Guanine nucleotide-binding protein in sea urchin eggs serving as the specific substrate of islet-activating protein, pertussis toxin. *FEBS Lett.* **207**, 28–34.

Paul, M. & Gould-Somero, M. (1976) Evidence for a polyspermy block at the level of sperm-egg plasma membrane fusion in *Urechis caupo*. *J. exp. Zool.* **196**, 105–112.

Pellaz, V. & Schorderet-Slatkine, S. (1989) Evidence for a pertussis toxin-sensitive G protein involved in the control of meiotic reinitiation of *Xenopus laevis* oocytes. *Expl Cell. Res.* **183**, 245–250.

Shilling, F., Chiba, K., Hoshi, M., Kishimoto, T. & Jaffe, L.A. (1989) Pertussis toxin inhibits 1-methyladenine-induced maturation in starfish oocytes. *Devl Biol.* **133**, 605–608.

Shilling, F., Mandel, G. & Jaffe, L.A. (1990) Activation by serotonin of starfish eggs expressing the rat serotonin 1c receptor. *Cell Regulation* **1**, 465–469.

Simonds, W.F., Goldsmith, P.K., Codina, J., Unson, C.G. & Spiegel, A.M. (1989) G_{i2} mediates α_2-adrenergic inhibition of adenylyl cyclase in platelet membranes: In situ identification with G_α C-terminal antibodies. *Proc. natn. Acad. Sci. USA* **86**, 7809–7813.

Stryer, L. & Bourne, H.R. (1986) G proteins: a family of signal transducers. *Ann. Rev. Cell Biol.* **2**, 391–419.

Swann, K., Ciapa, B. & Whitaker, M. (1987) Cellular messengers and sea urchin egg activation. In *Molecular Biology of Invertebrate Development*, pp. 45–69. Ed. J. D. O'Connor. Alan R. Liss, New York.

Turner, P.R. & Jaffe, L.A. (1989) G-proteins and the regulation of oocyte maturation and fertilization. In *The Cell Biology of Fertilization*, pp. 297–318. Eds H. Schatten & G. Schatten. Academic Press, San Diego.

Turner, P.R., Jaffe, L.A. & Fein, A. (1986) Regulation of cortical vesicle exocytosis in sea urchin eggs by inositol 1,4,5-trisphosphate and GTP-binding protein. *J. Cell Biol.* **102**, 70–76.

Turner, P.R., Jaffe, L.A. & Primakoff, P. (1987) A cholera toxin-sensitive G-protein stimulates exocytosis in sea urchin eggs. *Devl Biol.* **120**, 577–583.

Whitaker, M., Swann, K. & Crossley, I. (1989) What happens during the latent period at fertilization. In *Mechanisms of Egg Activation*, pp. 157–171. Eds R. Nuccitelli, G. N. Cherr & W. H. Clark, Jr. Plenum, New York.

White, J., Kielian, M. & Helenius, A. (1983) Membrane fusion proteins of enveloped animal viruses. *Q. Rev. Biophys.* **16**, 151–195.

Wong, S.K.-F., Slaughter, C., Ruoho, A.E. & Ross, E.M. (1988) The catecholamine binding site of the β-adrenergic receptor is formed by juxtaposed membrane-spanning domains. *J. biol. Chem.* **263**, 7925–7928.

J. Reprod. Fert., Suppl. **42** (1990), 117–132

Excitation, activation and sperm entry in voltage-clamped sea-urchin eggs

E. L. Chambers and D. H. McCulloh

Department of Physiology and Biophysics, University of Miami School of Medicine, P.O. Box 016430, Miami, FL 33101, USA

Keywords: excitation; activation; sperm incorporation; voltage clamp; activation current; sea urchin

Introduction

The discovery that a depolarization of the egg's membrane potential (e.g. Steinhardt *et al.*, 1971; Hagiwara & Jaffe, 1979) is an early event during fertilization in many eggs, that this depolarization occurs rapidly following sperm attachment, and can be of large magnitude (e.g. Chambers & de Armendi, 1979), raised the question of what role(s) this depolarization might have.

Jaffe (1976) made the remarkable observation that the transient depolarization of the egg to a positive membrane potential in the sea urchin prevents the entry of supernumerary spermatozoa (block to sperm entry). This phenomenon has now been described for sperm–egg interactions in a number of different species (e.g. Jaffe, 1986; Jaffe, 1990). A question now clearly answered is that depolarization is not required for activation of the egg to occur (Lynn & Chambers, 1984). We have also found that the depolarization of sea-urchin eggs from their resting membrane potential of approximately -75 mV is required for sperm entry to occur and these studies form the topic of this article.

The results of our studies on fertilization in voltage-clamped sea-urchin eggs (the membrane potential of the egg held invariant, set at a value chosen by the investigator) are best presented within the context of the accompanying flow diagram (Fig. 1). The early stages of sperm–egg interaction are shown connected by the coupling transitions A, B, B1 and B2.

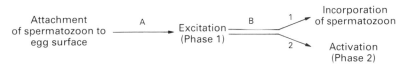

Fig. 1. Primary events of early fertilization.

By observing the distinctive current patterns generated in the voltage-clamped egg during the simultaneously video-recorded ($\times 2000$ magnification) events of sperm–egg interaction, each of the stages shown in Fig. 1 can be clearly distinguished. (For methods see McCulloh, 1989; also Lynn & Chambers, 1984; McCulloh *et al.*, 1987; Lynn *et al.*, 1988.) A major finding in our voltage-clamp studies is that the coupling transitions shown in Fig. 1 can be differentially blocked depending on the membrane potential (V_m) at which the egg is clamped.

The abbreviations used in this paper are listed in Table 1.

Voltage dependence of sperm entry and responses of Types I, II and III

In eggs voltage-clamped at V_m more positive than $+17$ mV, we observe that the spermatozoa attach firmly to the egg's surface, but none of the eggs elevate fertilization envelopes, nor do they cleave, as described earlier (Jaffe, 1976). The spermatozoa at these positive V_m values fail to elicit an

Table 1. Abbreviations used in this paper

EPR	—electrophysiological response
I_{on}	—the initial onset of current (amplitude)[a]
I_m	—the maximum amplitude of current of Type II EPRs, or of phase 1 of Type III EPRs[a]
I_{sm}	—the maximum amplitude of current during phase 1[a]
I_{off}	—the cut off of current which terminates Type II EPRs and phase 1 of Type III EPRs[b]
I_p	—amplitude of the major current peak during phase 2 of Types I and III EPRs[a]
$I_{(10\% \, Ip)}$	—amplitude of current equivalent to 10% of I_p[a]
mV	—millivolt
nC	—nanoCoulomb
pF	—picoFarad
V_m	—membrane potential

[a]Graphically identified in Fig 2.
[b]Graphically identified in Figs 7 & 8.

electrophysiological response (EPR) (Lynn & Chambers, 1984; Lynn *et al.*, 1988), and electrical continuity between the gametes is never achieved (patch-clamp studies by McCulloh & Chambers, 1986a, b). To state this in another way, the eggs with attached spermatozoa show no evidence of excitation or of activation (Fig. 1): the coupling transition step at A has been blocked.

At clamped V_m between $+10$ and -100 mV, within 1–2 sec after sperm attachment virtually every spermatozoon elicits an EPR, inducing excitation of the egg. An abrupt increase of the membrane conductance of the egg with an attached spermatozoon causes an abrupt step in the current trace, I_{on}, shown in Fig. 2 as an initial downward deflection in each of the current traces. (At clamped negative V_m the current is inward for I_{on} and all components of the EPRs.) Following I_{on}, three types of responses or EPRs occur (Fig. 2), depending on the clamped V_m: Types I and III have 3 phases, while Type II has only the first phase.

When eggs are clamped between $+15$ and -15 mV, essentially every spermatozoon which initiates an EPR causes a Type I response (Fig. 2a), termed the activation current. The spermatozoon enters the egg (Fig. 3), and the egg subsequently cleaves normally. As the clamped V_m is progressively made more negative, fewer and fewer of the EPRs are associated with sperm entry, until at clamped V_m values more negative than ~ -75 mV (the resting V_m of the unfertilized egg), sperm entry no longer occurs (Fig. 3). None the less, every time a spermatozoon is seen to enter an egg, the Type I response is observed.

For Type I responses, following I_{on}, a characteristic shoulder or phase-1 component of the activation current is generated (duration 10–12 sec after I_{on}; see Fig. 2a, I_{on} to I_{sm}). Phase 1 (excitation) corresponds to the latent period (Allen & Griffin, 1958). Excitation is followed by activation, which is manifested by a large increase in conductance, phase 2, during which peak current, I_p, is attained (Fig. 2a). During phase 2 a wave of cortical granule exocytosis sweeps around the egg. An increase of intracellular Ca^{2+} is known to occur during the exocytosis (e.g. Swann & Whitaker, 1986). Eggs with a Type I response undergo the transitions A, B, B1 and B2 as illustrated in Fig. 1.

Type I responses (associated with sperm entry) are replaced by responses of Types II and III at V_m values progressively more negative than -15 mV (see Figs 3, 5 and 6). Type II and III responses occur after attachment of a spermatozoon, but sperm entry does not occur, and the eggs do not cleave. The Type II response, or sperm transient current (Fig. 2b), has a single phase and ends with

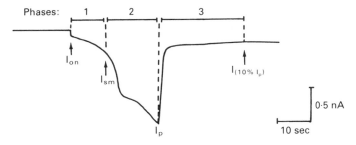

(a) Type I activation — spermatozoon enters (V = −33 mV)

(b) Type II transient — no sperm entry (V = −58 mV)

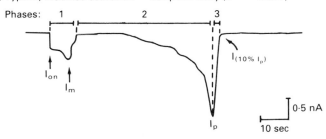

(c) Type III, modified activation — no sperm entry (V = −45 mV)

Fig. 2. The three types of electrophysiological responses observed after insemination of voltage-clamped sea-urchin eggs. For abbreviations see Table 1. (From Chambers, 1989.)

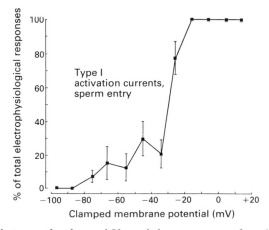

Fig. 3. Relationship between the clamped V_m and the percentage of total electrophysiological responses induced by spermatozoa which are associated with penetration of the spermatozoon into the egg (Type I responses). Values are mean ± standard error for 6–54 responses (total = 251).

a sharp cut off of the current. The egg otherwise remains in the unfertilized state, since the transition at B (Fig. 1) does not occur. On several occasions, following the cut off of current (the signal which announces that the spermatozoon will not penetrate the egg) the spermatozoon immediately swam away. More usually the spermatozoon remains attached for a period up to 1 min, and then floats away. Type II responses fall into two classes based upon their durations. Type II responses of long duration (Fig. 2b; Fig. 4a) last ~11 sec, and represent the isolated phase-1 component of the Type I response (Lynn *et al.*, 1988; David *et al.*, 1988). The percentage of all EPRs which are Type II responses of long duration is greatest at V_m values between -30 mV and -85 mV, and declines outside this range of V_m values (Fig. 5). Type II responses of short duration are discussed below.

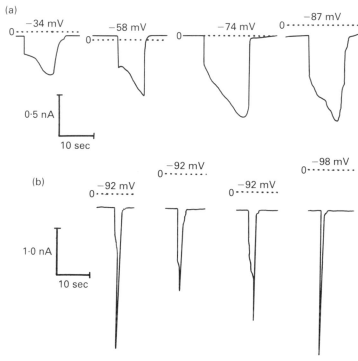

Fig. 4. Sperm transient currents (Type II), (a) of the long duration class, and (b) of the short duration class (note larger nA scale). The clamped V_m is shown above a dotted line which denotes the 0 current level. (From Lynn *et al.*, 1988.)

In the Type III response termed a modified activation current, phase 1 (Fig. 2c) from I_{on} to return of the current to the preinsemination holding value is identical to a Type II response of long duration. The range of V_m at which Type III responses occur (Fig. 6) is essentially the same as for Type II responses of long duration (compare Figs 5 and 6). After the rapid cut off of current at the end of phase 1 (which signals that the spermatozoon will not penetrate the egg), the current remains at the holding level (the level of current required to maintain the egg's V_m at the desired value before insemination). After a variable period of time, up to 40 sec, following which phase 2 occurs and a wave of cortical granule exocytosis ensues, indicative of activation. As the fertilization envelope elevates, the spermatozoon is carried off the surface of the egg. The fertilization cone which forms at the site of sperm attachment, and which persists after detachment of the spermatozoon, is filament-like and attenuated, unlike the mound-shaped fertilization cones which form in association with sperm entry in Type I responses.

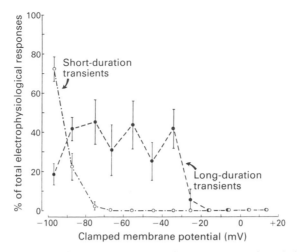

Fig. 5. Relationship between the clamped V_m and the percentage of total electrophysiological responses induced by spermatozoa which are sperm transient currents (Type II responses, no sperm entry) of long duration (3·1 sec or longer) (●‒‒‒●) or of short duration (<3·1 sec) (○‒·‒○). Values are mean ± standard error for 6–54 responses (total = 251). (From Lynn *et al.*, 1988.)

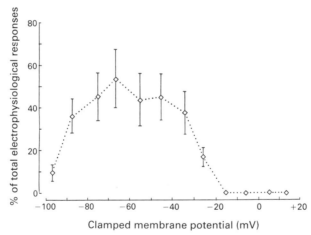

Fig. 6. Relationship between the clamped V_m and the percentage of total electrophysiological responses induced by spermatozoa which are modified activation currents (Type III responses, no sperm entry). Values are mean ± standard error for 6–54 responses (total = 251).

The amplitude of the major current peak, I_p, during phase 2 of the Type III response may be the same as for a Type I response, with full elevation of the fertilization envelope. Occasionally at clamped V_m more negative than -70 mV the amplitude may be much diminished and exocytosis may proceed only a portion of the way around the entire circumference of the egg, resulting in partial elevation of the fertilization envelope.

In modified activation currents (Type III responses) the transitions A and B2 have occurred but the transition at B1 is curtailed (Fig. 1). The sperm aster fails to appear, presumably due to the absence of the sperm centriole. Therefore, as a consequence of clamping the V_m at negative V_m, excitation is either completely (Type II response) or partly (Type III response) dissociated from activation.

The basis for considering that the initial conductance increase which causes phase 1 (first 10–12 sec) of Type I and III activation currents represent an excitatory (Fig. 1) rather than an activation phase is that this component, which obligatorily precedes sperm-induced activation, can occur in isolation (Type II response) *without any other manifestation of activation.*

At clamped V_m values progressively more negative than -80 mV, Type III responses (activation without sperm entry) become an increasingly smaller fraction of the EPRs and, together with Type II responses of the long duration type, are increasingly replaced by very short Type II responses with a duration of less than 3 sec (Figs 4b and 5) (Lynn *et al.*, 1988).

The effects of the clamped V_m on the early stages of sperm–egg interaction in terms of the coupling transition steps affected (see Fig. 1) are summarized in Table 2. Microinjection of neomycin to a final intracellular concentration of ~ 10 mM, which inhibits the formation of $Ins(1,4,5)P_3$), also inhibits the transition at B (E. L. Chambers, D. H. McCulloh, K. Swann & M. Whitaker, unpublished data). Exposure of eggs to cytochalasin, which inhibits the G-actin $\rightarrow$ F-actin transformation, inhibits the transition at B or at B1 (Lynn & Chambers, 1987; Lynn, 1989). Both of the effects exerted by cytochalasin are duplicated by clamping eggs at a V_m more negative than -25 mV. Moreover, cytochalasin has a suppressive effect on fertilization cone formation (Schatten & Schatten, 1981), similar to the attenuating effect of a clamped negative V_m observed in association with Type III responses (see above). For eggs microinjected with EGTA (Table 2) to a final intracellular concentration of 1 mM, phase 2 is obliterated and activation does not occur (presumably due to chelation of free Ca^{2+}), but sperm entry proceeds (unpublished results). EGTA blocks the transition at B2, but not at B1 (Fig. 1).

Table 2. Transition steps blocked during fertilization by voltage clamping eggs or by chemical treatment

Blocked at transition step	Blocking agent	Result
A	Clamped at V_m more positive than $+20$ mV	No EPR, no excitation
B	Clamped at V_m more negative than -25 mV, from -85 mV to -100 mV all eggs blocked at B; or egg microinjected with neomycin (clamped at -20 mV)	Type II EPR, no sperm entry
B1	Clamped V_m between -25 mV and -85 mV; or egg exposed to cytochalasin (clamped at -20 mV)	Type III EPR, no sperm entry
B2	Egg microinjected with EGTA (clamped at -20 mV)	Prolonged phase 1 without abrupt cut off, spermatozoon enters

Electrophysiological responses to sperm attachment in zygotes and oocytes

With the objective of determining the generality of the electrophysiological phenomena we observe in mature eggs after sperm attachment, we extended our studies to reinseminated zygotes (during the 1-cell stage) and to oocytes.

The voltage dependence of sperm entry and the EPRs observed after sperm attachment were similar to those in mature eggs. Spermatozoa enter oocytes and denuded zygotes (McCulloh *et al.*, 1987; McCulloh, 1989) clamped near 0 mV, but at clamped V_m values more negative than -20 mV sperm entry is inhibited. In oocytes the voltage dependence for sperm entry is shifted in the positive direction: at a clamped V_m of -12 mV 50% of the EPRs are associated with sperm entry, whereas for eggs the 50% point is at a clamped V_m of -30 mV.

In oocytes clamped at V_m near 0 mV prolonged current responses are observed in association with sperm entry. The EPRs in zygotes (e.g. Fig. 7a) are remarkably similar to those seen in oocytes (McCulloh *et al.*, 1987). Like the Type I EPR in mature eggs (Fig. 2a), the response in oocytes and zygotes has 3 phases, but the amplitude of current during the second phase is markedly attenuated, lacking a definitive peak (I_p). This attenuation can be explained as due to the greatly diminished (or absent) Ca^{2+} wave, which in mature eggs accompanies the opening of channels as exocytosis proceeds over the surface of the egg.

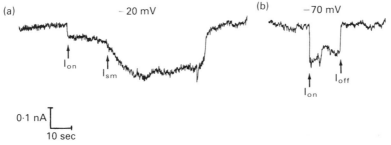

Fig. 7. Electrophysiological responses recorded from re-inseminated zygotes during the 1-cell stage, 20–30 min after initial insemination. Clamped V_m shown above each panel. (a) For a zygote clamped at -20 mV a prolonged response was observed and spermatozoa entered. (b) For a zygote clamped at -70 mV, an abbreviated response was observed with abrupt onset and termination; spermatozoa did not enter the egg. For (a) and (b) fertilization envelopes were removed 30 sec after initial insemination by passage through bolting cloth. At 15 min zygotes were washed 3 times in Ca^{2+}-free sea water, returned to regular sea water, and the electrode inserted into the zygote, which was then re-inseminated.

At a clamped V_m more negative than -20 mV, sperm transient currents like Type II EPRs in mature eggs are observed in oocytes and in zygotes in association with attached spermatozoa which fail to penetrate. An example is shown in Fig. 7(b) for a reinseminated zygote, but the illustration could equally well serve for a sperm transient current in an oocyte (McCulloh *et al.*, 1987). The characteristic abrupt I_{on} is shown, followed after a brief interval by a rapid cut off of the current (I_{off}).

When during responses of Types I, II and III do the gametes fuse?

The term 'gamete membrane fusion' is used in this article to signify that, at the site of apposition of the gametes, the sperm and egg plasma membranes have become continuous, eliminating the membrane barrier between the tip of the acrosome and the egg cortex, and resulting in the adjoining of the sperm and egg cytoplasms. When the term 'electrical continuity between the gametes' is used, this signifies that ions can pass readily between spermatozoon and egg at their site of apposition, but the plasma membranes have not necessarily undergone fusion.

We have defined gamete membrane fusion in the morphological sense, and as such electron microscopy should provide a direct answer to the question posed. Eggs voltage-clamped at -10 to -20 mV (V_m values permissive for sperm entry, Type I responses) were fixed with glutaraldehyde or a mixture of glutaraldehyde and osmium tetroxide at 1–2-sec intervals after I_{on}, serially sectioned, and viewed either by conventional transmission or high-voltage electron microscopy. Gamete membrane fusion, as defined, was detected at 5 sec after I_{on}, but not earlier (Longo *et al.*, 1986, 1990).

In an alternative method to estimate the time of the fusion event, a patch-clamp method was used (McCulloh & Chambers, 1986a, b). The change in membrane capacitance (proportional to surface area) was measured for an isolated patch of membrane on the living egg after attachment of a spermatozoon to the patch (spermatozoa were injected into the patch pipette). By keeping the area of the patch small, when an electrical connection between the attached spermatozoon and the egg occurred, the addition of the sperm membrane capacitance to that of the patch could be readily determined. The results showed that, at the same time as I_{on} occurred, the membrane capacitance of the patch increased by $\sim 0.2\,pF$, compatible with the estimated surface area of the sperm head.

If we equate the time for the increase in membrane capacitance with the time when the gamete membranes fuse, as defined above, this provides an estimate of ~ 5 sec earlier than determined by electron microscopy of eggs clamped at V_m values permissive for sperm entry.

We cannot entirely discount the possibility that in the electron microscope method the addition of fixative might have disrupted the gamete membrane fusion event while still in an early unstable state. However, since the increase in membrane capacitance reports the time when an electrical connection between the gametes is established, the passage of relatively small ions between the gametes could suffice for electrical continuity. Consequently, if the apposed gamete membranes underwent a transitional permeabilized state before pores evolved, traversing the gamete membranes of sufficient width to be detected by electron microscopy, then the time of onset of an electrical connection (capacitance method) could well precede the time of the fusion event as estimated by electron microscopy. A conservative estimate is that, with the fixation methods used, a cytoplasmic bridge (zone of cytoplasmic continuity) traversing the apposed acrosomal and egg plasma membranes would need to be 5 nm or wider to be detectable by electron miroscopy. Recent electron microscopic studies (Longo et al., 1990) of preparations fixed <5 sec after I_{on} suggest that a transitional stage exists, before actual gamete membrane fusion, in which the outer leaflets of the apposed sperm and egg unit membranes are eliminated. Palade & Bruns (1968) had earlier described the successive elimination of layers of the two apposed unit membranes as a probable intermediate in vesicle–plasma membrane fusion.

Electron microscope studies have not as yet been carried out on eggs clamped at negative V_m values in the range at which Type II and III responses (no sperm entry) occur. However, by means of the patch-clamp method described above, an increase of membrane capacitance of the patch following sperm attachment was observed simultaneously with I_{on} for both types of responses, as well as for Type I responses (i.e. whenever an I_{on} is recorded). Simultaneously with the cut off of the current which terminates Type II or phase 1 of Type III responses, the membrane capacitance of the patch also decreased, returning to the original value (transiently for Type III responses, because capacitance measurements cannot be continued after the fertilization envelope starts to elevate, due to loss of the seal between the orifice of the patch-clamp pipette and the egg surface). From these data we conclude that, for sperm transients and phase 1 of modified activation currents, electrical continuity between the gametes occurs at I_{on}, but is interrupted at the cut off of current. Whether or not a transient adjoining of the sperm and egg cytoplasms (gamete membrane fusion as defined) occurred between I_{on} and I_{off} remains undecided.

Localization of conductance changes in voltage-clamped eggs

We had long observed that when several spermatozoa attach to an egg in quick succession (within 2–3 sec) during phase 1 of Type I and III EPRs, or during Type II EPRs (which represent the isolated phase 1 component) the currents induced by each spermatozoon summed arithmetically. Two examples of Type II EPRs for which a second spermatozoon induced a superimposed response are shown in Fig. 8. This observation suggested to us that the channels responsible for the generation of the currents during phase 1 are located in the neighbourhood of the attached spermatozoon, rather than being globally distributed.

To localize conductance changes, the patch-clamp technique was used, with spermatozoa injected into the patch pipette (McCulloh & Chambers, 1986a, b), or spermatozoa were added to

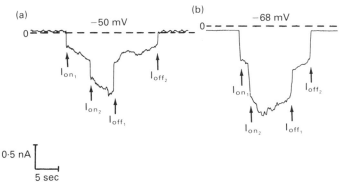

Fig. 8. Summation of sperm transient currents of long duration for an egg clamped at -50 mV (a) and at -68 mV (b). For each, $I_{on\,1}$ and $I_{on\,2}$ identify abrupt onset of current following attachment of the first and second spermatozoon, respectively, while $I_{off\,1}$ and $I_{off\,2}$ identify the abrupt cut off of current when electrical continuity between the gametes is interrupted for each spermatozoon. The 0 current level is shown by the broken line.

the bath (the patch inaccessible to the spermatozoa) (McCulloh & Chambers, 1985). These studies show that, during phase 1 of Type I and III EPRs or during Type II EPRs (the isolated phase 1 component), the increase of conductance is localized to the patch where the spermatozoon attaches. The most convincing evidence supporting this conclusion is that the entirety of the whole egg current during phase 1 can be accounted for as current which flows through the sperm-attached patch (McCulloh & Chambers, 1986a). Moreover, the increase of conductance was totally eliminated simultaneously with the cut off of current that terminates Type II EPRs, or phase 1 of Type III EPRs.

Our findings resemble those reported for the egg of the echiuroid worm, *Urechis*, for which evidence has been presented that the fertilizing spermatozoon opens channels limited to the site of sperm entry (Jaffe *et al.*, 1979; Gould-Somero, 1981).

During phase 2 our patch-clamp data, with the spermatozoa introduced into the bath outside the confines of the isolated patch, showed that the increase in conductance, which starts at the site of sperm attachment at the beginning of phase 2, sweeps as an encircling band over the surface of the egg to the opposite pole, while behind the advancing band, the conductance turns off. The major current peak, I_p (Fig. 2a, c), is generated (in the whole egg) as the zone of increased conductance reaches the antipode.

The phase 2 conductance changes are similar to those observed for the amphibian egg (Kline & Nuccitelli, 1985; Jaffe *et al.*, 1985; Kline, 1986). A transient inward current localized to a ring-shaped zone was found to progress over the entire egg surface as a wave starting from the point of activation.

Returning now to a more detailed analysis of the site of the channels responsible for the increase in conductance at I_{on}, during phase 1 and during Type II responses, capacitance measurements showed that, simultaneously with the occurrence of electrical continuity between the gametes, membrane conductance also increased. Moreover, when electrical continuity between the gametes ceased, terminating Type II and phase 1 of Type III responses, the membrane conductance cut off. (At this time, or within 1 or 2 sec, we occasionally observe actual detachment of the spermatozoon which caused the EPR from the surface of the egg). From these data we conclude that the channels responsible for the early increase in membrane conductance, which we have shown are localized to the site of the sperm-attached patch, may in fact be located in the membrane of the acrosome-reacted spermatozoon. These channels would be inserted in parallel with those in the egg membrane when electrical continuity between the gametes is established. The permeability of the sperm plasma membrane increases and its V_m depolarizes when the acrosome reaction occurs (Schackmann *et al.*, 1984). Consequently, the acrosome-reacted spermatozoa can be expected to have a high membrane conductance, relative to that of the unfertilized egg's exceptionally low membrane conductance.

Reference to Fig. 2(a) shows that, for Type I EPRs, the amplitude of the activation current at the shoulder maximum, I_{sm} (at end of phase 1), approximates the amplitude attained early during phase 3, immediately after the rapid cut off of current following I_p has levelled off. The amplitude of this current early during phase 3 can be accounted for by the persistence of channels in the sperm membrane. Even at this time, when the fertilization envelope has risen, the fertilization cone only partly encloses the spermatozoon (McCulloh *et al.*, 1988). In marked contrast to Type I EPRs, for Type III responses (Fig. 2c), early during phase 3 the current turns off all the way to the pre-insemination holding level. The explanation for this is that the spermatozoon had earlier been detached from the egg. Consequently, the sperm membrane channels were no longer present through which inward current could flow.

That persistence of sperm membrane channels accounts for the amplitude of the current seen early during phase 3 in Type I EPRs (after the channels in the egg membrane during phase 2 had shut down) is demonstrated in the EPR shown in Fig. 9. This depicts a rare occurrence, in which a typical Type I EPR evolved well after I_p and well into phase 3. However, the spermatozoon instead of remaining at the egg surface, stuck to the rising fertilization envelope, but was still connected to the egg cortex by means of a cytoplasmic strand. At the arrow labelled 'sperm off' the cytoplasmic strand suddenly snapped, thereby breaking the contact between spermatozoon and egg. At the same instant the current abruptly turned off, returning to the pre-insemination holding level.

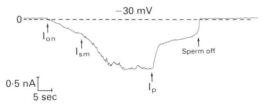

Fig. 9. Unusual case where an electrophysiological response starts as a typical Type I response in an egg clamped at -30 mV, but during phase 3 the rising fertilization envelope detaches the entering spermatozoon, at 'sperm off'.

Fusion and the possible existence of an intracellular sperm activation factor

If a sperm cytoplasmic activating factor is involved in activation of the egg, then electrical continuity between the gametes, accompanied or not by gamete membrane fusion as defined, would be an obligatory prerequisite to activation. For eggs clamped at a V_m permissive for sperm entry, we have unequivocally shown that gamete membrane fusion, as defined, occurs well before (at least 6 sec) the initiation of activation. This establishes the possibility that a sperm-activating factor is involved in activation.

In regard to eggs clamped at negative V_m values which do not permit sperm entry, we have shown that electrical continuity between the gametes is achieved, but is then interrupted after a brief interval. We do not know, however, whether gamete membrane fusion, as defined, had actually occurred before the cut off of electrical continuity. None the less, when spermatozoa caused activation to occur, this was always preceded by an episode of electrical continuity between the gametes (in other words, a phase 2 current pattern does not occur unless preceded by phase 1). Where electrical continuity between the gametes is interrupted, when activation does occur (Type III EPRs) the activation response is delayed (late onset of major inward current and of I_p), compared with eggs in which continuity between the gametes was maintained (Type I EPRs). This suggests, for Type III responses, prolongation of the time to achieve threshold concentration within the egg of a triggering agent during the latent period before activation would proceed.

In addition, all gradations of activation are observed during Type III responses, from a barely detectable phase 2 (associated with elevation of a partial fertilization envelope), to phase 2 responses with I_p nearly of the same amplitude as observed when sperm entry occurs (full elevation of the fertilization envelope). These gradations are reminiscent of what would be expected if various amounts of an activating factor diffused from the spermatozoon to the egg. When the amount of diffusing factor is insufficient to attain the threshold needed for activation to occur, Type II responses would occur.

In summary, considering the alternative possibility that a surface ligand–surface receptor interaction might be involved in activation of the egg, it is a significant fact that spermatozoa can attach to an egg and remain bound for minutes (at V_m values permissive as well as at negative V_m values not permissive for sperm entry) without causing any activation of the egg. Only if the attachment is followed by evidence that continuity between the gametes has been achieved, even if only transiently, does activation occur.

If diffusion of a cytoplasmic factor from the spermatozoon to the egg is involved, we might expect to find a correlation between the occurrence of activation and the interval during which electrical continuity between the gametes is maintained. This interval (I_{on} to I_{off}) equals the duration of Type II EPRs of long duration, or of short duration, and phase 1 of Type III EPRs. (We can compare these durations to those observed for phase 1 of Type I EPRs with respect to the interval during which continuity between the gametes is maintained but a different factor is being measured since the length of phase 1 is determined by the time when the major inward current of phase 2 (Fig. 2a, I_{sm}) starts, and not by the cut off of continuity between the gametes). Indeed, our data show that EPRs associated with activation (Types I and III) are profoundly suppressed (Fig. 10) at clamped V_m more negative than -80 mV when the percentage of Type II EPRs of short duration (Fig. 10) increases markedly. The transients of short duration, mean of 1·7 sec (Fig. 4b), have approximately 1/6th to 1/7th the duration of phase 1 of both Type I and III EPRs (see Table 3). These data are consistent with the conclusion that when the interval during which continuity exists between the gametes is very much shortened, activation is suppressed.

Table 3. Duration (sec) of Type II EPRs of the short and of the long duration class, and of phase 1 of Type I and III EPRs

Type II EPR, short duration	Type II EPR, long duration	Phase 1, Type III EPR	Phase 1, Type I EPR
1·7 ± 0·11 ($n=41$)	10·2 ± 0·49 ($n=32$)	11·1 ± 0·91 ($n=21$)	11·6 ± 0·34 ($n=32$)

Values are mean ± the s.e. for *n* determinations.

However, when Type II responses of short duration (seen only at a V_m more negative than -75 mV) are excluded, the relationship between the interval during which electrical continuity between the gametes is maintained, and activation is hardly evident. The mean duration of Type II responses of long duration, which are not followed by activation, is not significantly different from the mean duration of phase 1 of the Type III responses, which are followed by activation (Table 3; Fig. 11).

One possible explanation of the different sequelae for the two types of responses is that, for Type II responses of the long duration class, before cut off of continuity between the gametes, a cytoplasmic bridge or pores which formed at the site of sperm–egg apposition was/were of insufficient width to permit diffusion of an adequate amount of an activating factor from the spermatozoon to the egg.

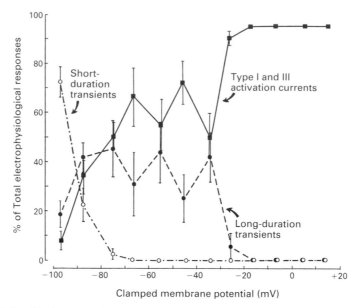

Fig. 10. Relationship between the clamped V_m and the percentage of total electrophysiological responses induced by spermatozoa which are long-duration sperm transient currents ($\bullet$ – – – $\bullet$); or short duration sperm transient currents ($\bigcirc$ – $\cdot$ – $\bigcirc$) or EPRs associated with activation (Type I and III responses, $\blacksquare$———$\blacksquare$). Values are mean $\pm$ s.e. for 6–54 responses (total = 251).

What accounts for the suppression of sperm entry at clamped negative V_m values?

The cut off of current (I_{off}) at the end of phase 1 in Type III responses, and which terminates Type II responses, signals the abrogation of electrical continuity between the gametes and the cessation of the process of sperm incorporation. The cut off of continuity between the gametes is clearly promoted by shifting the clamped V_m in the negative direction, as shown by the replacement at more negative V_m values of Type I EPRs (Fig. 3) where no cut off of current occurs at the end of phase 1, with Types II and III EPRs (Figs 5 & 6). The relationship to shifting the V_m in the negative direction, which also increases inward current, suggested that the amount of charge accumulated during phase 1 of Type III EPRs, or during type II EPRs of the long duration class (sperm transient currents) might have a role. To test this possibility we estimated the net charge (nC) which accumulates by using the equation: charge (nC) = [duration in sec] [$I_{on} + (I_m - I_{on})/2$].

Plots of the frequency of occurrence of the three types of responses versus net charge accumulation during phase 1 and Type II EPRs of the long duration class are shown in Fig. 11 (d, e, f). Net charge accumulation is clearly greater when the spermatozoa fail to enter. The largest net charge accumulation is observed for the Type II responses (Fig. 11f). (Recall that Type II EPRs represent the isolated phase 1 component, in which excitation is fully dissociated from activation; Fig. 1.)

The question then arose: could the suppression of sperm entry at clamped negative V_m value be related to the intracellular accumulation of a particular cation? This led to a series of experiments, presently in progress, in which we are examining the effects of altering the concentration of the different cations in sea water on the voltage dependence of sperm entry and the frequency of occurrence of the three types of EPRs (Chambers et al., 1988; McCulloh et al., 1989a). Up to now we have found that the concentration of Na^+ (replaced by choline$^+$) can be reduced to 1–2 mM (from 510 mM in regular sea water) without affecting voltage dependence, in spite of a 90–95% reduction in the amplitude of the currents. When the concentration of Ca^{2+} was changed (osmolarity maintained constant by varying the concentration of Na^+), a decrease to 1 and 3 mM-Ca^{2+}

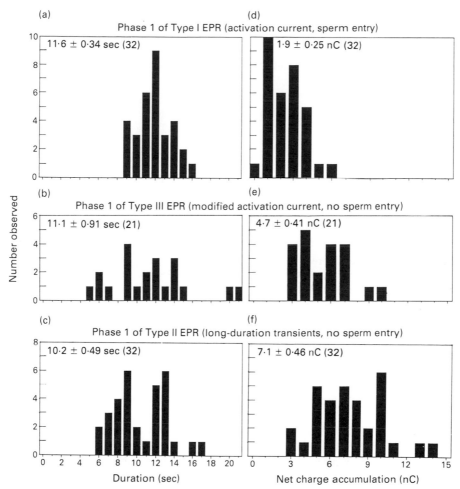

Fig. 11. Histograms of the duration (a, b, c) and net charge accumulation (d, e, f) for phase 1 of EPRs of Types I, III and II (long duration class). The voltage of the inseminated eggs was clamped at V_m values from $+10$ to $-85\,mV$. Mean $\pm$ s.e. values for (n) determinations are indicated in each panel.

(10 mM-Ca^{2+} in regular sea water) augmented and an increase to 22, 69 and 92 mM diminished the percentage of sperm entries (or Type I responses) at comparable clamped V_m values, and in proportion to the extent of change in Ca^{2+} concentration, i.e. the curve shown in Fig. 3 was shifted to the left (less inhibitory to sperm entry) when the external Ca^{2+} concentration was decreased, or to the right (more inhibitory to sperm entry) when the external Ca^{2+} concentration was increased.

The inhibitory effect of increased Ca^{2+} concentration is strikingly shown in Fig. 12 for an unclamped egg suspended in a sea water mixture containing 69 mM-Ca^{2+}, a concentration at which sperm entry is suppressed at essentially all clamped V_m values. In Fig. 12(a) an action potential (upper V trace) is elicited by applying a depolarizing pulse of current (lower trace). The responses shown in Fig. 12(b) and (c), each elicited by a single spermatozoon, last 8–11 sec and are longer than the action potential. The sperm-elicited responses are the voltage equivalent of Type II currents of the long duration class, but with an action potential superimposed at the beginning. Phase 2 of the activation potential did not follow, each of the spermatozoa subsequently floated off the surface and the egg otherwise remained in the unfertilized state. The sperm-induced responses shown here are never elicited in unclamped unfertilized eggs suspended in regular 10 mM-Ca^{2+} sea water at their spontaneously attained resting V_m. The reason is, once the spermatozoon initiates depolarization, the V_m is already at, or passes through a range permissive for sperm entry. On the other hand, for the experiment shown in Fig. 12, although sperm attachment was followed by full depolarization, with 69 mM-Ca^{2+} present in the external medium, none of the V_m values attained was permissive for sperm entry.

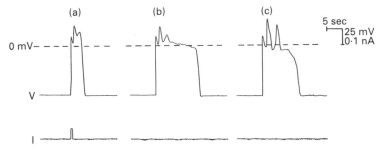

Fig. 12. Membrane potential recordings (V trace) from an unclamped egg in sea water containing 69 mM-Ca^{2+}. The resting membrane potential was ~ -84 mV. (a) Action potential elicited by a pulse of depolarizing current (I trace). (b, c) Membrane potential changes in the same egg as in (a) for which each sequence was initiated after attachment of a single spermatozoon.

To ascertain whether sperm entry in eggs clamped at negative V_m is blocked by Ca^{2+} influx, as suggested by our ion substitution experiments, we exposed eggs to several different Ca^{2+} channel-blocking agents (verapamil, nifedipine, and diltiazem) made up in regular 10 mM-Ca^{2+} sea water (McCulloh et al., 1989). We find that the Ca^{2+} blockers promote sperm entry in eggs clamped at V_m more negative that -20 mV, duplicating the effect of decreasing the concentration of Ca^{2+} in sea water.

Our data suggest that the voltage dependence of sperm entry is mediated by an effect of membrane potential on Ca^{2+} influx. Since the increase in membrane conductance during phase 1 is localized to the site of sperm attachment, an altered influx of Ca^{2+} at this site could be expected to affect the concentration of intracellular Ca^{2+} at the site of the entering spermatozoon.

Conclusions

For the unclamped egg suspended in regular sea water (resting $V_m \sim -75$ mV) the depolarization to a positive V_m value which follows sperm attachment (Chambers & de Armendi, 1979) is caused by the phase 1 and phase 2 conductance increases. This depolarization serves two functions: (1) it permits entry of the spermatozoon that caused the depolarization, and (2) it blocks the entry of other supernumerary spermatozoa.

The block to sperm entry in eggs clamped at positive V_m involves an entirely different mechanism from that observed at clamped negative V_m. At positive V_m the block is exerted before electrical continuity between the gametes can be detected (McCulloh & Chambers, 1986b), whereas at negative V_m the block is exerted only after electrical continuity between the gametes has been established.

Our data suggest that, for sperm entry to occur, it is essential that the depolarization diminishes the inward driving force on Ca^{2+} ions. If the egg maintained its resting negative V_m after continuity between the gametes had occurred, this could result in an excess influx of Ca^{2+} through open channels in the plasma membrane of the acrosome-reacted spermatozoon, elevating intracellular $[Ca^{2+}]$ at the crucial site where the events of gamete membrane fusion were being completed, and sperm incorporation initiated. The spermatozoon may therefore ensure its entry by contributing channels which depolarize the egg.

We thank Dr Frank Longo and Dr John Lynn for collaboration; Mr Pedro Ivonnet for the innumerable measurements required to ascertain the effects of ion-substituted media and Ca^{2+} blockers on the electrophysiological responses of voltage clamped eggs. This work was supported by NIH Research Grant HD 19126, NSF Research Grants DCB 83-16864 and DCB-8711787 (E.L.C.) and National Research Service Award HD 06505 (D.H.M.).

References

Allen, R. & Griffin, J.L. (1958) The time sequence of early events in the fertilization of sea urchin eggs. I. The latent period and the cortical reaction. *Expl Cell Res.* **15**, 163–173.

Chambers, E.L. (1989) Fertilization in voltage-clamped sea urchin eggs. In *Mechanisms of Egg Activation*, pp. 1–18. Eds R. Nuccitelli, G. N. Cherr & W. H. Clark. Plenum Press, New York.

Chambers, E.L. & de Armendi, J. (1979) Membrane potential, action potential and activation potential of eggs of the sea urchin, *Lytechinus variegatus*. *Expl Cell Res.* **122**, 203–218.

Chambers, E.L., Ivonnet, P.I. & McCulloh, D.H. (1988) Inhibition of sperm entry in sea urchin eggs voltage clamped at negative membrane potentials is affected by $[Ca^{2+}]_o$ but not by $[Na^+]_o$. *J. Cell. Biol.* **107**, 175a, abstr.

David, C., Halliwell, J. & Whitaker, M. (1988) Some properties of the membrane currents underlying the fertilization potential in sea urchin eggs. *J. Physiol. Lond.* **402**, 139–154.

Gould-Somero, M. (1981) Localized gating of egg Na^+ channels by sperm. *Nature, Lond.* **291**, 254–256.

Hagiwara, S. & Jaffe, L.A. (1979) Electrical properties of egg cell membranes. *Ann. Rev. Biophys. Bioeng.* **8**, 385–416.

Jaffe, L.A. (1976) Fast block to polyspermy in sea urchin eggs is electrically mediated. *Nature, Lond.* **261**, 61–71.

Jaffe, L.A. (1986) Electrical regulation of sperm-egg fusion. *Ann. Rev. Physiol.* **48**, 191–200.

Jaffe, L.A. (1990) First messengers at fertilization. *J. Reprod. Fert., Suppl.* **42**, 107–116.

Jaffe, L.A., Gould-Somero, M. & Holland, L. (1979) Ionic mechanism of the fertilization potential of the marine worm, *Urechis caupo (Echiura)*. *J. gen. Physiol.* **73**, 469–492.

Jaffe, L.A., Kado, R.T. & Muncy, L. (1985) Propagating potassium and chloride conductances during activation and fertilization of the egg of the frog, *Rana pipiens*. *J. Physiol., Lond.* **368**, 227–242.

Kline, D. (1986) A direct comparison of the extracellular current observed in the activating frog egg with the vibrating probe and patch clamp techniques. In *Ionic Currents in Development*, pp. 1–8. Ed. R. Nuccitelli. Alan R. Liss, New York.

Kline, D. & Nuccitelli, R. (1985) The wave of activation current in the *Xenopus* egg. *Devl Biol.* **111**, 471–487.

Longo, F.J., Lynn, J.W., McCulloh, D.H. & Chambers, E.L. (1986) Correlative ultrastructural and electrophysiological studies of sperm-egg interactions of the sea urchin, *Lytechinus variegatus*. *Devl Biol.* **118**, 155–166.

Longo, F.J., Cook, S., McCulloh, D.H., Ivonnet, P.I. & Chambers, E.L. (1990) Gamete interactions and the initiation of egg activation in sea urchins. In *Mechanisms of Fertilization: Plants to Humans*. Springer-Verlag, Berlin (in press).

Lynn, J.W. (1989) Correlation between time-dependent and cytochalasin B affected sperm entry in voltage clamped sea urchin eggs. In *Mechanisms of Egg Activation*, pp. 43–60. Eds R. Nuccitelli, G. N. Cherr & W. H. Clark. Plenum Press, New York.

Lynn, J.W. & Chambers, E.L. (1984) Voltage clamp studies of fertilization in sea urchin eggs. I. Effect of clamped membrane potential on sperm entry, activation, and development. *Devl Biol.* **102**, 98–109.

Lynn, J.W. & Chambers, E.L. (1987) Effects of cytochalasin B on egg activation currents in *Lytechinus variegatus* eggs voltage clamped at $-20\,mV$. *J. Cell Biol.* **105**, 359a, abstr.

Lynn, J.W., McCulloh, D.H. & Chambers, E.L. (1988) Voltage clamp studies of fertilization in sea urchin eggs. II. Current patterns in relation to sperm entry, non-entry, and activation. *Devl Biol.* **128**, 305–323.

McCulloh, D.H. (1989) Sperm entry in sea urchin eggs: recent inferences concerning its mechanism. In *Mechanisms of Egg Activation*, pp. 19–42. Eds R. Nuccitelli, G. N. Cherr & W. H. Clark. Plenum Press, New York.

McCulloh, D.H. & Chambers, E.L. (1985) Localization and propagation of membrane conductance changes during fertilization in eggs of the sea urchin, *Lytechinus variegatus*. *J. Cell Biol.* **101**, 230a, abstr.

McCulloh, D.H. & Chambers, E.L. (1986a) When does the sperm fuse with the egg? *J. gen. Physiol.* **88**, 38a–39a, abstr.

McCulloh, D.H. & Chambers, E.L. (1986b) Fusion and "unfusion" of sperm and egg are voltage dependent in the sea urchin *Lytechinus variegatus*. *J. Cell Biol.* **103**, 236a, abstr.

McCulloh, D.H., Lynn, J.W. & Chambers, E.L. (1987) Membrane depolarization facilitates sperm entry, large fertilization cone formation, and prolonged current responses in sea urchin oocytes. *Devl Biol.* **124**, 177–190.

McCulloh, D.H., Ivonnet, P.I. & Chambers, E.L. (1988) Actin polymerization precedes fertilization cone formation and sperm entry in the sea urchin egg. *Cell Motil. Cytoskeleton* **10**, 345, abstr.

McCulloh, D.H., Ivonnet, P.I. & Chambers, E.L. (1989a) Do calcium ions mediate the voltage dependent inhibition of sperm entry in sea urchin eggs? *Biophys. J.* **55**, 155a, abstr.

McCulloh, D.H., Ivonnet, P.I. & Chambers, E.L. (1989b) Blockers of Ca influx promote sperm entry in sea urchin eggs at clamped negative membrane potentials. *J. Cell Biol.* **109**, 126a, abstr.

Palade, G.E. & Bruns, R.E. (1968) Structural modifications of plasmalemmal vesicles. *J. Cell Biol.* **37,** 633–649.

Schackmann, R.W., Christen, R. & Shapiro, B.M. (1984) Measurement of plasma membrane and mitochondrial potentials in sea urchin sperm. *J. biol. Chem.* **259,** 13914–13922.

Schatten, G. & Schatten, H. (1981) Effects of motility inhibitors during sea urchin fertilization. *Expl Cell. Res.* **135,** 311–330.

Steinhardt, R.A., Lundin, L. & Mazia, D. (1971) Bioelectric responses of the echinoderm egg to fertilization. *Proc. natn. Acad. Sci., USA* **68,** 2426–2430.

Swann, K. & Whitaker, M.J. (1986) The part played by inositol trisphosphate and calcium in the propagation of the fertilization wave in sea urchin eggs. *J. Cell Biol.* **103,** 2333–2342.

GENERATION OF
SECOND MESSENGERS
IN
EGGS AND OOCYTES

Chairman
M. Whitaker

J. Reprod. Fert., Suppl. **42** (1990), 135–140

Printed in Great Britain
© 1990 Journals of Reproduction & Fertility Ltd

Facts and hypotheses of calcium regulation of MPF activity during meiotic maturation of starfish oocytes

M. Dorée, J.-C. Cavadore and A. Picard*

*CRBM, CNRS-INSERM, P.O. Box 5051, 34033 Montpellier Cedex, France; and
Laboratoire Arago, 66650 Banyuls, France

Keywords: calcium; MPF; cdc2 kinase; starfish oocytes; meiotic maturation

In the animal kingdom, female germ cells enter meiosis at the fetal or larval stage and arrest at prophase of the first meiotic cell cycle before they begin to grow. Under the influence of a variety of signals, fully-grown oocytes are released from cell cycle arrest and enter M-phase (see Masui & Clarke, 1979, for review). The action of these signals is indirect: they first induce the activation of an M-phase promoting factor (MPF) which in turn triggers the cytological and biochemical events observed at the onset of M-phase. Recently MPF has been identified as an M-phase specific H_1 histone kinase (Labbé *et al.*, 1988a, 1989a; Arion *et al.*, 1988) and shown to consist of a heterodimer of cdc2 and cyclin B (Labbé *et al.*, 1989b). Following MPF activation, either the oocytes complete meiotic maturation or they arrest again at first or second meiotic metaphase, depending on species.

Fertilization is required to bring about embryogenesis, and in some species to start or to complete meiotic maturation. While an increase in intracellular free calcium has been shown to be required in most if not all species for induction of development, the need for an intracellular calcium increase for MPF activation and meiosis reinitiation was questioned a few years ago and still remains a matter of controversy. The aim of this paper is to review and discuss the early and more recent evidence pointing to a possible role of Ca^{2+} in the control of MPF activity in starfish oocytes.

Does a release of Ca^{2+} occur after hormonal stimulation of starfish oocytes?

In starfish, 1-methyladenine is the naturally occurring maturation-inducing hormone (Kanatani *et al.*, 1969). 1-methyladenine induces release from prophase block by interacting with stereospecific receptors which appear to be localized exclusively on the plasma membrane (Kanatani & Hiramoto, 1970; Dorée & Guerrier, 1975; Moreau *et al.*, 1978a; Morisawa & Kanatani, 1978; Yoshikuni *et al.*, 1988). Transduction of the hormonal message results 2–5 min later in activation of the cdc2 kinase (Guerrier *et al.*, 1975; Labbé *et al.*, 1988b).

As early as 1978, prophase-blocked oocytes of the starfish *Marthasterias glacialis* injected with the calcium-sensitive photoprotein aequorin were reported to emit light, less than 2 sec after external application of 1-methyladenine (Moreau *et al.*, 1978b). This occurred in the absence of external Ca^{2+}, indicating that Ca^{2+} was released from intracellular stores. The calcium response was found to share the specificity of the biological response (MPF activation) with respect to the hormone, its active analogues and mimetics and to depend on agonist concentration. These findings supported the view that Ca^{2+} release was linked to transduction of the hormonal message in *Marthasterias glacialis* oocytes.

For a long time, all attempts of other groups to repeat these experiments in different starfish species were unsuccessful. For example, no change in the level of free calcium was detected following application of 1-methyladenine to single aequorin-injected oocytes of the starfish *Asterias forbesi* by Eisen & Reynolds (1984), who used aequorin in conjunction with a microscope-photomultiplier and microscope-image intensifier. In contrast, a large increase of intracellular free calcium was measured following fertilization of the same oocytes. Using the fluorescent dye fura-2 to measure calcium, Witchel & Steinhardt (1988) also failed, at first, to detect any change in intracellular calcium following hormonal stimulation in oocytes of the starfish *Asterina miniata*, although fertilization was accompanied by a large calcium spike. Even using the same starfish species as Moreau *et al.* (1978b), De Santis *et al.* (1987) were unable to detect a significant variation in intracellular free calcium during maturation. However, Witchel & Steinhardt (1989) have now succeeded in finding conditions under which 1-methyladenine consistently causes a global fura-2 detectable calcium spike in oocytes of the starfish *Asterina miniata*.

In the original experiments of Moreau *et al.* (1978b) the calcium response was greatly reduced and delayed by 1–2 min when the hormone was microinjected instead of added from outside, suggesting that Ca^{2+} was released as a direct consequence of 1-methyladenine interaction with its plasma membrane receptors. This interpretation was also supported by experiments *in vitro* showing that 1-methyladenine, its active analogues and its mimetic agent dithiothreitol triggered a specific release of Ca^{2+} from isolated cortical fragments (Dorée *et al.*, 1978). Ca^{2+} release occurred less than 0·1 sec after 1-methyladenine at 4°C, and was suppressed by competitive inhibitors of the hormone.

Ca^{2+} is not the second messenger of 1-methyladenine in meiosis reinitiation of starfish oocytes

Changes in intracellular free Ca^{2+} are restricted to the first 30 sec after application of 1-methyladenine to intact oocytes, then Ca^{2+} concentration returns to its basal level. In contrast, the presence of the hormone is required during several minutes for the cell machinery to be irreversibly released from prophase block (Guerrier & Dorée, 1975). The hormone therefore does not act simply by raising Ca^{2+} concentration in stimulated oocytes. In agreement with this view, it was shown that InsP$_3$ microinjection did not induce meiotic maturation in starfish oocytes, although it brought about cortical granule exocytosis and elevation of a fertilization membrane, due to a rapid increase of free calcium in cytoplasm (Picard *et al.*, 1985).

Despite these reservations, it was at first assumed that Ca^{2+} was acting as an intracellular second messenger for induction of entry into M-phase. It was even proposed that the hormone-induced calcium release was required in association with calmodulin to activate Ca^{2+} mediated processes regulating MPF activation. In apparent agreement with this view, it was first reported that anticalmodulin drugs like phenothiazines block hormone-induced meiotic maturation (Meijer & Guerrier, 1981). Unfortunately, the same drugs failed to change sensitivity to 1-methyladenine when they were microinjected instead of being added from outside (Dorée *et al.*, 1982). Moreover more specific calmodulin inhibitors like N(-6 aminohexyl)-5-chloro-1 naphthalenesulphonamide (W7) or anticalmodulin antibodies failed to inhibit 1-methyladenine-induced meiosis reinitiation in such conditions.

The key experiment in favour of the second messenger theory was that of Moreau *et al.* (1978b) who reported that microinjection of the calcium chelator EGTA *before* the peak of Ca^{2+} release suppressed nuclear envelope breakdown, whilst it had no effect when injected *after* the Ca^{2+} spike. However, during later experiments (Picard & Dorée, 1983a) prophase-blocked oocytes microinjected with EGTA and kept in Ca^{2+}-free sea water (conditions of Moreau's experiments) rapidly underwent irreversible cytological abnormalities, including enlargement of the perinuclear space and disappearance of the nucleolus. Those disorders did not occur when EGTA was injected a few minutes after 1-methyladenine addition. This could account for Moreau's initial observation that EGTA blocks meiotic maturation only if injected before hormonal stimulation. We therefore repeated the experiment carefully. When prophase-blocked oocytes were kept in natural sea water (containing Ca^{2+}), microinjection of EGTA did not inhibit hormone-induced meiosis reinitiation, although it prevented oocyte activation by fertilization, by ionophore A23187, or by subsequent microinjection of otherwise efficient Ca^{2+} buffers. EGTA was shown to be able to neutralize an increase of 48 µM in the free calcium concentration even as late as 30 min after its microinjection (Picard & Dorée, 1983a). Since free Ca^{2+} had been shown to increase by only 0·5–1 µM following 1-methyladenine addition, these results ruled out the hypothesis that an increase of intracellular Ca^{2+} was required for MPF activation at first meiotic metaphase in *Marthasterias glacialis* oocytes. These results were recently confirmed by Witchel & Steinhart (1989) with *Asterina miniata*.

There are several reports that free Ca^{2+} increases transiently before nuclear envelope breakdown at mitosis (Poenie *et al.*, 1985; Steinhardt & Alderton, 1988). Moreover microinjection of Ca^{2+} chelators reversibly inhibited nuclear envelope breakdown in sea urchin early embryos (Steinhardt & Alderton, 1988; Twigg *et al.*, 1988; Silver, 1989). Finally artificial increases in intracellular Ca^{2+} induced by InsP$_3$ microinjection were found to cause premature breakdown of the nuclear envelope, also in sea urchin early embryos (Twigg *et al.*, 1988). These results show that an elevated free Ca^{2+} concentration may be required for entry into mitotic metaphase, although it is not required for entry into first meiotic metaphase.

Contradictory effects of increasing intracellular or extracellular Ca^{2+} on meiotic maturation of starfish oocytes

Oocytes microinjected with Ca^{2+} buffers containing high levels of free Ca^{2+} require a much higher dose of hormone than do control oocytes for meiosis reinitiation. Ca^{2+} microinjected oocytes remained inhibited even 1 h after microinjection (Picard & Dorée, 1983a). In contrast, sensitivity to 1-methyladenine increases when oocytes are incubated in Ca^{2+}-free sea water, and even more upon addition of La^{3+} or Mn^{2+}, known to displace external membrane Ca^{2+} (A. Picard & M. Dorée, unpublished results).

Paradoxically, oocytes of the starfish *Marthasterias glacialis* also undergo meiotic maturation without hormone addition when transferred to artificial sea water containing a more than 10-fold higher calcium concentration than natural sea water (Guerrier *et al.*, 1978). Also unexplained is the fact that oocytes undergo meiotic maturation without hormone addition when transferred into Na^+-free sea water (Peaucellier *et al.*, 1987).

Ca^{2+} and MPF inactivation

Experiments in amphibians supported the view that the transient increase of free Ca^{2+} which follows fertilization or parthenogenetic activation of metaphase II arrested oocytes might directly trigger MPF inactivation which occurs at that time. Indeed addition of millimolar amounts of Ca^{2+} to MPF extracts had been shown to destroy its biological activity (Wasserman & Masui, 1976; Wu & Gerhart, 1980), although addition of ATP-α-S to the buffers was reported to protect MPF against Ca^{2+} (Hermann *et al.*, 1983).

In intact starfish oocytes, we found that ionophore A23187, fertilization, or microinjection of Ca^{2+}-rich buffers could not inactivate MPF, and none of these treatments advanced metaphasic oocytes into anaphase (Capony *et al.*, 1986).

The implication of these results was that a transient burst of free Ca^{2+} in the cytosol can perhaps induce MPF inactivation, but *only when it occurs at the right time* of the cell cycle. Recently, it was shown that high concentrations of EGTA have no effect on the timing of the onset, duration or extent of cyclin proteolysis *in vitro*. Moreover, adding up to 1 mM-CaCl$_2$ fails to trigger or accelerate cyclin destruction (Luca & Ruderman, 1989). These results suggest that elevation of intracellular free Ca^{2+} at the onset of anaphase is not a triggering event for cyclin degradation and MPF inactivation, although Whitaker & Patel (1990) show the opposite.

None the less, an intracellular burst of free Ca^{2+} has been reported to occur at anaphase onset in sea urchin early embryos (Poenie *et al.*, 1986), cultured mammalian cells (Izant, 1983; Keith *et al.*, 1985a, b; Ratan *et al.*, 1986) and plant cells (Saunders & Hepler, 1983; Wolniak *et al.*, 1983; Hepler, 1985). Moreover, when Ca^{2+}-buffering activity of cytoplasm was investigated throughout meiotic maturation in starfish oocytes, it was found to reach its lowest value at first meiotic anaphase (Picard & Dorée, 1983b). Some change in Ca^{2+}-regulation systems may therefore be temporarily related with MPF inactivation, although an increase of free Ca^{2+} does not appear to trigger cyclin degradation.

Microinjection of a peptide sequence perfectly conserved in p34[cdc2] homologues induces meiotic maturation and a transient increase of free calcium in starfish oocytes

All homologues of yeast p34[cdc2], from yeast to man, contain a perfectly conserved sequence EGVPSTAIREISLLKE (called PSTAIR) (Norbury & Nurse, 1989). On injection into starfish oocytes, MPF was activated and the germinal vesicle broke down when the peptide concentration was 0·4 mM or higher (Labbé *et al.*, 1989a). Besides inducing MPF activation and germinal vesicle breakdown, the peptide increased intracellular free Ca^{2+} from about 0·1 μM to 1 μM within 1 min after microinjection, then intracellular free Ca^{2+} decreased slowly toward its resting level. The transient burst of Ca^{2+} resulted in cortical granule exocytosis and elevation of a fertilization membrane. Co-injection of EGTA with the PSTAIR peptide suppressed cortical granule exocytosis, but it neither suppressed nor inhibited MPF activation and germinal vesicle breakdown. Thus the PSTAIR-induced MPF activation did not require elevation of free Ca^{2+}. The PSTAIR-induced increase of intracellular free Ca^{2+} also did not require MPF activation: indeed microinjection of p13[sucl], a yeast protein which interacts physically with cdc2, was found to prevent activation of MPF without affecting the PSTAIR-dependent increase of Ca^{2+} (Picard *et al.*, 1990).

Possible significance of Ca^{2+} transients during cell cycle in starfish oocytes

Although Ca^{2+} is not a second messenger in meiosis reinitiation, a transient increase of free Ca^{2+} has now been found to follow hormonal stimulation in different laboratories. Receptors for 1-methyladenine are at the cell membrane, thus transduction of the hormonal message may be expected to be associated with some change of plasma membrane properties. We believe that one of these changes is an increase of its fluidity, because such a change is expected to involve Ca^{2+} displacements from both protein and phospholipid components (Papahadjopoulos, 1968; Gordon *et al.*, 1980; Low *et al.*, 1979).

According to this view, the transient increase of free Ca^{2+} observed by some but not all groups of investigators is believed to be the landmark to fluidification of the plasma membrane.

The M-phase specific cdc2 kinase becomes activated following hormonal addition, starting about 2 min after 1-methyladenine addition. This is correlated with the increased phosphorylation of many proteins, occurring first in the cortical region of oocytes (Guerrier *et al.*, 1977). Non-ionic detergents have been shown to improve extraction of cdc2 kinase in an active form (Labbé *et al.*, 1988c). We propose that cdc2 kinase activation may first occur in the oocyte cortex as a consequence of a special mechanism involving membrane fluidification. Membrane fluidification may also be induced by external application of long, polyunsaturated fatty acids like arachidonic acid, and result in cdc2 kinase activation (Meijer *et al.*, 1984).

Before hormonal stimulation, cortical cdc2 (perhaps endoplasmic cdc2 too) is supposed to be associated with a membrane component which prevents it from activation: this is just the opposite of C-kinase, which is maintained in its *active* form through association with membrane components (Takai *et al.*, 1979; Uchida & Filburn, 1984). As for C-kinase, this association is supposed to be stabilized by calcium ions. Interaction of 1-methyladenine with its receptors triggers an increase in membrane fluidity correlated with Ca^{2+} displacement: this decreases cdc2 affinity for its membrane inhibitor.

Possibly, cdc2 interacts with the inhibitory component through its PSTAIR region, since peptide microinjection triggers kinase activation. Conversely, release of cdc2 from its membrane inhibitor may weaken Ca^{2+} bonds and result in Ca^{2+} mobilization. The model does not exclude other controls of cdc2 kinase activity, including dephosphorylation and interaction with cyclin B (Labbé *et al.*, 1989a, b; Dorée *et al.*, 1989).

The change in Ca^{2+} sequestering activities at onset of anaphase may also be related to some change of cdc2 interaction with membrane components. In agreement with this view, it has been shown in mammalian cells that a major part of cdc2 becomes sequestered at that time in triton-extractable vesicles which appear to fuse with each other in an interconnected tubular system (Bailly *et al.*, 1989).

References

Arion, D., Meijer, L., Brizuela, L. & Beach, D. (1988) Cdc2 is a component of the M phase-specific histone H1 kinase: evidence for identity with MPF. *Cell* **55**, 371–378.

Bailly, E., Dorée, M. & Bornens, M. (1989) $p34^{cdc2}$ is in part associated with the centrosome at G2/M transition and enters vesicles at anaphase in human cells. *EMBO J.* **8**, 3985–3996.

Capony, J.P., Picard, A., Peaucellier, G., Labbé, J.C. & Dorée, M. (1986) Changes in the activity of the maturation-promoting factor during meiotic maturation and following activation of amphibian and starfish oocytes: their correlation with protein phosphorylation. *Devl Biol.* **117**, 1–12.

De Santis, A., Ciccarelli, C. & Dale, B. (1987) Free intracellular cations in echinoderm oocytes and eggs. *Eur. Biophys. J.* **14**, 471–476.

Dorée, M. & Guerrier, P. (1975) Site of action of 1-methyladenine in inducing oocyte maturation in starfish: kinetical evidence for receptors localized on cell membrane. *Expl Cell Res* **91**, 296–300.

Dorée, M., Moreau, M. & Guerrier, P. (1978) Hormonal control of meiosis reinitiation in starfish oocytes: *in vitro* induced release of calcium ions from the plasma membrane in starfish oocytes. *Expl Cell Res.* **115**, 251–260.

Dorée, M., Picard, A., Cavadore, J.C., Le Peuch, C. & Demaille, J.G. (1982) Calmodulin antagonists and hormonal control of meiosis in starfish oocytes. *Expl Cell Res.* **139**, 135–144.

Dorée, M., Labbé, J.C. & Picard, A. (1989) M phase-promoting factor: its identification as the M phase-specific H1 histone kinase and its activation by dephosphorylation. *J. Cell. Sci.*, Suppl. **12**, 39–51.

Eisen, A. & Reynolds, G.T. (1984) Calcium transients during early development in single starfish (Asterias forbesi) oocytes. *J. Cell Biol.* **99**, 1878–1882.

Gordon, L.M., Sauerheber, R.D., Esgate, J.A., Dipple, I., Marchmont, R.J. & Houslay, M.D. (1980) The increase in bilayer fluidity of rat liver plasma membranes achieved by the local anesthetic benzyl alcohol affects the activity of intrinsic membrane enzymes. *J. biol. Chem* **255**, 4519–4527.

Guerrier, P. & Dorée, M. (1975) Hormonal control of meiosis reinitiation in starfishes: evidence for two successive phases respectively requiring and not requiring 1-methyladenine during the process of nuclear maturation. *Devl Biol.* **47**, 341–348.

Guerrier, P., Dorée, M. & Freyssinet, G. (1975) Stimulation précoce des activités protéines kinases au cours du processus hormonal de réinitiation de la méiose dans les ovocytes d'etoiles de mer. *C. r. hebd. Séanc. Acad. Sci. Paris* **281D**, 1475–1478.

Guerrier, P., Moreau, M. & Dorée, M. (1977) Hormonal control of meiosis in starfish: stimulation of protein phosphorylation induced by 1-methyladenine. *Molec. cell. Endocrinol.* **7**, 137–150.

Guerrier, P., Moreau, M. & Dorée, M. (1978) Control of meiosis reinitiation in starfish: calcium ions as the primary effective trigger. *Annls Biol. anim. Biochim. Biophys.* **18**, 441–452.

Hepler, P.K. (1985) Calcium restriction prolongs metaphase in dividing Tradescantia stamen hair cells. *J. Cell Biol.* **100**, 1363–1368.

Hermann, J., Bellé, R., Tso, J. & Ozon, R. (1983) Stabilization of the maturation-promoting facter (MPF) from *Xenopus laevis* oocytes. Protection against calcium ions. *Cell Differ.* **13**, 143–148.

Izant, J.G. (1983) The role of calcium ions during mitosis. Calcium participates in the anaphase trigger. *Chromosoma* **88**, 1–10.

Kanatani, H. & Hiramoto, H. (1970) Site of action of 1-methyladenine in inducing oocyte maturation in starfish. *Expl Cell Res.* **61**, 280–284.

Kanatani, H., Shirai, H., Nakanishi, K. & Kurokawa, T. (1969) Isolation and identification of meiosis-inducing substance in starfish *Asterias amurensis*. *Nature, Lond.* **211**, 273–277.

Keith, C.H., Maxfield, F.R. & Shelanski, M.L. (1985a) Intracellular free calcium levels are reduced in mitotic PtK2 epithelial cells. *Proc. natn. Acad. Sci., USA* **82**, 800–804.

Keith, C.H., Ratan, R., Maxfield, F.R., Bajer, A. & Shelanski, M.L. (1985b) Local cytoplasmic calcium gradients in living mitotic cells. *Nature, Lond.* **316**, 848–850.

Labbé, J.C., Lee, M.G., Nurse, P., Picard, A. & Dorée, M. (1988a) Activation at M-phase of a starfish homologue of the cell cycle control gene $cdc2^+$. *Nature, Lond.* **335**, 252–254.

Labbé, J.C., Picard, A. & Dorée, M. (1988b) Does the M-phase promoting factor (MPF) activate a major Ca^{2+} and cyclic nucleotide-independent protein kinase in starfish oocyte? *Dev. Growth Differ* **30**, 197–207.

Labbé, J.C., Picard, A., Karsenti, E. & Dorée, M. (1988c) A M-phase specific protein kinase in *Xenopus* oocytes: partial purification and possible mechanism of its periodic activation. *Devl Biol.* **127**, 157–169.

Labbé, J.C., Picard A., Peaucellier, G., Cavadore, J.C., Nurse, P. & Dorée, M. (1989a) Purification of MPF from starfish: identification as the Hl histone kinase p34^{cdc2} and a possible mechanism for its periodic activation. *Cell* **57**, 253–263.

Labbé, J.C., Capony, J.P., Caput, D., Cavadore, J.C., Derancourt, J., Kaghad, M., Lelias, J.M., Picard A. & Dorée, M. (1989b) MPF from starfish oocytes at first meiotic metaphase is an heterodimer containing one molecule of cdc2 and one molecule of cyclin B. *EMBO J.* **8**, 3053–3058.

Low, P.S., Lloyd, D.H., Stain, T.M. & Rogers, J.A. (1979) Calcium displacement by local anesthetics. Dependence on pH and anesthetic charge. *J. biol. Chem.* **254**, 4119–4125.

Luca, F.C. & Ruderman, J.V. (1989) Control of programmed cyclin destruction in a cell-free system. *J. Cell Biol.* **109**, 1895–1909.

Masui, Y. & Clarke, H. (1979) Oocyte maturation. *Int. Rev. Cytol.* **57**, 185–223.

Meijer, L. & Guerrier, P. (1981) Calmodulin in starfish oocytes. I. Calmodulin antagonists inhibit meiosis reinitiation. *Devl Biol.* **88**, 318–324.

Meijer, L., Guerrier, P. & Maclouf, J. (1984) Arachidonic acid, 12- and 15-hydroxyeicosatetraenoic acids, eicosapentaenic acid, and phospholipase A2 induce starfish oocyte maturation. *Devl Biol.* **106**, 368–378.

Morisawa, M. & Kanatani, H. (1978) Oocyte-surface factor responsible for 1-methyladenine-induced oocyte maturation in starfish. *Gamete Res.* **1**, 157–164.

Moreau, M., Guerrier, P. & Dorée, M. (1978a) Hormonal control of meiosis reinitiation in starfish oocytes: new evidence for absence of intracellular receptors for 1-methyladenine recognition. *Expl Cell Res.* **115**, 245–249.

Moreau, M., Guerrier, P., Dorée, M. & Ashley, C.C. (1978b) 1-methyladenine induced release of intracellular calcium triggers meiosis in starfish oocytes. *Nature, Lond.* **272**, 251–253.

Norbury, C. & Nurse, P. (1989) Control of the higher eukaryote cell cycle by p34^{cdc2} homologues. *Biochim. Biophys. Acta* **989**, 85–95.

Papahadjopoulos, D. (1968) Surface properties of acidic phospholipids: interaction of monolayers and hydrated liquid crystals with uni- and bi-valent metal ions. *Biochim. Biophys. Acta* **163**, 240–254.

Peaucellier, G., Picard, A., Robert, J.J., Capony, J.P., Labbé, J.C. & Dorée, M. (1987) Phosphorylation of ribosomal proteins during meiotic maturation and following activation in starfish oocytes: its relationship with changes of intracellular pH. *Expl Cell Res.* **174**, 71–88.

Picard, A. & Dorée, M. (1983a) Is calcium the second messenger of 1-methyladenine in meiosis reinitiation of starfish oocytes? *Expl Cell Res.* **145**, 325–337.

Picard, A. & Dorée, M. (1983b) Hormone-induced parthenogenetic activation of mature starfish oocytes. *Expl Cell Res.* **145**, 315–323.

Picard, A., Giraud, F., Le Bouffant, F., Sladeczek, F., Le Peuch, C. & Dorée, M. (1985) Inositol 1,4,5-trisphophate microinjection triggers activation but not meiotic maturation in amphibian and starfish oocytes. *FEBS Lett.* **182**, 446–450.

Picard, A., Cavadore, J.C., Lory, P., Bernengo, J.C., Ojeda, C. & Dorée, M. (1990) Microinjection of a conserved peptide sequence of p34^{cdc2} induces a Ca^{2+} transient in oocytes. *Science, NY* **247**, 327–329.

Poenie, M., Alderton, J., Tsien, R.Y. & Steinhardt, R.A. (1985) Changes of free calcium levels with stages of the cell division cycle. *Nature, Lond.* **315**, 145–149.

Poenie, M., Alderton, J., Steinhardt, R.A. & Tsien, R.Y. (1986) Calcium rises abruptly and briefly throughout the cell at the onset of anaphase. *Science, NY* **233**, 886–889.

Ratan, R.R., Shelanski, M.L. & Maxfield, F.R. (1986) The transition from metaphase to anaphase is accompanied by local changes in cytoplasmic free calcium in PtK2 kidney epithelial cell. *Proc. natn. Acad. Sci. USA* **83**, 5136–5140.

Saunders, M.J. & Hepler, P.K. (1983) Calcium antagonists and calcium inhibitors block cytokinin-induced bud formation in *Funaria*. *Devl Biol.* **99**, 41–49.

Silver, R. (1989) Nuclear envelope breakdown and mitosis in sand dollar embryos is inhibited by microinjection of calcium buffers in a calcium-reversible fashion, and by antagonists of intracellular Ca^{2+} channels. *Devl Biol.* **131**, 11–26.

Steinhardt, R.A. & Alderton, J.A. (1988) Intracellular free calcium triggers nuclear envelope breakdown in the sea urchin embryo. *Nature, Lond.* **332**, 364–366.

Takai, Y., Kishimoto, A., Iwasa, Y., Kawahara, Y., Mori, T. & Nishizuka, Y. (1979) Calcium-dependent activation of multifunctional protein kinase by membrane phospholipids. *J. biol. Chem.* **254**, 3692–3695.

Twigg, J., Patel, R. & Whitaker, M. (1988) Translational control of InsP3-induced chromatin condensation during the early cell cycles of sea urchin embryos. *Nature, Lond.* **332**, 366–369.

Uchida, T. & Filburn, C.R. (1984) Affinity chromatography of protein kinase C-phorbol ester receptor on polyacrylamide-immobilized phosphatidylserine. *J. biol. Chem.* **259**, 12311–12314.

Wasserman, W. & Masui, Y. (1976) A cytoplasmic factor promoting oocyte maturation: its extraction and preliminary characterization. *Science, NY* **191**, 1266–1268.

Whitaker, M.J. & Patel, R. (1990) Calcium and cell cycle control. *Development* **108**, 525–542.

Witchel, H.J. & Steinhardt, R.A. (1988) A global calcium increase is not required for germinal vesicle breakdown in oocytes of the starfish *Asterina miniata*. *J. Cell Biol.* **107**, 172a, abstr.

Witchel, H.J. & Steinhardt, R.A. (1989) 1-methyladenine can consistently induce a maturation-independent transient calcium increase in oocytes of the starfish *Asterina pectinifera*. *J. Cell Biol.* **109**, 31a, abstr.

Wolniak, S.M., Hepler, P.K. & Jackson, W.T. (1983) Ionic changes in the mitotic apparatus and the metaphase-anaphase transition. *J. Cell Biol.* **96**, 598–605.

Wu, M. & Gerhart, J.C. (1980) Partial purification and characterization of the maturation promoting factor from eggs of *Xenopus laevis*. *Devl Biol.* **79**, 465–477.

Yoshikuni, M., Ishikawa, K., Isobe, M., Goto, T. & Nagahama, Y. (1988) Characterization of 1-methyladenine binding in starfish oocyte cortices. *Proc. natn. Acad. Sci. USA* **85**, 1874–1877.

J. Reprod. Fert., Suppl. **42** (1990), 141–153

Second messengers at fertilization in sea-urchin eggs

Karl Swann and Michael J. Whitaker*

MRC Experimental Embryology and Teratology Unit, St George's Hospital Medical School,
Cranmer Terrace, London SW17 0RE, UK; and
*Department of Physiology, University College London, Gower Street, London WC1E 6BT, UK

Summary. The activation of the sea-urchin egg at fertilization is triggered by two ionic changes in the egg cytoplasm. First there is a wave of increase in cytoplasmic free calcium concentration (Ca^{2+}_i) that travels across the egg within the first minute of fertilization. The calcium wave is followed by a sustained rise in intracellular pH (pH_i). Fertilizing spermatozoa cause these two ionic changes by stimulating the hydrolysis of phosphatidylinositol 1,4,5-bisphosphate ($PtdInsP_2$). $PtdInsP_2$ hydrolysis produces inositol 1,4,5-trisphosphate, which releases calcium from intracellular stores, and diacylglycerol, which stimulates a plasma membrane sodium/hydrogen antiporter causing the rise in pH_i. A positive feedback cycle of intracellular calcium release and $InsP_3$ production appears to be part of the mechanism by which the calcium wave is propagated. It has been suggested that the spermatozoon triggers the calcium wave by acting on a cell surface receptor that couples to the egg phosphoinositidase C via a G-protein. We discuss evidence for an alternative hypothesis of egg activation in which a spermatozoon triggers the calcium wave by introducing a soluble activating factor into the egg cytoplasm.

Keywords: fertilization; calcium; phosphoinositides; cell messengers; sea-urchins

Introduction

How does a spermatozoon fertilize an egg? To answer this fundamental question in developmental biology we need to know what cell messengers used by the spermatozoon trigger the variety of biochemical and morphological changes that occur at fertilization. Experiments in sea-urchin eggs have shown that the spermatozoon mediates many of its effects through changes in the poly-phosphoinositide (PPI) messenger system. Parallels between events at fertilization and the way hormones cause PPI turnover in somatic cells have led to the suggestion that the spermatozoon triggers egg activation by acting as a giant hormone molecule on the egg membrane surface (Turner *et al.*, 1986; Jaffe, 1989). However, this hormone analogy may prove inappropriate. At fertilization, the sperm and egg membranes fuse to form one cell at about the same time, if not before, the observed changes in second messengers (Longo *et al.*, 1986; McCulloh & Chambers, 1986a; Turner *et al.*, 1984; Ciapa & Whitaker, 1986). Fertilization might therefore be regarded as a problem of intracellular, as opposed to transcellular, signalling. In this article we describe our current under- standing of the way the second messengers of the phosphoinositide system cause the early events associated with fertilization in sea-urchin eggs. We describe a model of fertilization for sea-urchins that has the sperm initiating events by fusing with the egg membrane and introducing a soluble factor into the egg cytoplasm.

The ionic hypothesis of fertilization

Mature sea-urchin eggs are arrested in interphase in a metabolically repressed state. The fertilizing spermatozoon not only provides the extra DNA to restore diploidy, but also activates the egg, releasing it from the repressed interphase block. The initiation of the cell cycle is accompanied by marked increases in respiration and in protein synthesis (Epel, 1978; Whitaker & Steinhardt, 1982).

One advantage of working on sea-urchin eggs is that the activation of the egg is invariably correlated with the formation of the fertilization envelope and the centring of the female pronucleus, both which are easily observed under the microscope. The fertilization envelope forms within 1 min of inseminating eggs and is a direct result of a concerted exocytosis of cortical granules that lie beneath the plasma membrane (Kay & Shapiro, 1985). A major advance in our understanding of fertilization has come from the realization that the multitude of biochemical and morphological events that occur in the egg all appear to be caused by two ionic changes in the cytoplasm (Whitaker & Steinhardt, 1982).

An increase in intracellular calcium, Ca^{2+}_i

The first, and most important, ionic change at fertilization is a single and transient increase in the intracellular free calcium concentration (Ca^{2+}_i) (Fig. 1; Whitaker & Steinhardt, 1982). A micromolar Ca^{2+}_i increase has been demonstrated to occur at fertilization in sea-urchin eggs using the photoprotein aequorin and the fluorescent dye, fura2 (Steinhardt *et al.*, 1977; Eisen *et al.*, 1984; Swann & Whitaker, 1986; Poenie *et al.*, 1985). The central role of this Ca^{2+}_i transient in activating the egg is clearly demonstrated by the fact that nearly all events at fertilization are effectively mimicked by applying calcium ionophores to eggs (Steinhardt & Epel, 1974; Whitaker & Steinhardt, 1982), or by injecting calcium-containing solutions (Hamaguchi & Hiramoto, 1981; Swann & Whitaker, 1986). It is also clear that the Ca^{2+}_i increase is essential at fertilization because injecting EGTA to chelate calcium prevents the spermatozoon from activating the egg (Zucker & Steinhardt, 1978; Hamaguchi & Hiramoto, 1981). Since fertilization, or ionophore-induced activation, and the occurrence of a normal Ca^{2+}_i increase are not prevented by removing external calcium, it is well established that the Ca^{2+}_i transient is largely the result of a release from intracellular stores (Steinhardt *et al.*, 1977; Schmidt *et al.*, 1982; Crossley *et al.*, 1988). The rapid unloading of an intracellular store at fertilization is also demonstrated by an increased loss of preloaded ^{45}Ca after insemination (Azarnia & Chambers, 1976).

An increase in intracellular pH

The second ionic change in the sea-urchin egg cytoplasm that plays a role in triggering development is a sustained rise in intracellular pH (pH_i) (Fig. 1; Johnson & Epel, 1976; Shen & Steinhardt, 1978). In *Lytechinus pictus* eggs the pH_i rises from 6·8 to 7·3 over the first 5 min at fertilization. This pH_i increase is important in acting co-operatively with the calcium transient to stimulate protein and DNA synthesis (Whitaker & Steinhardt, 1982). This fact helps to explain why weak bases that also raise pH_i stimulate protein synthesis in unfertilized eggs (Epel *et al.*, 1974; Whitaker & Steinhardt, 1985). Since the pH_i increase is caused by the activation of a plasma membrane sodium/hydrogen antiporter (Johnson & Epel, 1976; Payan *et al.*, 1983), an influx of sodium and efflux of hydrogen ions are observed shortly after fertilization (Mehl & Swann, 1961; Payan *et al.*, 1983). The existence of the sodium/hydrogen antiporter mechanism means that development of the sea-urchin egg is strictly dependent upon millimolar external sodium (Chambers, 1976).

Although the rise in pH_i is essential for development to proceed, it appears in some way to be secondary to the Ca^{2+}_i transient. Calcium ionophores cause a pH_i rise similar to that seen at fertilization (Whitaker & Steinhardt, 1981). Also, injecting the calcium chelator, BAPTA, prevents any pH_i increase in response to spermatozoa (Fig. 2). Thus, the Ca^{2+}_i transient somehow leads to the pH_i increase. The central questions to answer then are how the spermatozoon causes the transient increase in Ca^{2+}_i, and how this calcium change is linked to the rise in pH_i.

The fertilization wave

An important feature of the Ca^{2+}_i increase at fertilization is that it consists of a travelling wave. The Ca^{2+}_i increase starts at the point of sperm–egg contact and then travels across the egg in about

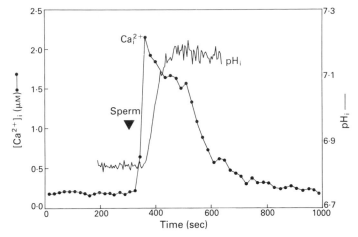

Fig. 1. The changes in Ca^{2+}_i and pH_i at fertilization in sea-urchin eggs (*Lytechinus pictus*) at 16°C. Superimposed traces are shown for two different eggs injected with fura-2 to measure Ca^{2+}_i or BCECF to measure pH_i (for methods see Poenie *et al.*, 1985; Paradiso *et al.*, 1987).

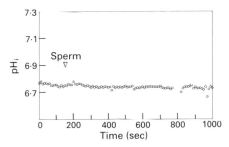

Fig. 2. BAPTA injection blocks the pH_i increase at fertilization. Record from a single *L. pictus* egg at 16°C that was injected with BCECF (as in Fig. 1) plus BAPTA (final concentration 1 mM). BAPTA-injected eggs became polyspermic (>10 spermatozoa/egg) under these conditions (I. Crossley, unpublished observations).

20–30 sec (Eisen *et al.*, 1984; Swann & Whitaker, 1986; Tsien & Poenie, 1986). The Ca^{2+}_i wave reaches levels of 1–10 μM and appears to be the direct and underlying cause of the wave of exocytosis and resultant fertilization envelope elevation that also crosses the egg in 20–30 sec (Jaffe, 1983; Whitaker & Steinhardt, 1982). This progressive exocytosis, or envelope elevation, is referred to as the fertilization wave (Sugiyama, 1956). There are two notable features of the fertilization wave that, by implication, also apply to the Ca^{2+}_i wave. One is that it is an autocatalytic wave, suggesting that a positive feedback cycle underlies the mechanism (Kacser, 1955). The other is that it is triggered with a distinct delay, or latent period, after sperm–egg contact (Allen & Griffin, 1958). Explaining fertilization requires us to explain both the nature of this calcium wave and the reasons for the delay, or latent period, that exists before it is triggered.

The most precise information on the delay and the calcium wave at fertilization has come from electrophysiological studies. The first detectable change in the egg after sperm–egg contact is an inward current (the sperm-current) that depolarizes the egg membrane potential causing an action potential to fire (Jaffe, 1976; Chambers & de Armendi, 1979; Lynn *et al.*, 1988). This sperm-induced inward current has an abrupt onset which is taken as the initial event at fertilization (Dale *et al.*, 1978; Whitaker & Steinhardt, 1982; Chambers & McCulloh, 1990). After the start of the sperm-current a second phase of inward current occurs. This secondary current is called the activation current and it coincides with the fertilization wave and Ca^{2+}_i transient at fertilization (David *et al.*, 1988). Since the start of the sperm-current is the first event at fertilization and the start of the activation current marks the initiation of the calcium wave, the interval between the starts of these two currents is a measure of the latent period of fertilization. The latent period in eggs of *L. pictus* varies considerably from 7 to 30 sec, but it has a mean period of about 15 sec (Shen & Steinhardt, 1984). From this it is clear that, whatever messengers the spermatozoon generates during the latent period to cause the calcium wave, they have to be made within seconds of the start of fertilization.

Phosphoinositide messengers and egg activation

Inositol 1,4,5-trisphosphate

An increased turnover of polyphosphoinositides within the first 5 sec of fertilization in sea-urchin eggs was first demonstrated by Turner *et al.* (1984). These data suggested that the turnover and subsequent hydrolysis of $PtdInsP_2$ might be an initial event at fertilization leading to the calcium wave, because $PtdInsP_2$ breakdown produces the calcium releasing messenger inositol 1,4,5-trisophosphate ($InsP_3$) (Berridge, 1987). Following this idea, Whitaker & Irvine (1984) showed that microinjection of $InsP_3$ in sea-urchin eggs causes an exocytosis, envelope elevation and pH_i rise identical to that seen at fertilization. Further experiments showed that injected $InsP_3$ causes a Ca^{2+}_i increase similar to that at fertilization. The Ca^{2+}_i transient explains the activation by $InsP_3$ because EGTA blocks the $InsP_3$-induced activation (Swann & Whitaker, 1986; Turner *et al.*, 1986). $InsP_3$ has also been shown to release calcium from a non-mitochondrial store in sea-urchin egg homogenates, or in egg cortical preparations (Clapper & Lee, 1985; Payan *et al.*, 1986). Since $InsP_3$ has been shown to be produced in the first 20–30 sec of fertilization (Ciapa & Whitaker, 1986), these data all suggest that $InsP_3$ is the cell messenger responsible for the sperm-induced Ca^{2+}_i transient.

$InsP_3$ and calcium influx

There have been two reports that $InsP_3$-induced exocytosis in sea-urchin eggs requires external calcium (Slack *et al.*, 1986; Irvine & Moor, 1986). A problem arises for the hypothesis that $InsP_3$ plays a role at fertilization because the exocytosis and activation of the egg by spermatozoa has no such external calcium requirement (Schmidt *et al.*, 1982). However, our attempts to repeat the results of Irvine & Moor (1986) have been unsuccessful. We found that there was no external calcium requirement for $InsP_3$-induced exocytosis (Crossley *et al.*, 1988). In fact, direct measurements of intracellular calcium with fura2 clearly show that the $InsP_3$-induced Ca^{2+}_i rise is the same in calcium-free or normal sea water (with $10\ mM$-Ca^{2+}) (Crossley *et al.*, 1988). A Ca^{2+}_i transient that is induced by high concentrations of injected $InsP_4$ is also unaffected by the absence of external calcium (Crossley *et al.*, 1988).

The influx of calcium at fertilization in sea-urchin eggs is largely voltage-dependent, since high-potassium sea water causes the same amount of ^{45}Ca uptake as seen at fertilization (Schmidt *et al.*, 1982). The calcium influx is functionally insignificant compared to the released intracellular calcium because depolarizing eggs of any species of sea-urchin does not cause activation (Whitaker & Steinhardt, 1985).

These data tend to rule out a role for inositol phosphates in gating calcium influx in sea urchin eggs. Moreover, any calcium influx that does occur does not play any role in activation. Admittedly, injection of $InsP_3$ is likely to affect calcium uptake because it does cause a depolarization similar to the activation potential at fertilization (Slack *et al.*, 1986). However, this is an indirect effect and is due to the fact that the released calcium opens non-selective cation channels in the plasma membrane (Obata & Kuroda, 1987; Whitaker, 1989). There is no evidence for a direct effect of $InsP_3$ on the plasma membrane in eggs.

Diacylglycerol

PtdInsP$_2$ hydrolysis also releases diacylglycerol whose messenger function is to stimulate protein kinase C (PKC). A role for this other wing of the PI messenger system at fertilization was first suggested by Swann & Whitaker (1985) who showed that the phorbol myristate acetate, which specifically activates PKC, causes a pH$_i$ rise in sea-urchin eggs. PKC activation appears to stimulate the sodium/hydrogen antiporter because the phorbol-induced pH$_i$ rise is inhibited by low sodium sea water and by the sodium/hydrogen antiporter antagonist, dimethylamiloride (Swann & Whitaker, 1985). In addition to phorbol esters, more natural PKC agonists, such as synthetic diacylglycerols, also cause a rise in pH$_i$ (Shen & Burgart, 1986; Lau *et al.*, 1986). Since increased diacylglycerol production first occurs during the Ca wave at fertilization (Ciapa & Whitaker, 1986), these data all strongly implicate diacylglycerol as the messenger that triggers the pH$_i$ at fertilization.

Shen (1989) has suggested that calcium–calmodulin rather than PKC is involved in stimulating the sodium/hydrogen antiporter at fertilization. He showed that (1) the PKC antagonist H7 blocks the phorbol ester-induced pH$_i$ increase but not that caused by spermatozoa, and (2) the calmodulin antagonist W7 blocks the fertilization-induced pH$_i$ changes, but not those caused by phorbol esters. These data do not rule out a role for PKC in causing the pH$_i$ increase because H7 does not always block the effects of PKC-induced phosphorylations stimulated by natural agonists in other cells (Watson *et al.*, 1988; Siefert & Schachele, 1988). However, they do emphasize a direct role for calcium in causing the pH$_i$ rise. As explained below, the production of diacylglycerol at fertilization appears to be a result of the calcium increase (Fig. 3). This could mean that both calmodulin and PKC are involved in stimulating the sodium/hydrogen exchanger (Shen & Buck, 1990). Given such a tight link between the Ca$^{2+}{}_i$ transient and diacylglycerol production, it will certainly be difficult to separate a direct role for calcium stimulating the sodium/hydrogen antiporter from an indirect effect of calcium causing diacylglycerol production which then affects PKC.

The mechanism of the fertililization wave

A positive feedback cycle involving calcium and InsP$_3$

One of the most important properties of InsP$_3$ as an egg activator is its ability to mimic the fertilization wave. Pressure pulse, and hence rapid, injections of small volumes of 5–10 μM-InsP$_3$ into one side of an egg can trigger a wave of envelope elevation that crosses the egg in about 20 sec (Whitaker & Irvine, 1984). Importantly, this InsP$_3$-induced wave cannot be explained by simple diffusion of the injected solution, and it appears that InsP$_3$ is triggering an autocatalytic wave that is inherent within the egg. This is presumably the same autocatalytic wave that is triggered by the spermatozoon. Whitaker & Irvine (1984) suggested a possible mechanism for such a wave involving InsP$_3$. The breakdown of polyphosphoinositides in sea-urchin egg membranes is stimulated by micromolar calcium concentrations (Whitaker & Irvine, 1984; Whitaker & Aitchison, 1985). Since PtdInsP$_2$ breakdown will produce InsP$_3$ which in turn releases more calcium, there appears to exist a positive feedback cycle of InsP$_3$ and Ca$^{2+}{}_i$ increase within the egg (Fig. 3). This positive feedback cycle could underlie the calcium and, therefore, the fertilization wave (Fig. 3). Support for this idea comes from the finding that intracellular neomycin, which inhibits the calcium-activated polyphosphoinositide hydrolysis (Whitaker & Aitchison, 1985), blocks the InsP$_3$-induced Ca$^{2+}{}_i$ wave, even though it does not alter the ability of InsP$_3$ to release calcium *per se* (Swann & Whitaker, 1986).

Although the fertilization wave may involve a Ca$^{2+}{}_i$-InsP$_3$ positive feedback cycle, the wave cannot be demonstrated to be triggered by calcium. Injection of small volumes of calcium-containing solutions, or local, external application of calcium ionophores, only causes a local exocytosis and local envelope elevation (Swann & Whitaker, 1986; Whitaker & Steinhardt, 1981).

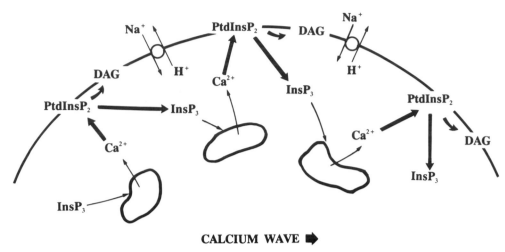

CALCIUM WAVE ➡

Fig. 3. The proposed mechanism of propagation of the calcium wave. There is a positive feed-back cycle in which $InsP_3$ causes calcium release which then stimulates further $InsP_3$ production via $PtdInsP_2$ hydrolysis. This cycle also produces diacylglycerol (DAG) which activates the Na^+/H^+ antiporter causing a rise in pH_i.

These data could be taken to argue against the theory of the positive feedback cycle. However, it is possible that the exact kinetics of a calcium increase that is needed to trigger the wave is not easily imitated by injection. Sea-urchin eggs appear to be different in this respect from frog eggs in which a local increase in Ca^{2+}_i easily triggers a propagating calcium wave (Busa & Nuccitelli, 1985; Kubota *et al.*, 1987). This may be because the calcium wave in frog eggs involves a calcium-induced calcium release mechanism (Busa *et al.*, 1985).

Calcium-stimulated polyphosphoinositide hydrolysis and the calcium wave

The existence of Ca^{2+}_i and $InsP_3$ waves is consistent with the finding that the measurable increase in $InsP_3$ at fertilization occurs during the wave (Ciapa & Whitaker, 1986). An initial increase in diacylglycerol production also occurs during the fertilization wave, supporting the idea that a Ca^{2+}_i increase causes the bulk, if not all, the polyphosphoinositide hydrolysis at fertilization. The finding that calcium ionophores or $InsP_3$ injection trigger the pH_i change at fertilization is also consistent with a calcium-dependent increase in diacylglycerol (Fig. 3) (Whitaker & Steinhardt, 1981; Whitaker & Irvine, 1984). Not only does the calcium wave appear to cause PPI hydrolysis but it may also stimulate the rapid resynthesis of $PtdInsP_2$; the kinases that phosphorylate PI and PIP are calcium dependent (Oberdorf *et al.*, 1989).

How does the spermatozoon trigger the calcium wave?

The wave of envelope elevation that is triggered by $InsP_3$ occurs with essentially no delay after injection (<1 sec). However, at fertilization there is a delay of at least 7 sec between the start of the sperm-induced current and the calcium wave (Shen & Steinhardt, 1984; Longo *et al.*, 1986; Lynn *et al.*, 1988). Therefore, the delay, or latent period, at fertilization may represent the time required for the spermatozoa to cause enough $InsP_3$ production, or enough of a local Ca^{2+}_i increase, to trigger the wave. It is not yet clear how the spermatozoon causes these initial changes.

The receptor-linked G-protein hypothesis

It has been suggested that the spermatozoon generates $InsP_3$ by acting on a cell surface receptor that couples to a phosphoinositidase C (PIC) through a GTP-binding protein, or G-protein (Fig. 4) (Turner *et al.*, 1986, 1987; Jaffe, 1989). This idea is mainly based upon the fact that stimulating G-protein activity with GTP-γ-S injection activates sea-urchin eggs, and that the G-protein blocker GDP-β-S inhibits envelope elevation at fertilization (Turner *et al.*, 1986). However, there are some difficulties in interpreting these results. GDP-β-S, at millimolar concentrations in the ooplasm, does not inhibit either sperm incorporation (Swann *et al.*, 1987), or the Ca^{2+}_i transient at fertilization (Fig. 5). So the original hypothesis that a G-protein is required by the spermatozoon to cause a calcium wave seems open to question. Stimulating G-proteins with GTP-γ-S *does* cause a Ca^{2+}_i transient similar to that seen at fertilization, but the lack of effect of GDP-β-S on the Ca^{2+}_i transient suggests that a G-protein may not be used at fertilization (Swann *et al.*, 1987). G-proteins coupled to PIC, or other enzymes, certainly exist in the egg (Turner *et al.*, 1987), but this does not mean they are involved at fertilization. They may, instead, be used during egg maturation (Shilling *et al.*, 1989), or even later in development.

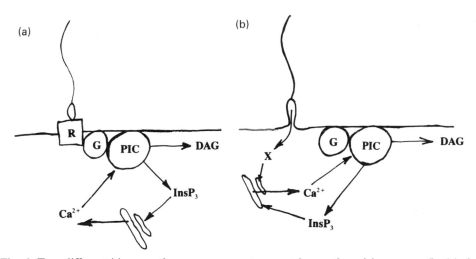

Fig. 4. Two different ideas on the way a spermatozoon triggers the calcium wave. In (a) the spermatozoon binds to a surface receptor (R) that is coupled to a phosphoinositidase C (PIC) via a guanine nucleotide binding protein (G). In (b) the sperm and egg membranes fuse and this allows a factor to diffuse into the egg and cause calcium release from an internal store.

In support of the idea that the G-protein is not used at fertilization we have recently found that GTP-γ-S and spermatozoa activate eggs in rather different ways. This is revealed by the sensitivity of these two activators to heparin. Heparin is a competitive $InsP_3$ antagonist (Worley *et al.*, 1987) which, when injected, reduces the sensitivity of sea-urchin eggs to $InsP_3$ (I. Crossley & M. Whitaker, unpublished observations). Heparin blocks the GTP-γ-S-induced activation and the Ca^{2+}_i transient, yet at the same concentrations it does not inhibit even one spermatozoon from causing a Ca^{2+}_i wave (I. Crossley & M. J. Whitaker, unpublished observations). In turkey erythrocyte membranes, for example, GTP-γ-S makes as much $InsP_3$ as maximal hormone stimulation (Harden, 1989), but this result in eggs is unexpected. Heparin does increase the latent period at fertilization, suggesting that a critical local $InsP_3$ level has to be reached before the wave is triggered. However, the finding that heparin cannot stop the spermatozoa triggering the wave suggests that the spermatozoon does not use the same activating mechanism as does GTP-γ-S.

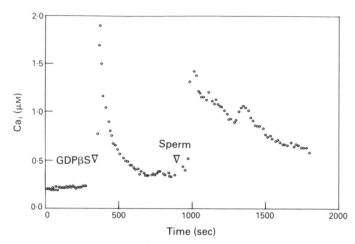

Fig. 5. GDP-β-S does not block the $Ca^{2+}{}_i$ transient at fertilization. An *L. pictus* egg at 16°C was injected with fura-2 (as in Fig. 1) and then reinjected with GDP-β-S to a final concentration of 5 mM. GDP-β-S injection itself caused a significant $Ca^{2+}{}_i$ transient increase. After this first transient increase declined, insemination resulted in another larger $Ca^{2+}{}_i$ increase (I. Crossley, unpublished observations).

We arrived at a similar conclusion by measuring diacylglycerol production in single eggs. Diacylglycerol production at fertilization is calcium-dependent, since it is abolished by micro-injecting BAPTA, a calcium chelator (Fig. 2), while diacylglycerol production induced by micro-injecting GTP-γ-S does not require a calcium increase (Whalley & Whitaker, 1988).

Fusion of the spermatozoon and egg

If the spermatozoon does not act via a receptor coupled to G-protein then what mechanism does it use to trigger the calcium wave? An alternative hypothesis of fertilization is that the spermatozoon introduces a soluble activating factor into the egg cytoplasm after gamete fusion (Dale *et al.*, 1985; Dale, 1988). Such a factor could cause a local increase in $Ca^{2+}{}_i$ or InsP$_3$ from within the egg (Fig. 4). This idea is feasible since the sperm and egg membranes fuse before the start of the calcium wave (Longo *et al.*, 1986; Hinkley *et al.*, 1986). In fact, experiments measuring capacitance changes at fertilization in sea-urchin eggs demonstrate that sperm–egg membrane fusion occurs simultaneously with the onset of the sperm-induced inward current (McCulloh & Chambers, 1986a). Since the sperm-current is the first detectable change that the spermatozoon causes in the egg, gametes are clearly in direct cytoplasmic contact at the very start of fertilization. The delay period between this initial fusion and the triggering of the calcium wave could, therefore, represent the time required for an activating factor to diffuse from the spermatozoon into the egg (Whitaker *et al.*, 1989).

The idea that the delay period at fertilization represents the diffusion time of an activating sperm factor may explain some observations made on voltage-clamped eggs. When eggs are held at potentials more negative than −50 mV and inseminated, spermatozoa often cause short-duration inward currents that do not lead to egg activation (Lynn *et al.*, 1988; David *et al.*, 1988). These abortive and brief duration sperm-currents appear to be caused by the fusion and subsequent 'unfusion' of the spermatozoon (McCulloh & Chambers, 1986b). The initial state of sperm–egg fusion is therefore reversible and lasts for short durations at negative holding potentials (McCulloh & Chambers, 1986b; Whitaker *et al.*, 1989; Chambers & McCulloh, 1990). If, at negative potentials, the spermatozoon is only briefly fused to the egg it is unlikely that sufficient time (the latent period) will elapse for enough factor to diffuse into the egg to trigger the calcium wave. There is a quantitative agreement between the incidence of sperm-currents that trigger the wave and the theoretical chances of the observed length of sperm-current leading to activation that is dealt with in more detail elsewhere (Whitaker *et al.*, 1989).

Cross-fertilization experiments provide further evidence for the hypothesis that fusion of the spermatozoon with the egg causes activation. Starfish spermatozoa will not normally penetrate, or activate, sea-urchin eggs. Presumably egg and sperm receptors are mismatched. However, if starfish spermatozoa are artificially fused to sea-urchin eggs using polyethylene glycol, then egg activation occurs (Kyozuka & Osanai, 1989). Since polyethyleneglycol treatment alone does not activate eggs, it appears that a spermatozoon needs only to fuse with the egg to trigger the calcium wave. Again a ready explanation of why fusion leads to activation is that it allows the spermatozoon to introduce an activating factor into the egg cytoplasm.

In contrast to the soluble sperm factor hypothesis that we suggest for sea-urchins, experiments on *Urechis* eggs have suggested that the spermatozoon may act on an egg surface receptor (Gould *et al.*, 1986; Gould & Stephano, 1987). When a bindin-like molecule from isolated *Urechis* spermatozoa is added to the outside of *Urechis* eggs, it causes activation and the same voltage changes that are seen at fertilization. Some caution should be exercised in interpreting these data, because non-specific agents such as trypsin, protamines and polyamines also activate *Urechis* eggs (Paul, 1975; Fujiwara *et al.*, 1983; Gould *et al.*, 1986). Nevertheless, the experiments of Gould *et al.* (1986) may mean that a hormone-like molecule exists on the spermatozoa of some species. If this is the case then there could be phyletic differences between sea-urchin and *Urechis* fertilization. *Urechis* eggs are fundamentally different from sea-urchin eggs in that they are activated by an influx of calcium, rather than by the internal release mechanism (Jaffe, 1983).

An hypothesis of egg activation

It is a very old idea that spermatozoa fertilize eggs by introducing an activating factor into the egg (Loeb, 1913). In recent years this idea has received less attention than the receptor–G-protein hypothesis. However, the experiments with GTP analogues now point away from this idea. Furthermore, the only protein that has been isolated from acrosomal tips of sea-urchin spermatozoa and that acts on the sea-urchin egg surface is bindin, and bindin does not activate eggs (Vacquier & Moy, 1977). Since bindin is a fusogenic protein (Glabe, 1985), its likely function is simply to fuse the spermatozoon to the egg. Given that the fusion of gamete membranes is the first event in egg activation (McCulloh & Chambers, 1986a; Chambers & McCulloh, 1990), fertilization ceases to be a problem of transmembrane signalling and the idea of an intracellular activating sperm factor may be the most straightforward explanation of fertilization (Fig. 6).

It is not yet clear what such a proposed sperm factor may be, or exactly how it works. Sea-urchin spermatozoa may contain a number of candidate activators, including calcium itself (Jaffe, 1983), InsP$_3$ (Whitaker & Irvine, 1984; Domino & Garbers, 1988; Iwasa *et al.*, 1989), cyclic GMP (Swann *et al.*, 1987) and cyclic-ADP ribose (Clapper *et al.*, 1987; Lee *et al.*, 1989). It has been reported that injection of sperm cytosol fractions trigger envelope elevation in sea-urchin eggs, or the fertilization current in ascidian eggs (Dale *et al.*, 1985; Dale, 1988) but the identify of the factor remains unknown. More recently, however, injection of mammalian sperm cytosol has been found to cause sustained repetitive $Ca^{2+}{}_i$ transients that mimic fertilization in hamster eggs (Swann, 1990). The active factor in mammalian spermatozoa appears to be protein. This provides the most convincing direct demonstration of a sperm factor because, unlike sea-urchin or *Urechis* eggs, the repetitive $Ca^{2+}{}_i$ transients in fertilizing hamster eggs are not mimicked by any form of parthenogenetic stimulation (see Miyazaki, 1990).

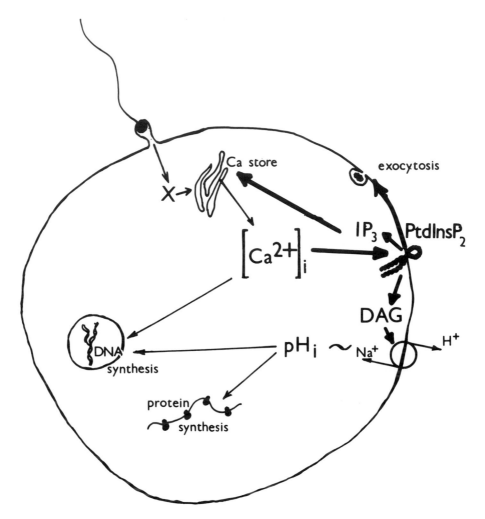

Fig. 6. A model of second messenger production and functions at fertilization in sea-urchin eggs. The spermatozoon activates the egg by introducing a soluble factor (X) into the egg cytoplasm. This factor causes a small amount of calcium release. The feedback cycle of PtdInsP$_2$ hydrolysis (see Fig. 4) amplifies this Ca$^{2+}_i$ increase and causes the pH$_i$ increase. These two ionic changes act together to stimulate protein and DNA synthesis.

Whatever the nature of the sperm factor in sea-urchins, its effect should be to increase Ca$^{2+}_i$ or InsP$_3$ to the point where the regenerative calcium wave is triggered. Once started, it appears that the calcium wave can proceed on its own via a positive feedback cycle of Ca$^{2+}_i$ increase and InsP$_3$ production. The wave is as important a feature of fertilization as the existence of a sperm factor. It acts as an amplification system that allows the spermatozoon to release all the internal stores of calcium and generate a large increase in diacylglycerol. The Ca$^{2+}_i$ and pH$_i$ changes that ensue provide the dual ionic signals that trigger the reinitiation of the cell cycle and the development of the egg (Fig. 6) (Whitaker & Steinhardt, 1985).

We thank Ian Crossley and Timothy Whalley for letting us present some of their unpublished data. The work was supported by the S.E.R.C., the Royal Society and the Wellcome Trust.

References

Allen, R.D. & Griffin, J.L. (1958) The time sequence of early events at fertilization in sea-urchins. *Expl Cell Res.* **15**, 163–173.

Azarnia, R. & Chambers, E.L. (1976) The role of divalent cations in activation of the sea-urchin egg. I. Effect of fertilization on divalent cation content. *J. exp. zool.* **198**, 65–77.

Berridge, M.J. (1987) Inositol trisphosphate and diacylglycerol; two interacting second messengers. *Ann. Rev. Biochem.* **56**, 159–163.

Busa, W.B. & Nuccitelli, R. (1985) An elevated cytosolic Ca^{2+}_i wave follows fertilization in eggs of the frog, *Xenopus laevis. J. Cell Biol.* **100**, 1325–1329.

Busa, W.B., Fergesun, J.E., Suresh, K.J., Williamson, J.R. & Nuccitelli, R. (1985) Activation of frog eggs by inositol 1,4,5-trisphosphate. *J. Cell Biol.* **101**, 677–682.

Chambers, E.L. (1976) Na is essential for activation of the inseminated sea-urchin egg. *J. exp. Zool.* **197**, 149–154.

Chambers, E.L. & de Armendi, J. (1979) Membrane potential, action potential and activation potential of the sea-urchin *Lytechinus variegatus. Expl Cell Res.* **122**, 203–218.

Chambers, T.L. & McCulloh, D.H. (1990) Excitation, activation and sperm entry in voltage-clamped sea-urchin eggs. *J. Reprod. Fert., Suppl.* **42**, 117–132.

Ciapa, B. & Whitaker, M.J. (1986) Two phases of inositol and diacylglycerol production at fertilization. *FEBS Lett.* **195**, 347–351.

Clapper, D. & Lee, H.C. (1985) Inositol trisphosphate induces calcium release from nonmitochondrial stores in sea-urchin egg homogenates. *J. biol. Chem.* **260**, 13947–13945.

Clapper, D.L., Walseth, T.F., Dargie, P.J. & Lee, H.C. (1987) Pyridine nucleotide metabolites stimulate calcium release from sea-urchin egg microsomes desensitized to inositol trisphosphate. *J. biol. Chem.* **262**, 9561–9568.

Crossley, I., Swann, K. & Whitaker, M.J. (1988) Activation of sea-urchin eggs by inositol(1,4,5) trisphosphate is independent of external calcium. *Biochem. J.* **252**, 257–262.

Dale, B. (1988) Primary and secondary messengers in activation of ascidian eggs. *Expl Cell Res.* **177**, 205–211.

Dale, B., De Felice, L.J. & Taglietie, V. (1978) Membrane noise and conductance increase during single spermatozoon-egg interaction. *Nature, Lond.* **316**, 541–542.

Dale, B., DeFelice, L.J. & Ehrenstein, G. (1985) Injection of a soluble sperm extract into sea-urchin eggs triggers the cortical reaction. *Experientia* **41**, 1068–1070.

David, C., Halliwell, J. & Whitaker, M.J. (1988) Some properties of the membrane currents underlying the fertilization potential in sea-urchin eggs. *J. Physiol., Lond.* **402**, 139–154.

Domino, S.E. & Garbers, D.L. (1988) The fucose-sulfate conjugate that induces an acrosome reaction in spermatozoa stimulates inositol 1,4,5-trisphosphate accumulation. *J. biol. Chem.* **263**, 690–695.

Eisen, A., Kiehart, D.P., Wieland, S.J. & Reynolds, G.T. (1984) Temporal sequences and spatial distribution of early events of fertilization in single sea-urchin eggs. *J. Cell Biol.* **99**, 1647–1654.

Epel, D. (1978) Mechanism of activation of sperm and egg during fertilization of sea-urchin gametes. *Curr. Top. Dev. Biol.* **12**, 185–246.

Epel, D., Steinhardt, R.A., Humphreys, T. & Mazia, D. (1974) An analysis of the partial metabolic depression of the sea-urchin egg by ammonia; the existence of independent pathways. *Devl Biol.* **40**, 245–255.

Fujiwara, A., Kusunoki, S., Tazawa, E. & Yaumasu, I. (1983) Stimulation of unfertilized eggs of the echiuroid, *Urechis unicinctuis* by polyamines. *Dev. Growth, Differ.* **25**, 445–452.

Glabe, C.G. (1985) Interaction of sperm adhesive protein, bindin with phospholipid vesicles. II Bindin induces fusion of mixed phase vesicles that contain phosphatidylcholine and phosphatidylserine in vitro. *J. Cell Biol.* **100**, 800–805.

Gould, M. & Stephano, J.L. (1987) Electrical responses of eggs to acrosomal protein similar to those induced by sperm. *Science, NY* **235**, 1654–1656.

Gould, M., Stephano, J.L. & Holland, L.Z. (1986) Isolation of protein from *Urechis* sperm acrosomal granules that binds sperm to eggs and initiates development. *Devl Biol.* **117**, 306–318.

Harden, T.K. (1989) The role of guanine nucleotide regulatory proteins in receptor selective direction of inositol lipid signalling. In *Inositol Lipids in Cell Signalling*, pp. 113–133. Eds R. H. Michell, A. H. Drummond & C. P. Downes. Academic Press, London.

Hamaguchi, Y. & Hiramoto, Y. (1981) Activation of sea-urchin eggs by microinjection of calcium buffers. *Expl Cell Res.* **134**, 171–179.

Hinkley, R.E., Wright, B.D. & Lynn, J.W. (1986) Rapid visual detection of sperm egg fusion using the DNA specific fluorocrome Hoechst 33342. *Devl Biol.* **118**, 148–154.

Irvine, R.F. & Moor, R.M. (1986) Microinjection of inositol 1,3,4,5-tetrakisphosphate activates sea urchin eggs by a mechanism dependent upon external Ca^{2+}. *Biochem. J.* **240**, 917–920.

Iwasa, K.H., Ehrenstein, G., DeFelice, L.J. & Russel, J.T. (1989) Sea urchin sperm contain enough inositol 1,4,5-trisphosphate to activate eggs. *J. Cell Biol.* **109**, 693a, abstr.

Jaffe, L.A. (1976) Fast block to polyspermy in sea urchin eggs is electrically mediated. *Nature, Lond.* **261**, 261–277.

Jaffe, L.A. (1989) Receptors, G-proteins and egg activation. In *Mechanisms of Egg Activation*, pp. 151–171. Eds R. Nuccitelli, G. N. Cherr & W. H. Clark, Jr. Plenum Press, New York.

Jaffe, L.F. (1983) Sources of calcium in egg activation; a review and hypothesis. *Devl Biol.* **99**, 265–276.

Johnson, C.H. & Epel, D. (1976) Intracellular pH and activation of sea-urchin eggs after fertilization. *Nature, Lond.* **262**, 661–664.

Kacser, H. (1955) The cortical changes on fertilisation in the sea-urchin egg. *J. exp. Biol.* **32**, 451–467.

Kay, E.S. & Shapiro, B.M. (1985) The formation of the fertilization membrane of the sea-urchin egg. In *Biology of Fertilization*, Vol. 3, pp. 45–80. Eds C. Metz & A. Monroy. Academic Press, New York.

Kubota, H.Y., Yoshimoto, Y., Yoneda, M. & Hiramoto, Y. (1987) Free calcium wave upon activation in Xenopus eggs. *Devl Biol.* **119**, 129–136.

Kyozuka, K. & Osanai, K. (1989) Induction of cross fertilization between sea-urchin eggs and starfish sperm by polyethylene glycol treatment. *Gamete Res.* **22**, 123–129.

Lau, A.F., Rayson, T. & Humphreys, T.C. (1986) Tumour promoters and diacylglycerol activate the Na^+/H^+ antiporter of sea-urchin eggs. *Expl Cell Res.* **166**, 23–30.

Lee, H.C., Walseth, T.F., Bratt, G.T., Hayes, R.N. & Clapper, D.L. (1989) Structural determination of a cyclic metabolite of NAD^+ with intracellular Ca^{2+}-mobilizing activity. *J. biol. Chem.* **264**, 1608–1615.

Loeb, J. (1913) *Artificial Parthenogenesis and Fertilization.* University of Chicago Press, Chicago.

Longo, F.J., Lynn, J.W., McCulloh, D.H. & Chambers, E.L. (1986) Correlative ultrastructural and electrophysiological studies of sperm egg interaction in the sea-urchin, *Lytechinus variegatus. Devl Biol.* **118**, 155–166.

Lynn, J.W., McCulloh, D.H. & Chambers, E.L. (1988) Voltage clamp studies of fertilization in sea-urchin eggs. II. Current patterns in relation to sperm entry, nonentry, and activation. *Devl Biol.* **128**, 305–323.

McCulloh, D.H. & Chambers, E.L. (1986a) When does the sperm fuse with the egg? *J. gen. Physiol.* **88**, 38–39a.

McCulloh, D.H. & Chambers, E.L. (1986b) Fusion and "unfusion" of sperm and egg are voltage dependent in the sea-urchin egg *Lytechinus variegatus. J. Cell Biol.* **103**, 286a, abstr.

Mehl, J.W. & Swann, M.M. (1961) Acid and base production at fertilization in sea-urchins. *Expl Cell Res.* **22**, 233–245.

Miyazaki, S. (1990) Cell signalling at fertilization of hamster eggs. *J. Reprod. Fert., Suppl.* **42**, 163–175.

Obata, S. & Kuroda, H. (1987) The second component of the fertilization potential in sea-urchin (*Pseudocentrotus depressus*) eggs involves Na^+ and K^+ permeability. *Devl Biol.* **122**, 432–438.

Oberdorf, J., Vilar-Rojas, C. & Epel, D. (1989) The localization of PI and PIP kinase activities in the sea-urchin egg and their modulation following fertilization. *Devl Biol.* **131**, 236–242.

Paradiso, A.M., Tsien, R.Y. & Machen, T.E. (1987) Digital image processing of intracellular pH in gastric oxyntic cells. *Nature, Lond.* **325**, 447–450.

Paul, M. (1975) Release of acid and changes in light scattering properties following fertilization of *Urechis caupo* eggs. *Devl Biol.* **43**, 299–312.

Payan, P., Girard, J.P. & Ciapa, B. (1983) Mechanisms regulating intracellular pH in sea-urchin eggs. *Devl Biol.* **100**, 29–38.

Payan, P., Girard, J.P., Sardet, C., Whitaker, M.J. & Zimmerberg, J. (1986) Uptake and release of calcium by isolated egg cortices of the sea-urchin *Parcentrotus lividus. Biol. Cell.* **58**, 87–90.

Poenie, M., Alderton, J., Tsien, R.Y. & Steinhardt, R.A. (1985) Changes in free calcium with stages of the cell division cycle. *Nature, Lond.* **315**, 147–149.

Schmidt, T., Patton, C. & Epel, D. (1982) Is there a role for calcium influx during fertilization of sea-urchin eggs? *Devl Biol.* **90**, 284–290.

Seifert, R. & Schachtele, C. (1988) Studies with protein kinase C inhibitors presently available cannot elucidate the role of protein kinase C in the activation of NADPH oxidase. *Biochem. Biophys. Res. Commun.* **152**, 585–592.

Shen, S.S. (1989) Na^+-H^+ antiport during fertilization of the sea-urchin egg is blocked by W-7 but is insensitive to K525a and H7. *Biochem. Biophys. Res. Commun.* **161**, 1100–1108.

Shen, S.S. & Buck, W.R. (1990) A synthetic peptide of the pseudosubstrate domain of protein kinase C blocks cytoplasmic alkalinization during activation of the sea-urchin egg. *Devl Biol.* (in press).

Shen, S.S. & Burgart, L.J. (1986) 1,2,-diacylglycerols mimic phorbol 12-myristate acetate activation of the sea-urchin egg. *J. Cell Physiol.* **127**, 330–340.

Shen, S.S. & Steinhardt, R.A. (1978) Direct measurement of intracellular pH during metabolic derepression of the sea-urchin egg. *Nature, Lond.* **272**, 253–254.

Shen, S.S. & Steinhardt, R.A. (1984) Time and voltage windows for reversing the electrical block to fertilization. *Proc. natn. Acad. Sci. USA* **81**, 1436–1439.

Shilling, F., Chiba, K., Hoshi, M., Kishimoto, T. & Jaffe, L.A. (1988) Pertussis toxin inhibits 1-methyladenine-induced maturation in starfish oocytes. *Devl Biol.* **113**, 605–608.

Slack, B.E., Bell, J.E. & Benos, D.J. (1986) Inositol-1,4,5 trisphosphate injection mimics fertilization potentials of sea-urchin eggs. *Am. J. Physiol.* **250**, C340–344.

Steinhardt, R.A. & Epel, D. (1974) Activation of sea urchin eggs by a calcium ionophore. *Proc. natn. Acad. Sci. USA* **71**, 1915–1919.

Steinhardt, R.A., Zucker, R. & Schatten, G. (1977) Intracellular calcium at fertilization in the sea-urchin egg. *Devl Biol.* **58**, 185–196.

Sugiyama, M. (1956) Physiological analysis of the cortical response of the sea-urchin egg. *Expl Cell Res.* **10**, 364–376.

Swann, K. (1990) Injection of a cytosolic factor from sperm imitates the membrane potential fertilization response in golden hamster eggs. *J. Physiol., Lond.* **427**, abstr.

Swann, K. & Whitaker, M. (1985) Stimulation of the Na/H exchanger of sea-urchin eggs by phorbol ester. *Nature, Lond.* **314**, 274–277.

Swann, K. & Whitaker, M.J. (1986) The part played by inositol trisphosphate and calcium in the propagation of the fertilization wave in sea-urchin eggs. *J. Cell Biol.* **103**, 2332–2342.

Swann, K., Ciapa, B. & Whitaker, M.J. (1987) Cellular messengers and sea-urchin egg activation. In *The Molecular Biology of Invertebrate Development*, pp. 45–69. Ed. D. O'Conner. Alan R. Liss, New York.

Tsien, R.Y. & Poenie, M. (1986) Fluorescence ratio imaging: a new window into intracellular ionic signalling. *Trends in Pharm. Sci.* **11**, 450–455.

Turner, P.R., Scheetz, M.P. & Jaffe, L.A. (1984) Fertilization increases the polyphosphoinositide content of sea-urchin eggs. *Nature, Lond.* **310**, 141–145.

Turner, P.R., Jaffe, L.A. & Fein, A. (1986) Regulation of cortical vesicle exocytosis by inositol 1,4,5-trisphosphate and GTP binding protein. *J. Cell Biol.* **102**, 70–76.

Turner, P.R., Jaffe, L.A. & Primakoff, P. (1987) A cholera toxin sensitive G-protein stimulates exocytosis in sea-urchin eggs. *Devl Biol.* **120**, 577–583.

Vacquier, V.D. & Moy, G.W. (1977) Isolation of bindin: The protein responsible for the adhesion of sperm to sea-urchin eggs. *Proc. natl. Acad. Sci. USA* **74**, 2456–2460.

Watson, S.P., McNalie, J., Shipman, L.J. & Godfrey, P.P. (1988) The action of the protein kinase C inhibitor, staurosporine, on human platelets. *Biochem. J.* **259**, 345–351.

Whalley, T. & Whitaker, M.J. (1988) Guanine nucleotide activation of phosphoinositidase C at fertilization in sea-urchin eggs. *J. Physiol., Lond.* **406**, 126*P*, abstr.

Whitaker, M. (1989) Phosphoinositide second messengers in eggs and oocytes. In *Inositol Lipids in Cell Signalling*, pp. 459–483. Eds R. H. Michell, A. H. Drummond & C. P. Downes. Academic Press, London.

Whitaker, M.J. & Aitchison, M.J. (1985) Calcium dependent polyphosphoinositide hydrolysis is associated with exocytosis in vitro. *FEBS Lett.* **182**, 119–124.

Whitaker, M.J. & Irvine, R.F. (1984) Inositol-1,4,5 trisphosphate microinjection activates sea-urchin eggs. *Nature, Lond.* **312**, 636–639.

Whitaker, M.J. & Steinhardt, R.A. (1981) The relation between the increased reduced nicotinamide nucleotides and the initiation of DNA synthesis in sea-urchin eggs. *Cell* **25**, 95–103.

Whitaker, M.J. & Steinhardt, R.A. (1982) Ionic regulation of egg activation. *Q. Rev. Biophys.* **15**, 593–666.

Whitaker, M.J. & Steinhardt, R.A. (1985) Ions and the control of development. In *Fertilization*, pp. 167–221. Eds C. Metz & A. Monroy. Academic Press, London.

Whitaker, M.J., Swann, K. & Crossley, I. (1989) What happens during the latent period at fertilization. In *Mechanisms of Egg Activation*, pp. 157–171. Eds R. Nuccitelli, G. N. Cherr & W. H. Clark Jr. Plenum Press, New York.

Worley, P.F., Baraban, S., Supattapone, S., Wilson, V.S. & Snyder, S.H. (1987) Characterization of inositol trisphosphate receptor binding in brain. *J. biol. Chem.* **262**, 12132–12136.

Zucker, R.S. & Steinhardt, R.A. (1978) Prevention of the cortical reaction in fertilized sea-urchin eggs by injection of calcium-chelating ligands. *Biochim. Biophys. Acta* **54**, 459–466.

J. Reprod. Fert., Suppl. **42** (1990), 155–161

Printed in Great Britain
© 1990 Journals of Reproduction & Fertility Ltd

Involvement of calcium and inositol phosphates in amphibian egg activation

W. B. Busa

Department of Biology, The Johns Hopkins University, Charles and 34th Sts, Baltimore, MD 21218, USA

Keywords: Xenopus laevis; frog egg activation; inositol 1,4,5-trisphosphate

Introduction

Early suggestions that transient changes in intracellular free calcium levels ($[Ca^{2+}]_i$) constitute a general, perhaps even universal, mediator of egg activation at fertilization (Tyler, 1941; Steinhardt *et al.*, 1974; Jaffe, 1983) have seen dramatic confirmation during the past decade as new technologies for $[Ca^{2+}]_i$ measurement have revealed large transient changes accompanying fertilization in several phyla, including echinoderms (Steinhardt *et al.*, 1977; Eisen *et al.*, 1984; Eisen & Reynolds, 1984), teleosts (Ridgway *et al.*, 1977; Gilkey *et al.*, 1978), and mammals (Cuthbertson *et al.*, 1981; Miyazaki *et al.*, 1986). In what follows, I shall briefly review my own contributions and those of my colleagues to the study of the calcium transient at fertilization in amphibian eggs—specifically, those of the African clawed toad, *Xenopus laevis*, and the painted frog, *Discoglossus pictus*.

Frog eggs generally, and *Xenopus* eggs in particular, prove exceptionally suitable subjects for studies on the cell physiology of fertilization. *Xenopus* eggs are very large ($\sim 1\cdot3$ mm in diameter), quite robust, available in large numbers, and are easily fertilized *in vitro* with a fair degree of synchronization. Female *Xenopus* can be induced to ovulate year-round by injection of human chorionic gonadotrophin, eggs are readily hand-expressed without harm to the females (males, however, are typically killed before harvesting of testes), and the adult animals are easy to maintain in good health and will live for many years under laboratory conditions. Other frogs, particularly *Rana* spp., offer some unique advantages and have occasionally been used (see, e.g., Elinson, 1975; Cross, 1981), but have not enjoyed as wide acceptance (perhaps for no better reason than historical bias!). Finally, *Discoglossus* eggs possess some bizarre features such as a unique functional polarization, and can be exploited for various purposes. The cell biology of oogenesis, fertilization and early development in frogs has been comprehensively reviewed by Gerhart (1980).

The eggs of frogs, like those of animals of many other phyla, have several characteristic responses to fertilization, including plasma membrane depolarization (the so-called 'activation potential'), exocytosis of cortical granules, modification of microvilli, reorganization of cortical cytoplasm, increase in intracellular pH, and, as discussed below, a propagated wave of intracellular calcium mobilization which is thought to be largely responsible for triggering several of these other responses.

The calcium transient at fertilization

Based on earlier observations that various aspects of frog egg activation could be artificially elicited by microinjection of Ca^{2+} (Hollinger & Schuetz, 1976; Cross, 1981) or treatment with the calcium ionophore, A23187, it was widely assumed that the frog egg, like medaka fish (Ridgway *et al.*, 1977) and sea urchin (Steinhardt *et al.*, 1977) eggs, would prove to be activated by a transient increase in $[Ca^{2+}]_i$ following fertilization. Such $[Ca^{2+}]_i$ transients were first observed in *Xenopus* eggs impaled with Ca^{2+}-selective microelectrodes (Busa & Nuccitelli, 1985). Shortly after the first detectable sign of fertilization, the activation potential, such electrodes invariably detect an increase in cytosolic free calcium concentrations from the egg's resting value of 0·40 μM (pCa 6·4±0·02) to a peak of 1·2 μM (pCa 5·9±0·06) over the course of 2 min, followed by a recovery back to the initial resting level over the next 8 min. No further changes in $[Ca^{2+}]_i$ are observed with these electrodes through the first cleavage division, an observation also made by Rink et al. (1980). Considerable force was required to achieve impalement with these large-diameter electrode tips, hence impalement depth was largely uncontrolled and in several instances was taken to be ≥ 100 μm. The small standard errors quoted above therefore suggest that the $[Ca^{2+}]_i$ transient at fertilization in these eggs involves most or all of the cytosolic volume and does not vary sharply as a function of depth. These observations presented the first direct evidence for a subcortical calcium transient in any egg, since the cytoplasm of the centrolecithal medaka egg can be regarded as exclusively cortical and earlier work on sea-urchin eggs had assumed that the calcium transient occurred throughout the cytoplasm (Whitaker & Steinhardt, 1982; Eisen et al., 1984). Clearly, we would expect that, if Ca^{2+} is to play a central role as a second messenger in activation of the cytoplasmic and nuclear responses to fertilization, its distribution should be widespread in the giant cell that is the egg, and the frog egg provided the first opportunity to confirm this (albeit in an indirect fashion; a more explicit study of this point would be useful).

In the egg of the medaka fish, the calcium transient at fertilization as revealed by the calcium-sensitive photoprotein, aequorin, propagates as a wave or ring of elevated $[Ca^{2+}]_i$ from the sperm entry point to its antipode (Gilkey et al., 1978). Similarly, a wave of cortical granule exocytosis and cortical reorganization is observed in fertilized Xenopus eggs (Hara & Tydeman, 1979; Takeichi & Kubota, 1984), giving rise to the expectation that here, too, the calcium transient at fertilization would propagate as a wave from the sperm entry point. Busa & Nuccitelli (1985) studied this by impaling eggs at two sites with as many calcium-selective electrodes; the electrode placed in the sperm-receptive 'animal' hemisphere (distinguished by its pigmentation from the 'vegetal' hemisphere, where sperm–egg fusion normally does not occur; Elinson, 1975) always reported the post-fertilization calcium transient before the electrode in the vegetal hemisphere, thus confirming that the calcium transient propagated as a wave as in medaka. Because the sperm entry point in Xenopus is readily visible as a localized accumulation of pigment granules, we could accurately determine the separation of each of these two electrodes from the sperm entry point and thus calculate the calcium wave's apparent propagation velocity as 9·7 ± 1·5 μm/sec at 22°C, quite similar to the 9–10 μm/sec propagation rate of the cortical granule exocytosis wave cited above. Significantly, the wave was essentially identical in magnitude and width at both extremes of the >1 mm diameter cell, demonstrating that an active propagation mechanism (and not simple diffusion) was at work. A similar, but much more slowly recovering, $[Ca^{2+}]_i$ transient has also been recorded in fertilized eggs of the painted frog, Discoglossus pictus (Nuccitelli et al., 1988).

Kubota et al. (1987) later confirmed the Xenopus egg wave's existence in a visually dramatic fashion with the photoprotein, aequorin, revealing a calcium wave sweeping the artificially activated Xenopus egg with a velocity of 7·8 ± 0·9 μm/sec, visually coincident with the wave of cortical granule exocytosis. The wave visualized by Kubota et al. (1987) differed slightly from that observed by Busa & Nuccitelli (1985) in that it was but 45 sec 'wide', compared with our own determination of a 10-min width. In large measure this must be an artefactual difference, since our electrodes can detect resting $[Ca^{2+}]_i$ levels and can observe the entirety of the calcium wave, while aequorin can only respond to $[Ca^{2+}]_i$ levels substantially above resting values and so can only visualize the narrow crest of the wide calcium wave. Additionally, however, an optical probe such as aequorin would be expected to report $[Ca^{2+}]_i$ values only from the extreme cortex of this opaque egg, while our electrode-based measurements were clearly subcortical, and this may have contributed to the observed difference to an undetermined extent. Indeed, it would be interesting to know whether and how the wave's characteristics differ between deep and cortical cytoplasm, since the latter possesses morphologically distinct specializations of the endoplasmic reticulum which have been proposed to play a role in wave initiation and/or propagation (Gardiner & Grey, 1983; Busa *et al.*, 1985).

A curious and as-yet unexplained characteristic of the electrode-determined calcium wave is its latency. Assuming a constant propagation velocity and projecting the wave back in time to the sperm entry point, we calculated that the propagated wave begins there a full minute after onset of the fertilization potential, and this was confirmed by a recording in which a calcium-selective electrode was fortuitously located only 20 μm from the sperm entry point but still took 64 sec to detect the onset of the wave. Unfortunately, such measurements cannot be taken as definitive, not least because our electrodes measured subcortical $[Ca^{2+}]_i$, while the wave must be assumed to originate in the cortex. Similar (but shorter) latencies have been detected in sea-urchin eggs with measurement techniques not subject to this problem (Eisen *et al.*, 1984). The issue of latency of wave initiation is therefore of some interest, especially as it may be relevant to the debate concerning the molecular mechanism of wave initiation (see, Swann & Whitaker, 1990; Jaffe, 1990).

Role of inositol trisphosphate in the calcium wave

While developmental cell physiologists were establishing the occurrence and roles of calcium transients in egg activation, somatic cell physiologists were elucidating the means by which certain calcium-mobilizing hormones elicit similar transients in a variety of other cell types, and thereby established the widespread role of the polyphosphoinositide cycle (PI cycle) and its product, *myo*-inositol 1,4,5-trisphosphate ($Ins(1,4,5)P_3$) in calcium-based cell signalling (for a recent review, see Berridge & Irvine, 1989). In light of its central role in triggering Ca^{2+} release from the endoplasmic reticulum into the cytosol in other cell types, $Ins(1,4,5)P_3$ (produced via hydrolysis of phosphatidylinositol 4,5-bisphosphate, or PIP_2) seemed a possible potential actor in the chain of events leading to Ca^{2+} wave propagation in the activating egg.

The demonstration by Turner *et al.* (1984) that fertilization evoked an immediate increase in flux through the PI cycle in sea-urchin eggs inspired numerous workers to consider this as a possible mechanism for wave initiation in eggs. Whitaker & Irvine (1984) soon demonstrated that microinjection of $Ins(1,4,5)P_3$ into unfertilized sea-urchin eggs triggered cortical granule exocytosis and intracellular alkalinization, two events in the programme of fertilization thought to be elicited by a $[Ca^{2+}]_i$ increase, and they inferred that eggs, like somatic cells, possess an $Ins(1,4,5)P_3$-sensitive calcium store which could provide the basis for the $[Ca^{2+}]_i$ transient at fertilization.

The first direct demonstration of such a calcium store in eggs again involved calcium-selective microelectrode recordings from frog eggs, iontophoretically injected with $Ins(1,4,5)P_3$ (Busa *et al.*, 1985). Such injections of sub-femtomole quantities of $Ins(1,4,5)P_3$ elicited propagated calcium waves which in their form, magnitude and propagation velocity were indistinguishable from the calcium wave seen at fertilization. This response to $Ins(1,4,5)P_3$ injection did not require Ca^{2+} in the external medium. Significantly, $Ins(1,4,5)P_3$ injections triggered not only a Ca^{2+} wave, but other early events of egg activation such as plasma membrane depolarization, cortical contraction and cortical granule exocytosis (Busa *et al.*, 1985; Picard *et al.*, 1985). The $[Ca^{2+}]_i$ response was highly specific for $Ins(1,4,5)P_3$: $Ins(1,4)P_2$ was an extremely inefficient activator, and no amount of fructose bisphosphate tested would mobilize Ca^{2+}. In contrast with the results of Irvine & Moor (1986) with sea-urchin eggs, we find that the synthetic isomer $Ins(2,4,5)P_3$ can also activate frog eggs, albeit with a much lower potency of about 12% (Busa, 1988; unpublished observations), indicating that formation of $Ins(1,3,4,5)P_4$ (a phosphorylation product of $Ins(1,4,5)P_3$, but not of $Ins(2,4,5)P_3$) is probably not required for calcium mobilization in the frog egg (see also Crossley *et al.*, 1988).

Various lines of evidence indicate that the $Ins(1,4,5)P_3$-sensitive calcium store in somatic cells is the endoplasmic reticulum (or a subset thereof). Similarly, an isolated microsomal fraction of sea urchin eggs co-sedimenting with endoplasmic reticulum markers releases calcium in response to

Ins(1,4,5)P$_3$ (Clapper & Lee, 1985). Recent elegant studies (Nuccitelli *et al.*, 1989) using centrifugally stratified (but otherwise intact) *Xenopus* eggs have demonstrated that iontophoretically injected Ins(1,4,5)P$_3$ elicits substantial calcium mobilization from a microsomal band, but not from bands comprised of mitochondria, lipids, or yolk platelets.

Employing a novel double-barrelled microelectrode (incorporating an Ins(1,4,5)P$_3$ iontophoresis barrel and an adjacent calcium-selective microelectrode), Busa *et al.* (1985) were able to distinguish between the local, direct response to injection of Ins(1,4,5)P$_3$ and the global $[Ca^{2+}]_i$ wave it elicits. By injecting subthreshold amounts we could observe Ins(1,4,5)P$_3$-mediated Ca^{2+} release (presumably from endoplasmic reticular stores) at the injection site without triggering a Ca^{2+} wave or activating the egg. Larger injections (or application of calcium ionophore) would trigger a Ca^{2+} wave, after which a local $[Ca^{2+}]_i$ response to injected Ins(1,4,5)P$_3$ could still be observed. This is of interest because once the egg is activated and has generated a Ca^{2+} wave, it is impossible by any means to trigger a second propagated Ca^{2+} wave; the activated egg loses its wave propagation mechanism but retains its Ins(1,4,5)P$_3$-sensitive calcium stores. This implies either that the Ins(1,4,5)P$_3$-sensitive calcium store is not responsible for the Ca^{2+} release constituting the propagated wave, or, if this store is involved, then some upstream component in the pathway regulating wave propagation does not return to its initial state following the wave.

In the case of the sea-urchin egg, Whitaker & Irvine (1984) originally proposed that the calcium wave is propagated via an autocatalytic action of the PI cycle based on the ability of micromolar $[Ca^{2+}]_i$ levels to activate phospholipase C: local activation of phospholipase C locally produces Ins(1,4,5)P$_3$, which locally elevates $[Ca^{2+}]_i$, which activates neighbouring phospholipase C molecules, thus propagating PI cycle activity and $[Ca^{2+}]_i$ increase across the cell (Fig. 1). To account for the observations described above, we proposed a different model for the frog egg: here, PI cycle activation at the site of sperm–egg fusion was proposed to initiate the calcium wave, while its further propagation was suggested to depend upon calcium-induced calcium release (CICR), a phenomenon best characterized in cardiac muscle (see, e.g., Fabiato & Fabiato, 1979) (Fig. 1). This model assumes that the calcium pool which supports CICR is distinct from the Ins(1,4,5)P$_3$-sensitive pool, and further that it is deactivated following the wave (much as the cortical endoplasmic reticulum disappears immediately behind the wave; Gardiner & Grey, 1983).

Unfortunately, definitive tests to distinguish between the models of Fig. 1 (and other possible models) have yet to be conceived. Some recent unpublished results, however, seem more in keeping with the autocatalytic PI cycle model than the CICR model of wave propagation in the frog egg. *Xenopus* eggs labelled with tritiated *myo*-inositol and artificially activated display a significant ($\sim 40\%$) decrease in label in PIP$_2$ (J. E. Ferguson & R. Nuccitelli, personal communication). The magnitude of this change is hard to account for by a model in which PI cycle activation occurs only at the sperm–egg fusion site, and suggests instead a cell-wide activation of PIP$_2$ hydrolysis. Such observations do not, however, address the question of whether global PI cycle activation is the basis or merely a consequence of calcium wave propagation, and the question of the mechanism of propagation will require further study.

Unanswered questions

Much remains to be learned concerning the mobilization of calcium during activation of the amphibian egg. Aside from the mystery of the mechanism of wave propagation just discussed, we still do not understand specifically how the spermatozoon triggers the calcium wave. If we assume that triggering involves PI cycle activation (Fig. 1), then the analogy of the spermatozoon as a hormone molecule naturally arises. Does the spermatozoon then bind to an integral membrane protein (a sperm receptor) which in turn activates a GTP-binding protein (see Jaffe, 1990), or is the first event of fertilization a direct fusion of sperm and egg membranes which permits a diffusible sperm component to be released into the egg cytoplasm (see Swann & Whitaker, 1990)? And what

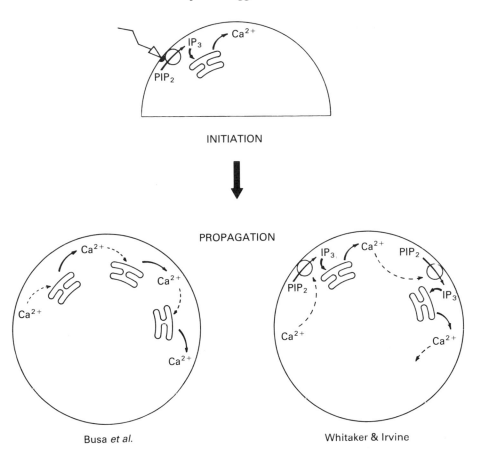

INITIATION

PROPAGATION

Busa *et al.*   Whitaker & Irvine

Fig. 1. The proposed mechanism of calcium wave initiation in the frog egg and two possible models of calcium wave propagation through eggs. Initiation of the wave at the sperm entry point is proposed to involve a localized activation of phospholipase C-mediated PIP_2 hydrolysis at that site, eliciting a localized Ins(1,4,5)P_3-mediated calcium release from internal stores. Further propagation of calcium release beyond the sperm entry point to yield a calcium wave has been suggested to involve either calcium-induced calcium release (Busa *et al.*, 1985) or autocatalytic PI cycle activity based on calcium-induced phospholipase C activation (Whitaker & Irvine, 1984).

is the role of the calcium wave, once triggered? Considerable evidence points to calcium as the primary messenger of egg activation (see Whitaker & Steinhardt, 1982, for review), yet recent data complicate this once simple view. *Xenopus* eggs can be artificially activated by treatment with phorbol esters (tumour-promoting analogues of diacylglycerol which, like diacylglycerol, activate protein kinase C) (Bement & Capco, 1989), even when $[Ca^{2+}]_i$ is clamped at low values by micro-injection of a calcium buffer such as BAPTA (Bement & Capco, 1990). Additionally, these workers observe that protein kinase C inhibitors such as sphingosine and H7 significantly inhibit calcium ionophore-induced activation. These observations are perhaps not surprising, given the well-established ability of protein kinase C activation to enhance cellular responses to calcium (Nishizuka, 1984). Quite surprising, however, is the observation that phorbol esters will trigger cortical granule exocytosis and early cleavage furrow formation in immature *Xenopus* oocytes (Bement & Capco, 1989), despite the fact that such immature cells are not activated by calcium ionophore (Charbonneau & Grey, 1984). Pharmacological effects such as these can be tricky to interpret, but they clearly underscore the fact that we are not yet ready to write the final chapter on amphibian egg activation.

References

Bement, W.M. & Capco, D.G. (1989) Activators of protein kinase C trigger cortical granule exocytosis, cortical contraction, and cleavage furrow formation in *Xenopus laevis* oocytes and eggs. *J. Cell Biol.* **108**, 885–892.

Bement, W.M. & Capco, D.G. (1990) Protein kinase C acts downstream of calcium at entry into the first mitotic interphase of *Xenopus laevis*. *Cell Regulation* **1**, 315–326.

Berridge, M.J. & Irvine, R.F. (1989) Inositol phosphates and cell signalling. *Nature, Lond.* **341**, 197–205.

Busa, W.B. (1988) Roles for the phosphatidylinositol cycle in early development. *Phil. Trans. R. Soc. Lond. B* **320**, 415–426.

Busa, W.B. & Nuccitelli, R. (1985) An elevated free cytosolic Ca^{2+} wave follows fertilization in eggs of the frog, *Xenopus laevis*. *Devl Biol.* **100**, 1325–1329.

Busa, W.B., Ferguson, J.E., Joseph, S.K., Williamson, J.R. & Nuccitelli, R. (1985) Activation of frog (*Xenopus laevis*) eggs by inositol trisphosphate. I. Characterization of Ca^{2+} release from intracellular stores. *J. Cell Biol.* **101**, 677–682.

Charbonneau, M. & Grey, R.D. (1984) The onset of activation responsiveness during maturation coincides with the formation of the cortical endoplasmic reticulum in oocytes of *Xenopus laevis*. *Devl Biol.* **102**, 90–97.

Clapper, D.L. & Lee, H.C. (1985) Inositol trisphosphate induces calcium release from nonmitochondrial stores in sea urchin egg homogenates. *J. biol. Chem.* **260**, 13947–13954.

Cross, N.L. (1981) Initiation of the activation potential by an increase in intracellular calcium in eggs of the frog, *Rana pipiens*. *Devl Biol.* **85**, 380–384.

Crossley, I., Swann, K., Chambers, E. & Whitaker, M. (1988) Activation of sea urchin eggs by inositol phosphates is independent of external calcium. *Biochem. J.* **252**, 257–262.

Cuthbertson, K.S.R., Whittingham, D.G. & Cobbold, P.H. (1981) Free Ca^{2+} increases in exponential phases during mouse oocyte activation. *Nature, Lond.* **294**, 754–757.

Eisen, A. & Reynolds, G.T. (1984) Calcium transients during early development in single starfish (*Asterias forbesi*) oocytes. *J. Cell Biol.* **99**, 1878–1882.

Eisen, A., Kiehart, D.P., Wieland, S.J. & Reynolds, G.T. (1984) Temporal sequence and spatial distribution of early events of fertilization in single sea urchin eggs. *J. Cell Biol.* **99**, 1647–1654.

Elinson, R.P. (1975) Site of sperm entry and a cortical contraction associated with egg activation in the frog *Rana pipiens*. *Devl Biol.* **47**, 257–268.

Fabiato, A. & Fabiato, F. (1979) Calcium and cardiac excitation-contraction coupling. *Ann. Rev. Physiol.* **41**, 473–484.

Gardiner, D.M. & Grey, R.D. (1983) Membrane junctions in *Xenopus* eggs: their distribution suggests a role in calcium regulation. *J. Cell Biol.* **96**, 1159–1163.

Gerhart, J.C. (1980) Mechanisms regulating pattern formation in the amphibian egg and embryo. In *Biological Regulation and Development*, Vol. 2, pp. 133–316. Ed. R. F. Goldberger. Plenum, New York.

Gilkey, J.C., Jaffe, L.F., Ridgway, E.B. & Reynolds, G.T (1978) A free calcium wave traverses the activating egg of the medaka, *Oryzias latipes*. *J. Cell Biol.* **76**, 448–466.

Hara, K. & Tydeman, P. (1979) Cinematographic observation of an "activation wave" (AW) on the locally inseminated egg of *Xenopus laevis*. *Wilhelm Roux' Archs Dev. Biol.* **186**, 91–94.

Hollinger, T.G. & Schuetz, A.W. (1976) "Cleavage" and cortical granule breakdown in *Rana pipiens* oocytes, induced by direct microinjection of calcium. *J. Cell Biol.* **71**, 395–401.

Irvine, R.F. & Moor, R.M. (1986) Micro-injection of inositol 1,3,4,5-tetrakisphosphate activates sea urchin eggs by a mechanism dependent on external Ca^{2+}. *Biochem. J.* **240**, 917–920.

Jaffe, L.A. (1990) First messengers at fertilization. *J. Reprod. Fert., Suppl.* **42**, 107–116.

Jaffe, L.F. (1983) Sources of calcium in egg activation: a review and a hypothesis. *Devl Biol.* **95**, 265–276.

Kubota, H.Y., Yoshimoto, Y., Yoneda, M. & Hiramoto, Y. (1987) Free calcium wave upon activation in *Xenopus* eggs. *Devl Biol.* **119**, 129–136.

Miyazaki, S., Hashimoto, N., Yoshimoto, Y., Kishimoto, T., Igusa, Y. & Hiramoto, Y. (1986) Temporal and spatial dynamics of the periodic increase in intracellular free calcium at fertilization of golden hamster eggs. *Devl Biol.* **118**, 259–267.

Nishizuka, Y. (1984) The role of protein kinase C in cell surface signal transduction and tumour promotion. *Nature, Lond.* **308**, 693–698.

Nuccitelli, R., Kline, D., Busa, W.B., Talevi, R. & Campanella, C. (1988) A highly localized activation current yet widespread intracellular calcium increase in the egg of the frog, *Discoglossus pictus*. *Devl Biol.* **130**, 120–132.

Nuccitelli, R., Ferguson, J. & Han, J.-K. (1989) The role of the phosphatidylinositol cycle in the activation of the frog egg. In *Mechanisms of Egg Activation*, pp. 215–230. Eds R. Nuccitelli, G. N. Cherr & W. H. Clark, Jr. Plenum, New York.

Picard, A., Giraud, F., Le Bouffant, F., Sladeczek, F., Le Peuch, C. & Doree, M. (1985) Inositol 1,4,5-triphosphate microinjection triggers activation, but not meiotic maturation in amphibian and starfish oocytes. *FEBS Lett.* **182**, 446–450.

Ridgway, E.B., Gilkey, J.C. & Jaffe, L.F. (1977) Free calcium increases explosively in activating medaka eggs. *Proc. natn. Acad. Sci. USA* **74**, 623–627.

Rink, T.J., Tsien, R.Y. & Warner, A.E. (1980) Free calcium in *Xenopus* embryos measured with ion-selective microelectrodes. *Nature, Lond.* **283**, 658–660.

Steinhardt, R.A., Epel, D., Carroll, E.J. & Yanagimachi, R. (1974) Is calcium ionophore a universal activator for unfertilised eggs? *Nature, Lond.* **252**, 41–43.

Steinhardt, R., Zucker, R. & Schatten, G. (1977) Intracellular calcium release at fertilization in the sea urchin egg. *Devl Biol.* **58,** 185–196.

Swann, K. & Whitaker, M.J. (1990) Second messengers at fertilization in sea-urchin eggs. *J. Reprod. Fert., Suppl.* **42,** 141–153.

Takeichi, T. & Kubota, H.Y. (1984) Structural basis of the activation wave in the egg of *Xenopus laevis. J. Embryol. exp. Morph.* **81,** 1–16.

Turner, P.R., Sheetz, M.P. & Jaffe, L.A. 1984) Fertilization increases the polyphosphoinositide content of sea urchin eggs. *Nature, Lond.* **310,** 414–415.

Tyler, A. (1941) Artificial parthenogenesis. *Biol. Rev.* **16,** 291–336.

Whitaker, M. & Irvine, R.F. (1984) Inositol 1,4,5-trisphosphate microinjection activates sea urchin eggs. *Nature, Lond.* **312,** 636–639.

Whitaker, M. & Steinhardt, R.A. (1982) Ionic regulation of egg activation. *Q. Rev. Biophys.* **15,** 593–666.

J. Reprod. Fert., Suppl. **42** (1990), 163–175

Cell signalling at fertilization of hamster eggs

S. Miyazaki

Department of Physiology, Tokyo Women's Medical College, Kawada-cho, Shinjuku-ku, Tokyo 162, Japan

Keywords: fertilization; intracellular calcium release; periodic Ca^{2+} transients; signal transduction; hamster egg

Sperm–egg interaction upon fusion causes an immediate change in membrane potential and a dramatic, transient increase in the intracellular calcium ion concentration ($[Ca^{2+}]_i$), as demonstrated in various eggs. These phenomena have been analysed extensively in sea-urchin eggs, and their significant roles in preventing polyspermy were elucidated during the 1970s (Jaffe, 1976; see review by Epel, 1978). For mammalian eggs, reports of studies on these phenomena first appeared in 1981; we reported recurring hyperpolarizations reflecting periodic Ca^{2+} transients at fertilization of golden hamster eggs (Miyazaki & Igusa, 1981a) and Cuthbertson *et al.* (1981), using luminescence measurement of loaded aequorin, demonstrated repeated Ca^{2+} rises in mouse eggs. Unfortunately, despite the accumulation of findings since then (see Miyazaki, 1988a, 1989), little has been mentioned about membrane potential changes and the $[Ca^{2+}]_i$ rise in review articles on mammalian fertilization. Recent advances in the study of transmembrane signalling and second messengers have led to the investigation of cell signalling in eggs at the early stage of fertilization. In this paper, I describe the physiological study of signal transduction during sperm–egg interaction that causes repetitive Ca^{2+} transients in hamster eggs.

Repetitive Ca^{2+} transients and the Ca^{2+} wave

Zona-free eggs are useful, because (1) microelectrode impalement is easier, (2) spermatozoa directly attach to the egg vitellus and so the timing of initiation of sperm–egg interaction can be identified, and (3) upon changing the external medium, or adding drugs, their effects on the zona pellucida are excluded. A disadvantage of zona-free eggs is that they are always polyspermic unless the number of applied spermatozoa is specially limited. Drugs and ions can be microinjected into eggs through glass micropipettes by applying either pressure or current pulses.

As shown in Fig. 1(a), the fertilizing hamster egg shows repetitive Ca^{2+} transients which are quite different from the Ca^{2+} rise in eggs of the sea urchin and other species. The egg for Fig. 1(a) was inseminated by a single spermatozoon (capacitated, acrosome-reacted spermatozoon) applied through a glass capillary. The egg was pre-injected with aequorin, and the luminescence generated by the aequorin–Ca^{2+} reaction was intensified and visualized as light spots on the TV monitor screen using a supersensitive TV camera system (a photon-counting imaging method: see Miyazaki *et al.*, 1986, for details). The luminescence intensity in the egg was obtained by processing the TV signal and is plotted from the time of sperm attachment to the egg surface (Fig. 1a).

The first Ca^{2+} rise occurs at about the time when flagellar motion of the spermatozoon stops 10–30 sec after the attachment, when the sperm and egg membranes are likely to fuse. The second and often the third response occurs at relatively short intervals of 40–50 sec and later responses occur at fairly constant intervals of 2–3 min. Each Ca^{2+} rise lasts for 12–18 sec and a series of Ca^{2+} transients persists for 1 h or even longer. The Ca^{2+} rise occurs in the entire egg in each response and is discrete in its occurrence. The series of Ca^{2+} rises declines in magnitude with time to a constant value (Fig. 1a). Direct measurement of $[Ca^{2+}]_i$ with a Ca^{2+}-sensitive microelectrode revealed that the peak $[Ca^{2+}]_i$ was 1–2 μM in the first 3 responses and 0·6–0·7 μM in later, constant responses (Igusa

(a) Aequorin luminescence

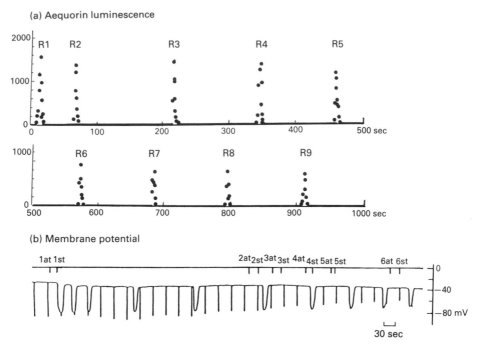

(b) Membrane potential

Fig. 1. Ca^{2+} transients and hyperpolarizing responses at fertilization of the hamster egg. **(a)** Ca^{2+} transients in a hamster egg with a single spermatozoon attached, shown by aequorin luminescence. Light intensity in a restricted area of the egg on the TV monitor screen was measured and is presented as arbitrary units on the ordinate. Abscissa: time after sperm attachment. R1–R9 = the 1st to 9th Ca^{2+} transient. (From Miyazaki et al., 1986.) **(b)** Membrane potential change during fertilization: 1–6 at = attachment of the 1st to 6th spermatozoon; 1–6 st = cessation of flagellar motion of the 1st to 6th spermatozoon. Constant current pulses of 0·5 nA and 0·3 sec duration were applied continuously to monitor changes in membrane conductance. (From Miyazaki, 1989.)

& Miyazaki, 1986). The $[Ca^{2+}]_i$ increase in the cytoplasm measured at the tip of the Ca^{2+} electrode was not significantly different between 3 and 30 µm from the egg surface (egg diameter, 70 µm).

With precise analysis of the spatial distribution of the Ca^{2+} rise using photon-counting imaging (see Fig. 2), a propagating increase in $[Ca^{2+}]_i$ was observed in the first response, starting from the sperm attachment site and spreading over the entire egg within 3–6 sec (Fig. 2a) (Miyazaki et al., 1986). This 'Ca wave' has been demonstrated in eggs of other species (see review by Jaffe, 1985). In hamster eggs the Ca^{2+} rise spreads so fast that propagating exocytosis of cortical granules may be hard to detect. Interestingly, the spreading Ca^{2+} rise in hamster eggs is repeated in the second and sometimes the third response, starting from the same focus, but spreading more rapidly ($\sim$2 sec) (see Fig. 2b & c). In subsequent responses, $[Ca^{2+}]_i$ increases almost synchronously in the whole egg within 1 sec. It therefore seems that the early 2–3 Ca^{2+} transients are triggered by the fused spermatozoon whilst succeeding periodic Ca^{2+} rises are built up, based on characteristics of Ca^{2+} dynamics in the inseminated egg.

Hyperpolarizing responses as a fertilization potential

An advantage of the hamster egg is that an increase in $[Ca^{2+}]_i$ can be monitored by a hyperpolarizing response in membrane potential using a conventional microelectrode inserted into the egg.

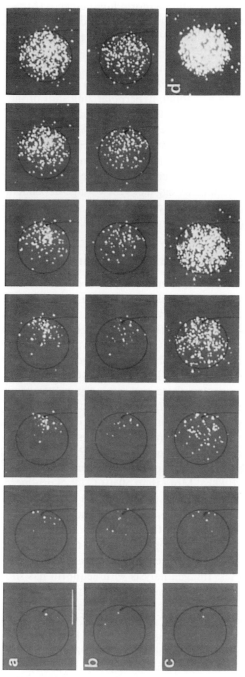

Fig. 2. Ca^{2+} waves at fertilization of the hamster egg and InsP$_3$-induced Ca^{2+} release in the unfertilized hamster egg. **(a–c)** Propagating Ca^{2+} rise in the first (a), second (b) and third (c) responses in a hamster egg with a spermatozoon attached (on the right), shown by aequorin luminescence using photon counting imaging. For each image light spots on the TV monitor screen were accumulated from their appearance. The video-recorded, processed image was played back, and video frames were stopped and then photographed (from left to right) at 0, 0·5, 1·0, 1·5, 2, 2·5 and 3 sec (up to 2 sec in c). The scale bar indicates 50 μm. (From Miyazaki *et al.*, 1986.) **(d)** Ca^{2+} release induced by injection of InsP$_3$ into an unfertilized egg in Ca-free medium. All light spots were accumulated during the time indicated by the horizontal bar in Fig. 3(b). (After Miyazaki, 1988b.)

The hyperpolarizing response is caused by a Ca^{2+}-activated K^+ conductance (Miyazaki & Igusa, 1982) and there is an exact one-to-one correspondence between a hyperpolarization response and a Ca^{2+} transient, as confirmed by combined recording of membrane potential and $[Ca^{2+}]_i$ with a Ca^{2+} electrode (Igusa & Miyazaki, 1986) or with aequorin luminescence (Miyazaki, 1988b).

As shown in Fig. 1(b), an inseminated hamster egg exhibits periodic hyperpolarization responses starting from the resting potential (-30 to -20 mV) and reaching -80 to -70 mV. The egg in Fig. 1(b) is an example of a polyspermic egg. Multiple spermatozoa cause more frequent hyperpolarization responses at intervals of 50–60 sec. The responses do not always coincide with the stopping of flagellar motion of additional spermatozoa (see 'st' in Fig. 1b). The series of hyperpolarization responses is superimposed on a gradual, hyperpolarizing shift of the resting potential to about -40 mV (Fig. 1b). The shift seems to be caused by a gradual increase in the basal $[Ca^{2+}]_i$, which was detected with the Ca^{2+} electrode (Igusa & Miyazaki, 1986).

Hyperpolarization responses were neither observed before insemination nor induced by non-acrosome-reacted spermatozoa which do not stop their flagellar motion on the egg surface. The fertilization potential of the hamster egg therefore consists of hyperpolarization responses superimposed on the hyperpolarizing shift. The hamster egg lacks the voltage-dependent block of sperm–egg fusion (Miyazaki & Igusa, 1982), unlike the sea-urchin egg (Jaffe, 1976). Therefore, the biological significance of a hyperpolarization response (the membrane potential change itself) is unknown.

G protein-mediated repetitive Ca^{2+} transients

Whitaker & Irvine (1984) first demonstrated that microinjection of inositol 1,4,5-trisphosphate ($InsP_3$) into unfertilized sea-urchin eggs causes the elevation of the fertilization membrane that is caused by Ca^{2+}-dependent exocytosis of cortical granules. Fertilization of sea-urchin eggs causes hydrolysis of phosphatidylinositol 4,5-bisphosphate (PIP_2) of the plasma membrane, which cleaves into $InsP_3$ and diacylglycerol (DAG) (Ciapa & Whitaker, 1986). Turner *et al.* (1986) have shown evidence that signal transduction in fertilized sea-urchin eggs involves activation of a GTP-binding protein (G protein) leading to PIP_2 breakdown and $InsP_3$-induced Ca^{2+} mobilization from intracellular stores. For sea-urchin eggs, however, there are some arguments against the idea that spermatozoa activate a G protein (Swann *et al.*, 1987; Swann & Whitaker, 1990).

Microinjection of GTP or its hydrolysis-resistant analogue GTPγS [guanosine-5'-0-(3-thiotriphosphate)] into unfertilized hamster eggs by pressure causes repetitive hyperpolarization responses (see Fig. 3a). With a critical concentration of GTP or GTPγS (200 μM or 12 μM in the egg, respectively, assuming uniform distribution), a single Ca^{2+} transient was elicited with a delay of 160–200 sec after injection (Miyazaki, 1988b). More than 50 μM GTPγS produced repetitive Ca^{2+} transients with an initial delay of 25–40 sec to the first response and intervals of 45–60 sec between responses. GTPγS-induced hyperpolarization responses (Fig. 3a) and sperm-induced hyperpolarization responses (Fig. 1b) have some similarities: both of them are generated at similar intervals, associated with a hyperpolarizing shift of the resting potential, and they are blocked by GDPβS at similar concentration ranges (see below). A difference between them is seen in the more noticeable attenuation of GTPγS-induced responses. Image analysis with aequorin has shown that the first 2–3 responses induced by injection of GTPγS are associated with the Ca^{2+} rise in the entire egg whilst succeeding Ca^{2+} rises occur at a localized area of the cytoplasm (Miyazaki, 1988b). Possible desensitization in GTPγS-induced hyperpolarization responses are described below.

The activation of G proteins by GTPγS should be antagonized by GDPβS [guanosine-5'-0-(2-thiodiphosphate)], the hydrolysis-resistant analogue of GDP. Pre-injection of GDPβS dose-dependently inhibited the occurrence of hyperpolarization responses induced by subsequent injection of GTPγS (Miyazaki, 1988b). Treatment with 7 mM-GDPβS in the egg completely blocked the response induced by 70 μM-GTPγS, without affecting the $InsP_3$-induced hyperpolarization response (see below for $InsP_3$-induced response). Similarly, pre-injection of GDPβS inhibited the occurrence of responses induced by subsequent insemination. Treatment with 8 mM-GDPβS

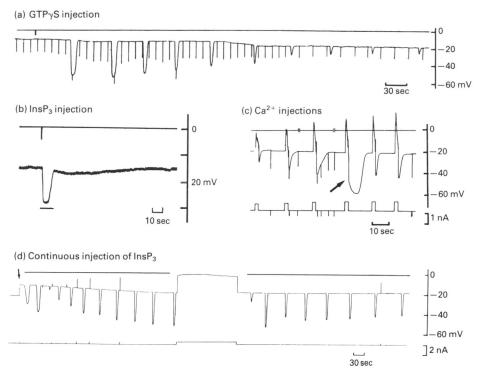

Fig. 3. Hyperpolarizing responses (HRs) induced by injection of GTPγS, InsP$_3$ or Ca^{2+}. **(a)** HRs induced by injection of GTPγS (2 mM in the pipette or 70 μM in the egg) into an unfertilized hamster egg. Rapid injection was performed at the moment indicated by the vertical bar in the top trace. **(b)** An HR induced by injection of InsP$_3$ (2·4 μM in the pipette or 48 nM in the egg) in Ca^{2+}-free medium, recorded from the egg for Fig. 2(d). (a & b from Miyazaki, 1988b.) **(c)** A regenerative HR (arrow) induced by iontophoretic injection of Ca^{2+} with current pulses. (From Igusa & Miyazaki, 1983.) **(d)** Continuous injection of InsP$_3$ through a micropipette with a blunt tip. The membrane potential decreased upon impalement of the pipette (arrow), but the reduced membrane resistance gradually recovered, resulting in an increase in the amplitude of HRs. Repetitive HRs were blocked by backing current (positive d.c. current) to prevent the leakage of InsP$_3$ from the pipette. (From Swann *et al.*, 1989.)

completely blocked hyperpolarization responses in an egg to which several spermatozoa successively fused.

These findings suggest that the induction of repetitive Ca^{2+} transients by spermatozoa involves activation of a G protein. When GDPβS was injected during a series of hyperpolarization responses, succeeding responses were blocked (Miyazaki, 1988b). This suggests that the periodic Ca^{2+} rises upon fertilization require persistent activation, not transient activation as a trigger, of the G protein-mediated process. It seems that InsP$_3$ is persistently produced to cause repeated Ca^{2+} rises.

The putative G protein is not sensitive to pertussis toxin or cholera toxin. Neither toxin (injected into the egg) stimulated or inhibited the occurrence of the GTPγS-induced or sperm-induced Ca^{2+} transients (Miyazaki, 1988b).

Second messenger- and third messenger-induced Ca^{2+} release

InsP$_3$-induced Ca^{2+} release

InsP$_3$ is well known to be a second messenger in various cells, inducing Ca^{2+} release from non-mitochondrial stores, possibly from the smooth endoplasmic reticulum (Berridge & Irvine, 1984).

A single, rapid injection of InsP$_3$ into unfertilized hamster eggs by pressure causes an immediate Ca^{2+} transient, as demonstrated by a hyperpolarization response (Fig. 3b) and by aequorin luminescence (Fig. 2d). The Ca^{2+} transient is induced in an approximately all-or-none fashion, spreads over the entire egg within 1 sec and lasts for 13–18 sec (Miyazaki, 1988b). The minimum effective concentration of InsP$_3$ was 80 nM in the injection pipette or 2 nM in the egg (if calculated under the assumption of uniform distribution in the cytoplasm). The Ca^{2+} transient was elicited in Ca-free medium (Figs 2d & 3b), indicating that InsP$_3$ induces Ca^{2+} release from intracellular stores in the hamster egg.

A single injection of InsP$_3$ by pressure usually produces only one Ca^{2+} release. Additional (and much smaller) Ca^{2+} rises were generated only when an extremely high concentration of InsP$_3$ was used (Miyazaki, 1988b). Injected InsP$_3$ may be immediately turned over. InsP$_3$ can be injected repeatedly in the same egg by current pulses. When the iontophoretic injection current of InsP$_3$ (negative pulse) is increased little by little, a Ca^{2+} release was induced in an all-or-none fashion (Miyazaki *et al.*, 1988). Once a Ca^{2+} release is produced, the same injection pulse causes little or no Ca^{2+} release for 90–120 sec; that is, there is a refractory period for induction of Ca^{2+} release. It is likely that the refractory period corresponds to the time required to recharge Ca^{2+} stores.

InsP$_3$ can be applied continuously by leakage through the injection pipette having a blunt tip. As shown in Fig. 3(d), periodic Ca^{2+} transients are produced at intervals of 40–60 sec, despite continuous application of InsP$_3$ (Swann *et al.*, 1989). The series of Ca^{2+} rises are blocked by applying a backing current (positive d.c. current) to the injection pipette (Fig. 3d). Thus, continuous production of InsP$_3$ would cause periodic Ca^{2+} release, such as is seen at fertilization.

Ca^{2+}-dependent Ca^{2+} release

It is known that Ca^{2+} itself can induce Ca^{2+} release from sarcoplasmic reticulum (SR) (see Endo, 1977). A Ca^{2+}-induced Ca^{2+} release mechanism has been assumed in fertilized eggs as a base for propagating Ca^{2+} release (see Jaffe, 1985). When Ca^{2+} is iontophoretically injected from a CaCl$_2$-filled micropipette into an unfertilized hamster egg by applying positive current pulses, a regenerative hyperpolarizing response is induced with an apparent threshold (see Fig. 3c) (Igusa & Miyazaki, 1983). This response was observed even in Ca-free medium. The regenerative response is followed by a refractory period of 60–120 sec of similar length to the refractory period of IP$_3$-induced Ca^{2+} release. During the refractory period, the injected Ca^{2+} *per se* causes only a small hyperpolarization due to a Ca^{2+}-activated K$^+$ conductance (see Fig. 3c), and the conductance increase at the peak of the hyperpolarization is roughly proportional to the injection current of Ca^{2+}. Therefore, the regenerative hyperpolarization response is thought to be a non-linearly enhanced increase in [Ca^{2+}]$_i$ induced by Ca^{2+}; that is, there exists an apparent Ca^{2+}-induced Ca^{2+}-release mechanism in the hamster egg.

Caffeine sensitizes Ca^{2+}-induced Ca^{2+} release from smooth endoplasmic reticulum and thereby induces Ca^{2+} release in muscle cells (Endo, 1977), but it is ineffective in hamster eggs (S. Miyazaki & T. Fujiwara, unpublished). The endoplasmic reticulum membrane in hamster eggs may possess Ca^{2+}-dependent Ca channels different from those in the SR membrane, or Ca^{2+} release may occur when Ca^{2+} stores are overloaded to a critical level upon application of Ca^{2+} into the cytoplasm.

Propagating Ca^{2+} release

A possible signalling pathway in the fertilized hamster egg is schematized in Fig. 6, based on the findings described above. InsP$_3$ is probably the second messenger and the initial inducer of Ca^{2+} release around the sperm attachment site. Released Ca^{2+} in turn would operate as the third messenger to cause Ca^{2+} release from neighbouring Ca^{2+} stores, and successive Ca^{2+}-induced Ca^{2+} release will result in a propagating Ca^{2+} release. With *Xenopus* eggs, Busa *et al.* (1985) have shown evidence for two functionally different Ca^{2+} pools mobilized by different effectors: InsP$_3$

causes a Ca^{2+} release from one type of pool and then major Ca^{2+} release occurs from another type of pool. In sea-urchin eggs, Swann & Whitaker (1986) have shown evidence for a recycling process between Ca^{2+}-stimulated production of $InsP_3$ and $InsP_3$-induced Ca^{2+} release as a base for the propagating Ca^{2+} wave. Further study is necessary for characterization of Ca^{2+} stores functioning at fertilization of hamster eggs.

The second and third Ca^{2+} transients are similar to the first one in peak $[Ca^{2+}]_i$ amplitude and propagating nature. They occur with relatively short intervals (shorter than the refractory period in response to $InsP_3$ or Ca^{2+} injection). The second and third responses may be due to Ca^{2+} release from reserve Ca^{2+} stores mobilized by the strong stimulus of spermatozoa. Possible mechanisms for the later periodic Ca^{2+} transients will be discussed below.

Feedback inhibition through protein kinase C

Another second messenger, diacylglycerol, derived from polyphosphoinositide (PI) turnover activates protein kinase C (PKC) (Nishizuka, 1984). One of the effects of PKC is thought to be to operate as part of a negative feedback loop regulating G protein-mediated Ca^{2+} transients in hamster eggs (Swann *et al.*, 1989). As shown in Fig. 3(a), GTPγS-induced hyperpolarization responses decline in amplitude with time. When GTPγS is iontophoretically injected into unfertilized hamster eggs by current pulses, a large hyperpolarization response appears with a delay of about 80 sec (mean value) after injection, followed by a series of much smaller responses (see Fig. 4a). Additional injection of GTPγS does not compensate for the attenuation in the series of hyperpolarization responses, indicating an apparent desensitization of the GTPγS-induced Ca^{2+} transients.

GTPγS-induced hyperpolarization responses were inhibited by the PKC activator phorbol 12-myristate 13-acetate (TPA) (100 nM) (see Fig. 4b) and the synthetic diacylglycerol, 1,2-dioctanoyl-glycerol (diC8) (250 nM) (Swann *et al.*, 1989). Conversely, the PKC inhibitor sphingosine (10 μM) enhanced the number of large hyperpolarization responses after GTPγS injection (Fig. 4c). Since TPA and sphingosine do not affect $InsP_3$-induced responses, a reasonable target for the inhibition by PKC is the putative G protein (Fig. 6). The apparent desensitization in GTPγS-induced Ca^{2+} transients could be due to PKC phosphorylating the G protein that controls PI turnover (Sagi-Eisenberg, 1989).

We have found that serotonin (5-hydroxytryptamine, 5-HT) is an agonist that produces receptor-mediated Ca^{2+} transients through activation of a G protein and PI turnover in hamster eggs (Miyazaki *et al.*, 1990). 5-HT-induced Ca^{2+} transients undergo desensitization as well, and they are inhibited by TPA and enhanced by sphingosine. Therefore, it cannot be ruled out that PKC also phosphorylates and inhibits the signalling function of receptors (see Cochet *et al.*, 1984; Lynch *et al.*, 1985).

Does this feedback inhibition operate at fertilization of hamster eggs? When eggs were inseminated in the presence of 100 nM-TPA, hyperpolarization responses were significantly reduced in frequency but not completely blocked (Swann *et al.*, 1989). Neither TPA nor sphingosine substantially affected the frequency or size of hyperpolarization responses once they had been initiated in inseminated eggs, when they were applied during the series of rhythmic hyperpolarization responses. Fertilizing spermatozoa may stimulate G protein-mediated Ca^{2+} transients in a way that precludes feedback inhibition by PKC.

Possible mechanism of cyclic Ca^{2+} transients

Models of $[Ca^{2+}]_i$ oscillation

The cyclic Ca^{2+} transients at fertilization of hamster eggs are of general interest, because there are a number of recent papers reporting that various cells respond to neurotransmitters, hormones

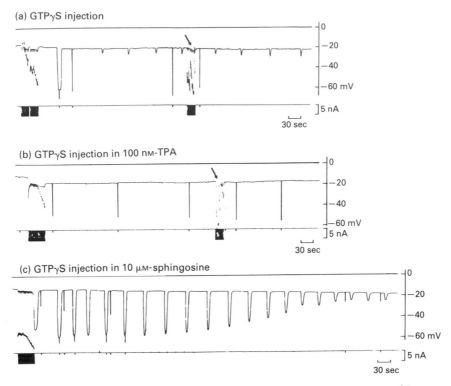

Fig. 4. Effects of protein kinase C activator and inhibitor on GTPγS-induced Ca^{2+} transients. **(a)** HRs induced by iontophoretic injection of GTPγS by current pulses (20 pulses of 5 nA, 1·5 sec duration). Additional injection of GTPγS had no effect (arrow). Constant small pulses were applied to monitor membrane conductance. **(b)** Complete inhibition of GTPγS-induced HRs by 100 nM-TPA. **(c)** Augmentation of the series of HRs by 10 μM-sphingosine. (From Swann *et al.*, 1989.)

and growth factors with oscillatory increases in $[Ca^{2+}]_i$ (see reviews by Berridge *et al.*, 1988; Berridge & Galione, 1988), although the functional significance of the oscillation is still unknown. As to the mechanism of $[Ca^{2+}]_i$ oscillation, Woods *et al.* (1987) have proposed receptor-controlled oscillations, based on their work on hepatocytes. In this model, the production of $InsP_3$ oscillates in such a way that an increase of $InsP_3$ is curtailed by a negative feedback loop through PKC onto the G protein. Berridge & Galione (1988) have proposed a second messenger-controlled oscillator model in which $InsP_3$ is supplied continuously and keeps an $InsP_3$-sensitive pool discharged while the Ca^{2+}-sensitive pool takes up Ca^{2+} ions mobilized from the $InsP_3$-sensitive pool and then undergoes Ca^{2+}-induced Ca^{2+} release, resulting in $[Ca^{2+}]_i$ oscillation. The cyclic Ca^{2+} rises in hamster eggs seem to be partly explained by the latter model rather than the former, because continuous production of $InsP_3$ through activation of a G protein is suggested by our data and continuous application of $InsP_3$ causes periodic Ca^{2+} rises. Sphingosine augmented the series of GTPγS-induced hyperpolarization responses but did not change the time course of each response (see Fig. 4c) (Swann *et al.*, 1989), suggesting that feedback inhibition by PKC does not operate in 'each' Ca^{2+} transient in hamster eggs, unlike the situation in hepatocytes.

Contribution of Ca^{2+} influx

An interesting feature of repetitive Ca^{2+} transients in hamster eggs is their dependence on extracellular Ca^{2+}. Periodic hyperpolarization responses induced by spermatozoa are reduced in

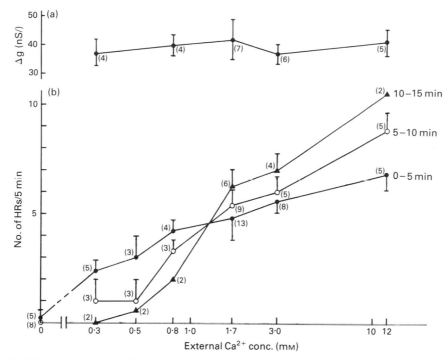

Fig. 5. Effect of external Ca^{2+} concentration on conductance increase at the peak of HR (a) and on the frequency of HRs (b) in inseminated hamster eggs. Eggs were inseminated in standard medium ($[Ca^{2+}]_o - 1.7$ mM) and then solutions with different $[Ca^{2+}]$ were perfused. The numbers of HRs occurring in every 5 min after start of the perfusion are plotted as mean $\pm$ s.d. against the logarithm of $[Ca^{2+}]_o$. Parentheses indicate the number of eggs examined. (After Igusa & Miyazaki, 1983.)

frequency and eventually stop after perfusion of Ca^{2+}-free medium (Igusa & Miyazaki, 1983). GTPγS-induced responses disappear in Ca^{2+}-free medium except the first 1–2 (Miyazaki, 1988b). Hyperpolarization responses are produced by continuous application of InsP$_3$ but only the initial 3–4 responses occur in Ca-free medium (S. Miyazaki & T. Fujiwara, unpublished). Thus, to maintain repeated Ca^{2+} rises, Ca^{2+} influx across the plasma membrane is necessary. Hyperpolarization responses are not due to periodic, transient increase in Ca^{2+} influx, because conductance increase and reversal potential of each response were little affected by the change in external Ca^{2+} concentration $[Ca^{2+}]_o$ (see Fig. 5a) (Igusa & Miyazaki, 1983). Therefore, later responses are also due to periodic Ca^{2+} releases from internal stores. Ca^{2+} influx affects the frequency of Ca^{2+} release (or interval between each Ca^{2+} release) in inseminated hamster eggs (Fig. 5b). The interval was shortened by increasing Ca^{2+} influx upon elevating $[Ca^{2+}]_o$ or applying hyperpolarizing current to make the electrical driving force for Ca^{2+} greater (Igusa & Miyazaki, 1983). Conversely, the interval was prolonged by decreasing Ca^{2+} influx upon reducing $[Ca^{2+}]_o$, or adding Ca^{2+} antagonists (Co^{2+} or Mn^{2+}), or applying depolarization to make the driving force smaller.

Linkage of Ca^{2+} influx to internal Ca^{2+} release

We have proposed a model, based on a linkage of continuous Ca^{2+} influx to internal Ca^{2+} release (Igusa & Miyazaki, 1983). Continuous Ca^{2+} influx will set the basal $[Ca^{2+}]_i$ at slightly above the resting level, as reflected in the hyperpolarizing shift of the resting potential and measured with the Ca^{2+} electrode. It is probable that a substantially elevated $[Ca^{2+}]_i$ level is a prerequisite for repeated Ca^{2+} release, both for the stimulation of Ca^{2+} release and the recharging of Ca^{2+} stores. The elevated basal $[Ca^{2+}]_i$ will be a stimulus to Ca^{2+}-induced Ca^{2+} release. Interestingly, the threshold iontophoretic injection current for Ca^{2+}-induced regenerative hyperpolarization responses in fertilized eggs is about one-tenth of that necessary in unfertilized eggs (Igusa & Miyazaki, 1983): the sensitivity of Ca^{2+}-induced Ca^{2+} release becomes much higher after insemination. Another possibility is that elevated Ca^{2+} level may sensitize $InsP_3$-induced Ca^{2+} release. It has been shown that $InsP_3$-induced Ca^{2+} release is remarkably enhanced by submicromolar concentrations of Ca^{2+} in smooth muscle (Iino, 1987). On the other hand, the elevated $[Ca^{2+}]_i$ level will facilitate the rate of reloading of the Ca^{2+} stores. Consequently, the interval between Ca^{2+} releases will depend on the basal $[Ca^{2+}]_i$ and, therefore, the rhythm of periodic hyperpolarization responses will be affected by Ca^{2+} influx.

At present, the pathway for Ca^{2+} through the egg plasma membrane is unknown. The hamster egg possess voltage-gated Ca channels that generate a Ca-dependent action potential (Miyazaki & Igusa, 1981b). Since hyperpolarization responses occur even when the egg is hyperpolarized below $-100\,mV$ (Miyazaki & Igusa, 1982), the putative Ca channel responsible for continuous Ca influx may be different from the voltage-gated Ca channel.

The Ca^{2+} extrusion system is also important for formation of repetitive Ca^{2+} rises. The recovery phase of the hyperpolarization response is 10 sec or less. A Ca^{2+} pump has been suggested to exist because of the prolongation of the recovery phase of the hyperpolarization response, caused by the application of La^{3+}, high $[Ca^{2+}]_o$ or quercetin (Georgiou et al., 1987) or by raising external pH (Georgiou et al., 1988). A Na^+–Ca^{2+} exchange system has also been suggested by the observation that there is a prolonged recovery phase upon removal of external Na^+ (Igusa & Miyazaki, 1983; Georgiou et al., 1988).

Biological significance of repetitive Ca^{2+} transients

The fused spermatozoon is the stimulus for generating periodic Ca^{2+} rises in hamster eggs. If we assume that ligand–receptor binding occurs at fertilization to activate a G protein and the subsequent signalling pathway (illustrated in Fig. 6), as is usually the case in other cells, a receptor for spermatozoa or a substance derived from spermatozoa must be postulated to exist in the egg plasma membrane. For example, substance X in the sperm plasma membrane may be a ligand of the receptor (Fig. 6). However, such a 'sperm receptor' has not so far been identified. Alternatively, an unknown substance Y in the sperm plasma membrane may activate G proteins of the egg (Fig. 6), or substance Z may come from the spermotozoon through cytoplasmic continuity and activate G proteins and other signalling pathway(s) in such a way that precludes feedback inhibition by PKC. These points remain to be elucidated.

Early Ca^{2+} transients are undoubtedly significant for the exocytosis of cortical granules of the egg, the released substance of which modifies the zona pellucida and prevents polyspermy (see review by Yanagimachi, 1988). Cortical granule breakdown lasts for 5–15 min in mouse and hamster eggs (Fukuda & Chang, 1978), and so several Ca^{2+} transients seem to be responsible for the block to polyspermy in these species.

It has been suggested that Ca^{2+} ions play a major role in activation and development of mammalian eggs (see Whittingham, 1980). There are various means of inducing parthenogenetic activation of mammalian eggs. Apropos intracellular Ca^{2+}, application of Ca ionophore A23187 causes activation of hamster eggs in Ca^{2+}- and Mg^{2+}-free medium (Steinhardt et al., 1974). Microinjection of Ca^{2+} into unfertilized mouse eggs can induce egg activation and development up to the blastocyst stage in vitro (Fulton & Whittingham, 1978). The initiation of the series of Ca^{2+} transients in inseminated hamster eggs has been shown to be related to egg activation, defined as the resumption of the second meiosis and the formation of a second polar body, which occurs about 1 h after insemination (Igusa et al., 1983). Ca^{2+} ions may be involved in the release of eggs from the meiotic block; for example, by inactivation of cytostatic factors which prevent meiotic resumption, as has been suggested for amphibians (Masui et al., 1977; Maller & Krebs, 1977).

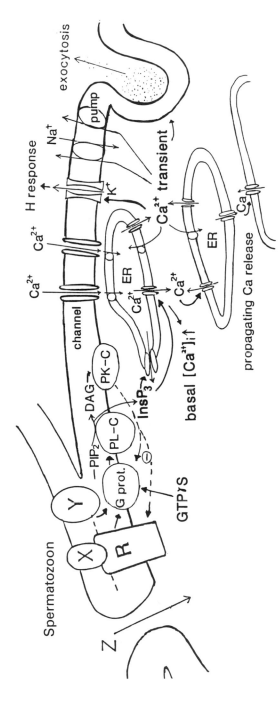

Fig. 6. A schematic drawing of the possible mechanism of cell signalling in the fertilized hamster egg. Thick arrowhead indicates each action. Thin arrowhead indicates movement of ions or substances. R: receptor; PL-C: phospholipase C. Other abbreviations are given in the text.

The function of the long series of Ca^{2+} transients is still largely unknown. The elevated basal $[Ca^{2+}]_i$ level may also be important. Ca^{2+} ions may function in the formation of pronuclei, or may regulate the cytoskeletal systems that incorporate the entire spermatozoon into the egg cytoplasm or in the migration of sperm and egg pronuclei.

There are therefore many important points unsolved in cell signalling at fertilization in mammalian eggs, and these will stimulate further studies in the future.

I thank Dr Y. Igusa, Dr N. Yamashita, Dr N. Hashimoto, Dr Y. Yoshimoto, Dr T. Kishimoto, Dr Y. Hiramoto, Dr Y. Katayama, Dr T. Fujiwara and Dr K. Swann for collaboration in these studies; and Miss Y. Tsuno for preparing the manuscript.

References

Berridge, M.J. & Galione, A. (1988) Cytosolic calcium oscillators. *FASEB J.* **2**, 3074–3082.

Berridge, M.J. & Irvine, R.F. (1984) Inositol trisphosphate, a novel second messenger in cellular signal transduction. *Nature, Lond.* **312**, 315–321.

Berridge, M.J., Cobbold, P.H & Cuthbertson, K.S.R. (1988) Spatial and temporal aspects of cell signalling. *Physiol. Trans. Royal Soc. B*, **320**, 325–343.

Busa, W.B., Ferguson, J.E., Joseph, S.K., Williamson, J.R. & Nuccitelli, R. (1985) Activation of frog (*Xenopus laevis*) egg by ionositol trisphosphate. I. Characterization of Ca^{2+} release from intracellular stores. *J. Cell Biol.* **101**, 677–6832.

Ciapa, B. & Whitaker, M.J. (1986) Two phases of inositol polyphosphate and diacylglycerol production at fertilization. *FEBS Lett.* **195**, 347–351.

Cochet, C., Gill, G.N., Meidenhelder, J., Cooper, J.A. & Hunter, T. (1984) C-kinase phosphorylates the epidermal growth factor receptor and reduces its epidermal growth factor-stimulated tyrosine kinase activity. *J. biol. Chem.* **259**, 2553–2558.

Cuthbertson, K.S.R., Whittingham, D.G. & Cobbold, P.H. (1981) Free Ca^{2+} increases in exponential phases during mouse oocyte activation. *Nature, Lond.* **316**, 541–542.

Endo, M. (1977) Calcium release from the sarcoplasmic reticulum. *Physiol. Rev.* **57**, 71–108.

Epel, D. (1978) Mechanisms of activation of sperm and egg during fertilization of sea urchin gametes. *Curr. Top. Devl Biol.* **12**, 185–261.

Fukuda, Y. & Chang, M.C. (1978) The time of cortical granule breakdown and sperm penetration in mouse and hamster eggs inseminated *in vitro*. *Biol. Reprod.* **19**, 261–266.

Fulton, B.P. & Whittingham, D.G. (1978) Activation of mammalian oocytes by intracellular injection of calcium. *Nature, Lond.* **273**, 149–151.

Georgiou, P., Bountra, C., McNiven, A.I. & House, C.R. (1987) The effect of lanthanum, quercetin and dinitrophenol on calcium-evoked electrical responses in hamster eggs. *Q. J. exp. Physiol.* **72**, 227–241.

Georgiou, P., House, C.R., McNiven, A.I. & Yoshida, S. (1988) On the mechanism of a pH-induced rise in membrane potassium conductance in hamster eggs. *J. Physiol., Lond.* **402**, 121–138.

Igusa, Y. & Miyazaki, S. (1983) Effects of altered extracellular and intracellular calcium concentration on hyperpolarizing responses of the hamster egg. *J. Physiol., Lond.* **340**, 611–632.

Igusa, Y. & Miyazaki, S. (1986) Periodic increase of cytoplasmic calcium in fertilized hamster eggs measured with calcium-sensitive electrodes. *J. Physiol., Lond.* **377**, 193–205.

Igusa, Y., Miyazaki, S. & Yamashita, N. (1983) Periodic hyperpolarizaing responses in hamster and mouse eggs fertilized with mouse sperm. *J. Physiol., Lond.* **340**, 633–647.

Iino, M. (1987) Calcium dependent inositol trisphosphate-induced calcium release in the guinea-pig taenia caeci. *Biochem. Biophys. Res. Commun.* **142**, 47–52.

Jaffe, L.A. (1976) Fast block to polyspermy in sea urchin eggs is electrically mediated. *Nature, Lond.* **261**, 68–71.

Jaffe, L.F. (1985) The role of calcium explosions, waves and pulses in activating eggs. In *Biology of Fertilization*, pp. 127–165. Eds C. B. Metz & A. Monroy. Academic Press, New York.

Lynch, C.J., Charest, R., Bocckino, S.B., Exton, J.H. & Blackmore, P.F. (1985) Inhibition of hepatic adrenergic effects and binding by phorbol myristate acetate. *J. biol. Chem.* **260**, 2844–2851.

Maller, J.L. & Krebs, E.G. (1977) Progesterone stimulated meiotic cell division in *Xenopus* oocytes. *J. biol. Chem.* **252**, 1712–1718.

Masui, T., Meyerhof, P.G., Miller, M.A. & Wasserman, W.J. (1977) Roles of divalent cations in maturation and activation of vertebrate oocytes. *Differentiation* **9**, 49–57.

Miyazaki, S. (1988a) Fertilization potential and calcium transients in mammalian eggs. *Dev. Growth & Differ.* **30**, 603–610.

Miyazaki, S. (1988b) Inositol 1,4,5-trisphosphate-induced calcium release and guanine nucleotide-binding protein-mediated periodic calcium rises in golden hamster eggs. *J. Cell Biol.* **106**, 345–354.

Miyazaki, S. (1989) Signal transduction of sperm-egg interaction causing periodic calcium transients in hamster eggs. In *Mechanisms of Egg Activation*, pp. 231–246. Eds R. Nuccitelli, G. N. Cherr & W. H. Clark Jr. Plenum Press, New York.

Miyazaki, S., Hashimoto, N., Yoshimoto, Y., Kishimoto, T., Igusa, Y. & Hiramoto, Y. (1986) Temporal and spatial dynamics of the periodic increase in intracellular free calcium at fertilization of golden hamster eggs. *Devl Biol.* **118**, 259–267.

Miyazaki, S. & Igusa, Y. (1981a) Fertilization potential in golden hamster eggs consists of recurring hyper-polarizations. *Nature, Lond.* **290**, 702–704.

Miyazaki, S. & Igusa Y. (1981b) Ca-dependent action potential and Ca-induced fertilization potential in golden hamster eggs. In *The Mechanism of Gated Calcium Transport Across Biological Membranes*, pp. 305–311. Eds S. T. Ohnishi & M. Endo. Academic Press, New York.

Miyazaki, S. & Igusa Y. (1982) Ca-mediated activation of a K current at fertilization of golden hamster eggs. *Proc. natn. Acad. Sci. USA* **79**, 931–935.

Miyazaki, S., Igusa Y. & Swann, K. (1988) Involvement of GTP-binding protein in signal transduction of sperm-egg interaction at fertilization of hamster eggs. *J. Physiol. Soc. Japan* **50**, 390, abstr.

Miyazaki, S., Katayama, Y. & Swann, K. (1990) Synergistic activation by serotonin and GTP analogue and inhibition by phorbol ester of cyclic Ca^{2+} rises in hamster eggs. *J. Physiol., Lond.* **426**, 209–227.

Nishizuka, Y. (1984) The role of protein kinase C in cell surface signal transduction and tumour promotion. *Nature, Lond.* **308**, 693–698.

Sagi-Eisenberg, R. (1989) GTP-binding proteins as possible targets for protein kinase C action. *Trends Biochem. Sci.* **14**, 355–357.

Steinhardt, R.A., Epel, D., Caroll, E.J. & Yanagimachi, R. (1974) Is calcium ionophore a universal activator for unfertilized eggs? *Nature, Lond.* **252**, 41–43.

Swann, K. & Whitaker, M.J. (1986) The part played by inositol trisphosphate and calcium in the propagation of the fertilization wave in sea urchin eggs. *J. Cell Biol.* **103**, 2333–2342.

Swann, K. & Whitaker, M.J. (1990) Second messengers at fertilization in sea-urchin eggs. *J. Reprod. Fert., Suppl.* **42**, 141–153.

Swann, K., Ciapa, B. & Whitaker, M.J. (1987) Cellular messengers and sea urchin egg activation. In *Molecular Biology of Invertebrate Development*, pp. 45–69 Ed. A. O'Conner. Alan R. Liss, New York.

Swann, K., Igusa, Y. & Miyazaki, S. (1989) Evidence for an inhibitory effect of protein kinase C on G-protein mediated repetitive calcium transients in hamster eggs. *EMBO J.* **8**, 3711–3718.

Turner, P.R., Jaffe, L.A. & Fein, A. (1986) Regulation of cortical vesicle exocytosis in sea urchin egg by inositol 1,4,5-trisphosphate and GTP-binding protein. *J. Cell Biol.* **102**, 70–76.

Whitaker, M.J. & Irvine, R.F. (1984) Inositol 1,4,5-trisphosphate microinjection activates sea urchin eggs. *Nature, Lond.* **312**, 636–639.

Whittingham, D.G. (1980) Parthenogenesis in mammals. In *Oxford Reviews of Reproductive Biology*, Vol. 2, pp. 162–221, Ed. C. A. Finn. Clarendon Press, Oxford.

Woods, N.M., Cuthbertson, K.S.R. & Cobbold, P.H. (1987) Agonist-induced oscillations in cytoplasmic free calcium concentrations in single rat hepatocytes. *Cell Calcium* **8**, 79–100.

Yanagimachi, R. (1988) Mammalian fertilization. In *The Physiology of Reproduction*, pp. 135–185. Eds E. Knobil & J. Neill. Raven Press, New York.

J. Reprod. Fert., Suppl. **42** (1990), 177–188

Printed in Great Britain
© 1990 Journals of Reproduction & Fertility Ltd

Cortical granules and the cortical reaction in mammals

D. G. Cran and C. R. Esper*

*Department of Molecular Embryology, AFRC Institute of Animal Physiology and Genetics Research, Babraham, Cambridge CB2 4AT, UK and *Departamento de Reproducao Animal, Faculdade de Ciencias Agrarias e Veterinarias de Jaboticabal, Rodovia Carlos Tonanni KM5, 18.870 Jaboticabal—SP, Brazil*

Keywords: cortical granules; exocytosis; polyspermy block; distribution; second messengers

Introduction

Fertilization is a unique event, being the only interaction between two totally dissimilar cell types leading to a cascade of events which results in the production of a new individual. Its fundamental importance has resulted in a closely orchestrated series of changes to allow species recognition, passage of the spermatozoa across the oocyte investments, penetration into the maternal cytoplasm and the subsequent triggering of intracellular processing leading to embryogenesis.

An obligatory feature in the animal kingdom is the necessity of re-establishing diploidy at fertilization (a certain degree of polyploidy may be tolerated in certain plant species). Embryos which contain more than a diploid complement generally die at an early stage of development and, as can be seen in man, even the presence of an extra chromosome will lead to severe abnormalities. There have developed, therefore, mechanisms whereby only a single male and female pronucleus undergo syngamy. Not surprisingly, the strategy employed varies considerably from group to group. In the fishes, for example, passage of more than one spermatozoon across the micropyle of the chorion is limited by the size of the constriction next to the plasma membrane (Fig. 1a). Following fusion of the fertilizing spermatozoon with the egg, ingrowth of cytoplasm into the channel prevents any subsequent entry. In organisms such as the sea urchin and *Xenopus* (Fig. 1b), after passage of the spermatozoon into the maternal cytoplasm, there is a massive and immediate exocytosis of the cortical granules, the result of which is the formation and elevation of the fertilization envelope which prevents the ingress of any further spermatozoa. In birds, polyspermy is the rule with multiple sperm entry (Fig. 1c) and selection occurs between the male pronuclei by an undetermined mechanism resulting in the fusion of only one with that of the female. The remainder of the pronuclei degenerate. In organisms with external fertilization, the oocyte comes into contact with vast numbers of spermatozoa; an immediate protective response by the oocyte is obligatory to ensure that polyspermy does not ensue. In mammals, in addition to protective mechanisms resulting from direct oocyte/sperm interactions, there is a major selection of numbers as the sperm population passes up the female reproductive tract. Thus only a very small fraction of the original ejaculate survives to encounter the oocyte/cumulus complex and at this point any spermatozoa which have spontaneously undergone the acrosome reaction are further eliminated from the survivors. In the hamster (Cummins & Yanagimachi, 1982) it has been estimated that the sperm/oocyte ratio does not exceed 1 until some 50% of the oocytes have been fertilized. Thus the potential of several spermatozoa simultaneously arriving at the oolemma *in vivo* is quite low. However, like the above examples, the potential for polyspermic fertilization remains and a mechanism to prevent this has therefore evolved which, as in the sea urchin, involves the exocytosis of cortical granules and subsequent interaction with the zona pellucida (Fig. 1d).

Exocytosis is generally divided into two types, continuous and triggered. The former consists of the non-regulated turnover of membranes and release into the extracellular space of proteins and extracellular matrix components. This form of release exists in most cell types (Baker, 1988) but there is little information relating to the oocyte. However, it would be surprising if some form of release were not occurring to regulate its immediate environs. The latter form of exocytosis takes place when a change in response to a particular signal is required. For example, the action of several hormones falls into this category and it is clear that the triggering of the cortical reaction and that of the acrosome reaction are examples of an exocytotic event taking place in response to

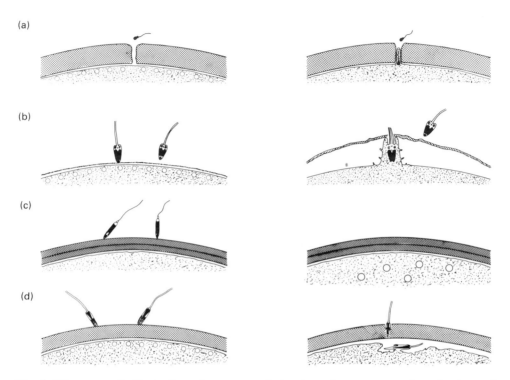

(a)

(b)

(c)

(d)

Fig. 1. Diagrammatic illustration of sperm–egg fusion in various groups and mechanisms of establishing a block to polyspermy. **(a)** Fish: sperm entry is through the micropyle which, following shedding of the cortical granules (circles), is subsequently blocked by an outgrowth of cytoplasm (right). **(b)** Sea urchin: after sperm entry the cortical granules are shed, resulting in the elevation of the fertilization envelope (dotted area) which prevents further ingress. **(c)** Birds: spermatozoa pass through the outer and inner envelopes surrounding the egg, resulting in multiple penetration. The large circles throughout the cytoplasm denote pronuclei. Establishment of monospermy takes place at an intracellular level. **(d)** Mammals: after passage of a spermatozoon through the zona pellucida, cortical granules (circles) are released with the result that it becomes refractory to further penetration (in some mammals the block may be established at the level of the vitelline membrane).

an external stimulus. These two exocytotic events are unusual, however, in that they take place only once in the lifetime of the cell. In most receptor-stimulated secretion of this type the product is continually being produced and thus, within limits, the cell can be repeatedly stimulated. During fertilization, as a result of the interaction of the two cell types, a series of signals is produced to ensure the realization of developmental potential (see Fig. 2), of which the stimulation of the cortical reaction is one end point. This review will centre on the cortical granules, and will examine the nature of their distribution within the oocyte and putative mechanisms leading to their fusion with the plasma membrane following interaction between the spermatozoon and the oocyte plasma membrane.

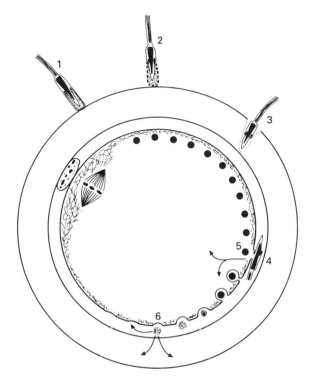

Fig. 2. Diagram demonstrating points at which cellular interactions or signalling mechanisms are operative during fertilization. (1) Sperm binding to the zona pellucida. (2) Induction of the acrosome reaction. (3) Penetration through the zona pellucida. (4) Fusion with the plasma membrane and induction of intracellular primary signalling mechanisms. (5) Production of second messengers leading to cortical granule exocytosis and general activation. (6) Interaction of the constituents of cortical granules on the zona pellucida and plasma membrane.

Techniques for examining cortical granules

The study of cortical granules in the mammal raises problems not encountered in lower species. In particular, the detection of exocytosis is particularly difficult. In the sea urchin it has been unambiguously shown that the elevation of the fertilization envelope is a direct consequence of granule shedding. In the mammal, changes in the zona pellucida are more subtle and are not associated with any overt structural change. Since the end result of the loss of the granules is to prevent sperm binding and passage through the zona, this has been used as a parameter of exocytosis (e.g. Endo *et al.*, 1987) as has the increased resistance to protease digestion (Colonna *et al.*, 1989) the so-called 'zona hardening'. While these approaches have their uses, they nevertheless may be several steps removed from the primary event and there is the potential for confusion with other factors. Of particular relevance is the fact that, since they are a measure of an end point, they are unable to determine a partial reaction such as might be necessary for the assemblage of dose–response curves. For such information there is no recourse but to examine the granules directly. There are essentially four approaches that can be made to visualize the granules which measure between 200 and 600 nm in diameter.

(1) The most unambiguous approach is to use electron microscopy and this has been used on several occasions (Nicosia *et al.*, 1977; Cran & Cheng, 1985). However, this procedure suffers from the major drawback that the experimental turnover time is long and only a relatively few oocytes

can be examined for any particular treatment. It has the advantage, however, that structural details and the identification of different populations can be ascertained unambiguously. (2) Of more wide-spread application is the use of 1-μm sections of oocytes embedded in a variety of resins (Cran *et al.*, 1988). Providing the granules can be easily visualized and not obscured by cytoplasmic inclusions, as in the pig, data from a considerable number of oocytes can readily be obtained. (3) Both these preceding techniques suffer from the deficiency that only a small proportion of the cell is examined and, therefore, there exists the possibility that fluxes in distribution and patterns of arrangement may be overlooked. In a few species such as the hamster it is possible to examine the granules directly (Cran & Moor, 1990). Indeed it was this observation, first made by Austin (1956), that led to the suggestion that the loss of the granules into the perivitelline space followed by their interaction with the zona pellucida was involved in the establishment of monospermy. It is perhaps surprising that this facility of observation has not been exploited more frequently, since quantitative and distributive information is readily obtainable. However, such an approach is only of use for oocytes which have a clear cytoplasm against which the granules stand out in contrast. (4) Perhaps the approach that will have most universal applicability is that which exploits the binding properties of certain lectins to the granules (Cherr *et al.*, 1988; Lee *et al.*, 1988; Ducibella *et al.*, 1988). These authors have shown that various lectins, in particular *Lens culinaris* (LCA), bind specifically to the granules which can therefore be visualized by a fluorescent marker and such a procedure has been utilized in a quantitative study by Ducibella *et al.* (1988). Confidence in this approach can be had from the observation that quantitative data on the hamster using the 'direct' method (see below) is in a similar range as that obtained for the mouse using the lectins. It is to be hoped that in the next few years a similar approach will prove to be fruitful in a wider range of species, particularly in the large domestic species.

Changes in distribution and number during oocyte maturation

In most cell types in which there is secretion of granules there is a constant movement of the granules from the site of production (usually the Golgi) to the plasma membrane. The situation in the oocyte is very different. During oocyte growth there is a period of intense metabolic activity during which the granules are formed and during which the vast majority move from the Golgi to lie within a few micrometres of the plasma membrane. Following the cessation of growth there is relatively little change either biochemically or structurally in the oocyte (Moor & Warnes, 1978; Cran *et al.*, 1980) while the ovarian follicle within which the oocyte lies undergoes profound change in terms of structural dynamics and steroidogenic capacity. This phase can last from several days to weeks. It is only during the final maturation phase stimulated by the preovulatory surge of luteinizing hormone (LH) that the oocyte is triggered again into intense activity which touches upon every aspect of the cell's function from transcriptional activity to nuclear breakdown (Warnes *et al.*, 1977). A fundamental aspect of these changes is major cytoplasmic remodelling (Zamboni, 1970; Szollosi *et al.*, 1972; Kruip *et al.*, 1983; van Blerkom & Runner, 1984; Cran, 1985; Hyttel *et al.*, 1986a, b, 1987) which affects every organelle in the cell and is particularly evident in the domestic species (e.g. cow, pig, sheep). A characteristic of the distributive changes in the organelles is a generalized centripetal movement such that immediately before ovulation the subplasmalemmar region is relatively free of organelles. The exception to this, of course, is the cortical granules which remain in the cortex. It would seem, therefore, that they are maintained under a positional restraint. Several lines of evidence would suggest that there is some kind of interaction between them and the peripheral cytoskeleton. Actin filaments lying under the plasma membrane have been observed in oocytes from a wide variety of species (Burgess & Schroeder, 1977; Bryan, 1982; Whitaker & Baker, 1983; Battaglia & Gaddum-Rosse, 1986; Le Guen *et al.*, 1989). In the sea urchin there is also suggestive evidence of a direct connection with filamentous structures (Chandler, 1988). In the mammal such direct information is, however, lacking. The presence of a very tight spatial relationship between the plasma membrane and the cortical granules is strikingly demonstrated by the change in the distribution of the organelles following centrifugation. If oocytes are subjected to centrifugal force the membranous organelles will become stratified into clear zones (Cran, 1987). Such a procedure has been used to identify pronuclei before microinjection of foreign DNA and, although there is some subsequent cell death, a fairly high percentage survive (Wall *et al.*, 1985). A constant feature of oocytes treated in this way is the positional maintenance of the cortical granules under the oolemma. Treatment with drugs that alter the cytoskeleton (e.g. nocodazole and cytochalasin) followed by mild centrifugation results in an almost total discharge of the granules (Cran, 1987), thus implying some kind of functional relationship between the two structural elements.

It has been shown that actin represents some 2% of total cellular protein in the oocyte and egg (Longo, 1987) and that there is a very low rate of actin synthesis in the maturing oocyte of the mouse (Wassarman, 1983). Several workers have shown that, at least in the mouse, there is a thickening of the cortical actin layer over the meiotic spindle (Nicosia *et al.*, 1977; Maro *et al.*, 1984; Reima & Lehtonen, 1985; Longo, 1987) and that these changes and those in plasma membrane glycoproteins are induced by the formation of the chromosomes (Longo & Chen, 1985; van Blerkom & Bell, 1986). Longo (1987) has shown that there is a marked reduction in the thickness of the actin layer in cortical regions other than that adjacent to the nucleus during oocyte maturation. Since the amount of actin remains constant the conclusion is drawn that there is a redistribution which is accompanied by a change in the receptors for actin. Such a finding would account for the centrifugal movement of the cortical granules during maturation providing that there is, indeed a physical link with the granules (Fig. 3). Further evidence for this last point has come from work by Le Guen *et al.* (1989) on sheep eggs. They have shown that, in ovulated oocytes which presumably are fully mature and capable of undergoing a cortical reaction in response to a fertilizing spermatozoon, the granules are closely apposed to the plasma membrane but treatment with cytochalasin D, apart from causing profound internal structural changes to the cytoplasm also, in some regions, induces a loss of association with the plasma membrane. Their evidence would suggest that there is a continued direct relationship between the actin filaments and the plasma membrane and it is reasonable to suggest that a change in the nature of this association following fertilization is one factor that leads to membrane fusion.

(a)   (b)

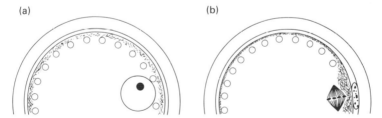

Fig. 3. Suggested mechanism accounting for the centrifugal movement of cortical granules during maturation. **(a)** Immature oocyte. The entire edge of the oocyte is surrounded by a subplasmalemmar layer of actin microfilaments which interact with the cortical granules. **(b)** Mature oocyte. There has been a redistribution of actin with a resulting thinning in the non nuclear cortex. This results in a close apposition between the granules and plasma membrane.

Not only are there major distributive events taking place during maturation in a radial direction, but following the formation of the first meiotic spindle there are changes of a circumferential nature. In immature oocytes, i.e. fully grown with a germinal vesicle, no preferential distribution of the granules with regard to the location of the nucleus can be detected although there are regions of higher and lower density which may be a reflection of their origin from the Golgi. The cow is a marked example of this, with large clumps of granules extending many micrometres into the peripheral cytoplasm being present. In the hamster, during maturation there is a marked change in the pattern of distribution as seen by tagging with fluorescently labelled LCA lectin (Cran & Moor, 1990). At about the time of the telophase/anaphase transition there is, in the region of the dividing nucleus, a marked clustering of the granules with, in addition, clumping suggestive of fusion of the granule contents following exocytosis into the perivitelline space. At an ultrastructural level a large organelle population largely consisting of mitochondria intermingled with cortical granules may be seen surrounding the nucleus. In addition Okada *et al.* (1986) have shown that in this species there is premature exocytosis of the granules at about this time. The temporal correlation of the increase of supranuclear actin alluded to above and these changes in the organelle population would suggest that there is likely to be a functional relationship.

In metaphase II oocytes of the hamster and the mouse there is a clear polarity of the granule population with respect to the metaphase spindle, the granules being almost totally excluded from this region. In the mouse this was first described by Nicosia *et al.* (1977) who indicated, on the basis of ultrastructural studies, that the cortical granule-free zone (CGFZ) occupied some 25% of the total oocyte surface area. This figure has recently been revised upward by Ducibella *et al.* (1988) who, examining entire populations of granules, have indicated that the figure is likely to be nearer 40%. In the hamster the CGFZ is considerably smaller at between 8 and 14%. How is this considerable loss achieved? There are clearly three possibilities. Firstly, during abstriction of the first polar body granules are lost from the parent cell. Polar bodies, however, contain relatively few granules and this loss could not account for such a large decrease. Secondly, as demonstrated by Okada *et al.* (1986) and Nicosia *et al.* (1977), premature exocytosis at about the time of polar body abstriction may occur. Thirdly, Ducibella *et al.* (1988) has found that subsequent to the formation of the CGFZ in the mouse there is approximately a 25% increase in granule concentration in the granule-containing zonae. It would appear, therefore, that in this species premature loss (Nicosia *et al.*, 1977) and circumferential migration may play a predominant role in creating this phenomenon. In the hamster the situation differs. In spite a clearing of a tenth of the surface area there is an increase in the total population of the cortical granules per oocyte (D. G. Cran, unpublished observations), suggesting that while the processes described for the mouse may also be taking place in this species there is continued production of granules as has been described for a number of other species (Sathananthan & Trounson, 1982a, b; Cran & Cheng, 1985).

Mechanisms of induction of the cortical reaction

Many treatments have been shown to induce the loss of cortical granules. These include electrical stimulation (Zamboni *et al.*, 1976; Gulyas, 1980), the use of ionophores (Steinhardt *et al.*, 1974; Gwatkin *et al.*, 1976), and the direct injection of calcium into the oocyte (Fulton & Whittingham, 1978). In addition, various other treatments have been found to change the status of the cortical granules in mammals such as the induction of hypothermia (Gulyas, 1976), addition of cations to the outside of the plasma membrane (Gwatkin *et al.*, 1976) and treatment with cryoprotectants (Schalkoff *et al.*, 1989). All these treatments, however, are highly artificial and while they are unlikely to provide much indication as to likely signalling mechanisms leading to the cortical reaction *in vivo*, may nevertheless throw some light on the process of exocytosis.

There is good evidence implicating an increase in cytoplasmic calcium to micromolar levels with exocytosis in a wide range of systems (Jackson & Crabb, 1988). This is also the case with mammalian oocytes, and the release of calcium may be elegantly demonstrated by preloading zona-free oocytes with aequorin and subsequently allowing them to undergo fertilization. Release of calcium may be visualized as emission photons of light. When this is carried out for the hamster it is clear that waves of calcium release are produced following fertilization (Miyazaki *et al.*, 1986; Igusa & Miyazaki, 1986; Miyazaki, 1990). The first transients take the form of a propagating wave starting at the point of sperm attachment and spreading around the circumference of the cell. There then follows subsequent waves which do not necessarily bear a direct spatial relationship to the point of attachment of the spermatozoon.

If it is accepted that the release of free calcium into the cytoplasm is the main driving force for exocytosis (and many other intracellular processes) it is necessary to ask what is the nature of the interactions between the spermatozoon and the egg which leads to the stimulation of the production of intracellular second messengers, what are these messengers and what is the structural basis of the calcium stores.

Sperm–oolemma interaction

Two possible, not necessarily mutually exclusive, interactions between the fertilizing spermatozoon and the oocyte surface leading to the initiation of the signalling mechanisms may be envisaged. In the first hypothesis receptor binding occurs between the post-equatorial segment of the spermatozoa and the oolemma, leading to the activation of specific intracellular G proteins and subsequently that of second messengers. In the second, the spermatozoon carries cytoplasmic factors into the oocyte which activate the system independent of the plasma membrane. Evidence for either of these possibilities in the mammal is as yet far from conclusive. Species specificity in the majority of mammals studied is conferred by interaction between the sperm surface and a moiety of the integral zona protein ZP3 (Bleil & Wassarman, 1980). At the level of the plasma membrane, while some degree of species specificity still exists, it is much less than with the zona (Yanagimachi, 1988). This lack of specificity is exemplified by the use of the zona-free hamster test for the penetrating ability of foreign spermatozoa. However, this does not necessarily rule out the possibility of some form of generalized membrane/membrane interaction, possibly unmasked by acrosomal enzymes bound to the surface of the spermatozoon as has been suggested by Yanagimachi (1988). Some further support for this idea has come from work by Kline *et al.* (1988) for *Xenopus*. These workers managed to insert receptors for serotonin and acetylcholine into the plasma membrane of the oocyte. Subsequent challenge with the agonists resulted in elevation of the fertilization membrane. Thus, while it would seem that stimulation of an artificial receptor results in the initiation of the cortical reaction in this species it remains to be seen how widespread it is.

Due to the nature of fertilization in the sea urchin with the rapid formation of the acrosomal process, it has been an attractive proposition that direct insertion of a sperm-associated compound is involved in activation (Swann & Whitaker, 1990). It is rather difficult to imagine how this could take place in the mammal since fusion and entry into the oocyte cytoplasm appears to be a rather gradual process without, from a morphological point of view, there being any evidence for 'injection' of material into the maternal cytoplasm. As far as we are aware only 2 reports have appeared providing direct evidence that the passage of a sperm-associated factor into oocyte cytoplasm results in activation (Stice & Robl, 1989; Swann & Whitaker, 1990). These workers have shown that a soluble protein or protein-associated fraction from homogenized spermatozoa which is not acrosomal in origin and is heat- and trypsin-sensitive will, when microinjected, activate oocytes. Further, this compound will only act intracellularly, having no effect when applied externally. It is clearly not going to be a simple matter to unravel this problem of the initial stages of activation and represents one of the challenges for the future.

Intracellular signal transduction

Over the past 5 years or so there has been much information on the role of phosphoinositides and derived metabolites, particularly inositol (1,4,5)-trisphosphate ($InsP_3$), as intracellular second messengers, and the chemistry and probable functions in an idealized cell of the phosphoinositide cycle have been exhaustively reviewed elsewhere (Berridge & Irvine, 1984, 1989). In a series of experiments on hamster oocytes Miyazaki (1988, 1990) has demonstrated that injection of $InsP_3$ at an intracellular concentration as low as 2 nM leads to a transient depolarization of the plasma membrane which is directly related to a single episodic release of Ca^{2+} into the cytoplasm. At very high (6 μM) intracellular levels there was evidence of continuing pulsatile release. GTP-γ-S, a non-hydrolysable G protein analogue, also induced calcium release but in this case spikes of release, at regular intervals continued for some time following injection, a situation very similar to that pertaining after fertilization (Miyazaki, 1988). In an attempt to relate InsP$_3$ injection, Ca^{2+} release and induction of the cortical reaction, Cran *et al.* (1988) injected hamster and sheep oocytes with various concentrations of InsP$_3$ and GTP-γ-S. As with a variety of invertebrate systems (e.g. Turner *et al.*, 1986), it was found that both compounds induced the cortical reaction. However, while the levels of GTP-γ-S required to induce the reaction were similar to those for Ca^{2+} release, those of InsP$_3$ were 200–400 times higher. This has now been repeated using whole cell preparations which are more accurate than counts derived from sections (D. G. Cran, unpublished observations). Using this approach it was possible to detect an effect of injection of InsP$_3$ at levels of approximately 10 nM$_i$, but while there was a significant reduction, cortical granule numbers were still some 60% of those of the control. This compares with a full cortical reaction in which numbers are reduced to 20% or lower of those of the control (D. G. Cran, unpublished observations). Kurasawa *et al.* (1989) have recently demonstrated in the mouse that injection of IP$_3$ inhibits fertilization and induces an electrophoretic shift of ZP2 to ZP2$_f$, a change which is also associated with fertilization (Bleil *et al.*, 1981). An effect was found at an intracellular concentration of some 10 nM but as with cortical granule exocytosis a maximal change was not evoked until a dosage some 10-fold higher was used. In mice the block to polyspermy is not established until some 8 min or so following fertilization (Gwatkin *et al.*, 1973; Schmell *et al.*, 1983) and loss of cortical granules in response to microinjection of InsP$_3$ takes some 5 min (Cran, 1989). It would seem therefore that, unlike the sea urchin in which exocytosis takes place in an almost explosive manner, exocytosis in mammals is likely to be a more gradual process. Since InsP$_3$ appears to be directly involved in Ca^{2+} release in oocytes it is tempting to suggest that a mechanism similar to that suggested by Berridge & Irvine (1989) and others in which Ca^{2+} may feed back onto recharged Ca^{2+} pools to release further Ca^{2+} and/or also provide continued stimulation of phospholipase C and thus induce a self-propagating system (Miyazaki, 1990).

The hydrolysis of phosphoinositide bisphosphate leads to the production of two second messengers—InsP$_3$ and diacylglycerol, the latter activating protein kinase C. Several reports have implicated protein kinase C in the regulation of exocytosis (Baker, 1984; Creutz *et al.*, 1983, 1985). In addition, Endo *et al.* (1987) have shown that the phorbol esters 12-O-tetradecanol phorbol 13-acetate (TPA) and 4β-phorbol didecanoate (4β-PD) and the diacylglycerol *sn*-1,2-dioctanoyl glycerol (diC$_8$) when applied to mouse oocytes will inhibit sperm penetration but not binding. In addition, there is a shift in mobility of ZP2 to ZP2$_f$. The implication from these results is that activation of protein kinase C is having an effect, either directly or indirectly on cortical granule exocytosis and therefore on the block to polyspermy. We have conducted a similar series of experiments on the hamster looking both at effects of phorbol esters and diacylglycerol on fertilization and the cortical reaction (Fig. 4). There was a dose-dependent effect of both phorbol myristate acetate (PMA) and 4β-PD on exocytosis which was mirrored by similar changes in the capacity to undergo fertilization. At 10 nM of the two phorbol esters binding was indistinguishable from that of the controls but at 100 nM it (and fertilization) were almost completely abolished. These results were supported by the observation that the inactive alpha stereoisomer of 4β-PD was completely without effect (Fig. 4). The diacylglycerol diC$_8$ resulted in a decrease in both cortical granule number and fertilization of only some 20%, a result which would not be expected if addition to the medium resulted in the activation of protein kinase C to a similar extent as that found after treatment with phorbol esters. In this regard treatment with 500 μM-diC$_8$ resulted in complete loss of fertilization and binding (C. R. Esper & D. G. Cran, unpublished observations). It is possible that the disparity between the two sets of data may be explicable in terms of a limited capacity of diC$_8$ to traverse the plasma membrane, resulting in suboptimal intracellular levels. There have been a number of reports indicating the existence of an interaction between the two signalling pathways (see Berridge, 1986). However, it is too early to know what is the likely physiological relevance for the oocyte.

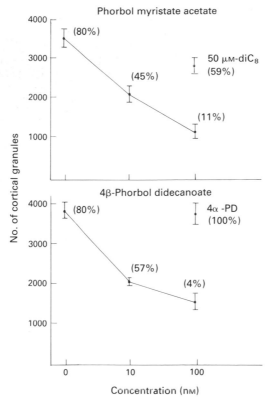

Fig. 4. Effect of phorbol esters and the diacylglycerol diC_8 on cortical granule number and percentage of fertilization (parentheses) of mature hamster oocytes.

Intracellular calcium stores

As we have seen, a recurring theme during fertilization and early embryonic development is the release of calcium from non-mitochondrial stores. What is the nature of these stores? To date we know very little regarding their nature in oocytes and eggs and indeed knowledge regarding location and function in somatic cells is still limited. During maturation in domestic species such as the cow, sheep and pig, depots of what has the morphology of smooth endoplasmic reticulum are found close to the plasma membrane (Kruip *et al.*, 1983; Cran, 1985). This clearly would be an appropriate site for Ca^{2+} release immediately following fertilization. In the hamster, after incubation with the Ca^{2+}-binding fluorescent dye, fluo-3, there is an accumulation of fluorescence in discrete patches throughout the cytoplasm (D. G. Cran, unpublished observations) (Fig. 5). All such fluorescence is lost following treatment with the ionophore A23187. The structural nature of these areas is not known. Clearly much work remains to be done to elucidate the nature and function of calcium stores in mammalian oocytes and eggs.

Recently there has been much interest in the literature regarding the location of $InsP_3$ receptor-binding sites and the nature and significance of structural identities called 'calciosomes' which appear to be largely involved in the storage of calcium. The latter are discrete organelles some 100 nm in diameter which do not appear to have any physical connection with any other form of organelle (Volpe *et al.*, 1988; Hashimoto *et al.*, 1988). They have been shown to contain a calcium-binding protein similar to that of calsequestrin of muscle sarcoplasmic reticulum. The organelles also contain Ca^{2+} ATPase which, unlike calsequestrin, is confined to the membrane. In addition, the calciosomes do not react with endoplasmic reticulum-specific markers. The evidence therefore

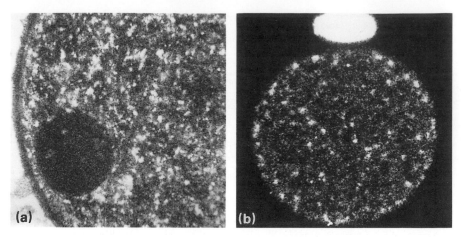

Fig. 5. Confocal optical sections of mature hamster oocyte incubated for 45 min in Fluo-3. (a) Immature oocyte. (b) Mature oocyte. Fluorescence can be detected at discrete sites throughout the cell. Note the exclusion from the nucleus in (a).

seems to point to there being a discrete organelle involved in calcium regulation. Immunological evidence, however, would appear to militate against the likelihood of their playing a primary role in calcium release into the cytoplasm. There is a general consensus that the $InsP_3$ receptor is located on endoplasmic reticulum (see Gill, 1989), but there is some disparity regarding the details of distribution. Ross *et al.* (1989) have observed labelling on the rough endoplasmic reticulum, the nuclear envelope and also on smooth endoplasmic reticulum located close to the plasma membrane. This is similar to unpublished results by Mignery *et al.* quoted by Gill (1989). A fourth location has been detected by Furuichi *et al.* (1989) who have also detected binding of the antibody to the plasma membrane. Clearly this heterogeneity of location would seem to indicate some secondary role for calciosomes. The significance of the multiple binding sites can, at present, only be a matter of conjecture. It is possible that the presence of receptors on the plasma membrane may be indicative of a role in $InsP_3$-mediated Ca^{2+} translocation across the plasma membrane. Certainly the presence of multiple binding sites would suggest that there is likely to exist a complex interaction between the various Ca^{2+} pools within cells. With regard to the mammalian oocyte there is, at present, no information regarding $InsP_3$ binding sites. It is to be hoped that this will be rectified within the next few years and that some refinement of knowledge of the nature of the Ca^{2+}-regulated processes taking place during the period surrounding fertilization will be made.

We thank Dr E. R. S. Roldan for critical appraisal of the manuscript.

References

Austin, C.R. (1956) Cortical granules in hamster eggs. *Expl Cell Res.* **10**, 533–540.

Baker, P.F. (1984) Multiple controls for secretion? *Nature, Lond.* **310**, 629–630.

Baker, P.F. (1988) Exocytosis in electropermeabilized cells: clues to mechanism and physiological control. In *Current Topics in Membranes and Transport*, Vol. 32, pp. 115–138. Eds N. Duzgunes & F. Bronner. Academic Press, London.

Battaglia, D.E. & Gaddum-Rosse, P. (1986) The distribution of polymerised actin in the rat egg and its

sensitivity to cytochasin B during fertilization. *J. exp. Zool.* **237**, 97–105.

Berridge, M.J. (1986) Cell signalling through phospholipid metabolism. *J. Cell Sci., Suppl.* **4**, 137–153.

Berridge, M.J. & Irvine, R.F. (1984) Inositol trisphosphate, a novel second messenger in signal transduction. *Nature, Lond.* **312**, 315–321.

Berridge, M.J. & Irvine, R.F. (1989) Inositol phosphates and cell signalling. *Nature, Lond.* **341**, 197–205.

Bleil, J.D. & Wassarman, P.M. (1980) Mammalian sperm-egg interaction: Identification of a glycoprotein in mouse egg zonae pellucidae possessing receptor activity for sperm. *Cell* **20**, 873–882.

Bleil, J.D., Beall, C.F. & Wassarman, P.M. (1981) Mammalian sperm-egg interaction: fertilization of mouse eggs triggers modification of the major zona glycoprotein ZP2. *Devl Biol.* **86**, 189–197.

Bryan, J. (1982) Redistribution of actin and fascin during fertilization in sea urchin eggs. *Cell. Differ.* **11**, 279–280.

Burgess, D.R. & Schroeder, T.B. (1977) Polarized bundles of actin filaments within microvilli of sea urchin eggs. *J. Cell Biol.* **74**, 1032–1037.

Chandler, D.E. (1988) Exocytosis and endocytosis: membrane fusion events captured in rapidly frozen cells. In *Current Topics in Membranes and Transport*, Vol. 32, pp. 169–202. Eds N. Duzgunes & F. Bronner. Academic Press, London.

Cherr, G.N., Drobnis, E.Z. & Katz, D.F. (1988) Localization of cortical granule constituents before and after exocytosis in the hamster egg. *J. exp. Zool.* **246**, 81–93.

Colonna, R., Tatone, C., Malgaroli, A., Eusebi, F. & Mangia, F. (1989) Effects of protein kinase C stimulation and free Ca^{2+} rise in mammalian egg activation. *Gamete Res.* **24**, 171–183.

Cran, D.G. (1985) Qualitative and quantitative structural changes during porcine oocyte maturation. *J. Reprod. Fert.* **74**, 237–245.

Cran, D.G. (1987) The distribution of organelles in mammalian oocytes following centrifugation prior to injection of foreign DNA. *Gamete Res.* **18**, 67–76.

Cran, D.G. (1989) Cortical granules during oocyte maturation and fertilization. *J. Reprod. Fert., Suppl.* **38**, 49–62.

Cran, D.G. & Cheng, W.T.-K. (1985) Changes in cortical granules during porcine oocyte maturation. *Gamete Res.* **11**, 311–319.

Cran, D.G. & Moor, R.M. (1990) Programming the oocyte for fertilization. In *Fertilization in Mammals*, Eds B. Bavister, J. Cummins & E. R. S. Roldan. Plenum Press, New York (in press).

Cran, D.G., Moor, R.M. & Hay, M.F. (1980) Fine structure of the sheep oocyte during antral follicle development. *J. Reprod. Fert.* **59**, 125–132.

Cran, D.G., Moor, R.M. & Irvine, R.F. (1988) Initiation of cortical reaction in hamster and sheep oocytes in response to inositol trisphosphate. *J. Cell Sci.* **91**, 139–144.

Creutz, C.E., Dowling, L.G., Sando, J.J., Villar-Palasi, C., Whipple, J.H. & Zaks, W.J. (1983) Characterization of chromobindins: soluble proteins that bind to the chromaffin granule membrane in the presence of Ca^{2+}. *J. biol. Chem.* **258**, 14664–14674.

Creutz, C.E., Dowling, L.G., Kyger, E.M. & Franson, R.C. (1985) Phosphatidylinositol-specific phospholipase C activity of chromaffin-binding proteins. *J. biol. Chem.* **260**, 7171–7173.

Cummins, J.M. & Yanagimachi, R. (1982) Sperm-egg ratios and the site of the acrosome reaction during *in vivo* fertilization in the hamster. *Gamete Res.* **5**, 239–256.

Ducibella, T., Anderson, E., Aalberg, J. & Rangarajan, S. (1988) Quantitative studies of changes in cortical granule number and distribution in the mouse oocyte during meiotic maturation. *Devl Biol.* **130**, 184–197.

Endo, Y., Schultz, R.M. & Kopf, G.S. (1987) Effects of phorbol esters and a diacylglycerol on mouse eggs: inhibition of fertilization and modification of the zona pellucida. *Devl Biol.* **119**, 199–209.

Fulton, B.P. & Whittingham, D.G. (1978) Activation of mammalian oocytes by intracellular injection of calcium. *Nature, Lond.* **273**, 149–151.

Furuichi, T., Yoshikawa, S., Miyawaki, A., Wada, K., Maeda, N. & Mikoshiba, K. (1989) Primary structure and functional expression of the inositol 1,4,5-trisphosphate-binding protein P_{400}. *Nature, Lond.* **342**, 32–38.

Gill, D.L. (1989) Receptor kinships revealed. *Nature, Lond.* **342**, 16–18.

Gulyas, B.J. (1976) Ultrastructural observations on rabbit, hamster and mouse eggs following electrical stimulation in vitro. *Am. J. Anat.* **147**, 203–218.

Gulyas, B.J. (1980) Cortical granules of mammalian cells. *Int. Rev. Cytol.* **65**, 357–392.

Gwatkin, R.B.L., Williams, D.T., Hartmann, J.F. & Kniazuk, M. (1973) The zona reaction of hamster and mouse eggs: production in vitro by a trypsin-like protease from cortical granules. *J. Reprod. Fert.* **32**, 259–265.

Gwatkin, R.B.L., Rasmusson, G.H. & Williams, D.T. (1976) Induction of the cortical reaction by membrane active agents. *J. Reprod. Fert.* **47**, 299–303.

Hashimoto, S., Bruno, B., Lew, D.P., Pazzan, T., Volpe, P. & Meldolesi, T. (1988) Immunocytochemistry of calciosomes in liver and pancreas. *J. Cell. Biol.* **107**, 2523–2531.

Hyttel, P., Callesen, H. & Greve, T. (1986a) Ultrastructural features of preovulatory oocyte maturation in superovulated cattle. *J. Reprod. Fert.* **76**, 645–656.

Hyttel, P., Xu, K.P., Smith, S. & Greve, T. (1986b) Ultrastructure of in vitro oocyte maturation in cattle. *J. Reprod. Fert.* **78**, 615–625.

Hyttel, P., Xu, K.P., Smith, S., Callesen, H. & Greve, T. (1987) Ultrastructure of the final nuclear maturation of bovine oocytes in vitro. *Anat. Embryol.* **176**, 35–40.

Igusa, Y. & Miyazaki, S. (1986) Periodic increase of cytoplasmic free calcium in fertilized hamster eggs measured with calcium-sensitive electrodes. *J. Physiol., Lond.* **377**, 193–205.

Jackson, R.C. & Crabb, J.H. (1988) Cortical exocytosis in the sea urchin egg. In *Current Topics in Membranes and Transport*, Vol. 32, pp. 45–85. Academic Press, London.

Kline, D., Simoncini, L., Mandel, G., Mane, R.A., Kado, R.T. & Jaffe, L.A. (1988) Fertilization events induced by neurotransmittors after injection of mRNA in *Xenopus* eggs. *Science, NY* **241**, 464–467.

Kruip, T.A., Cran, D.G., van Beneden, T.H. & Dieleman, S.J. (1983) Structural changes in bovine oocytes during final maturation in vivo. *Gamete Res.* **8**, 29–47.

Kurasawa, S., Schultz, R.M. & Kopf, G.S. (1989) Egg-induced modifications of the zona pellucida of mouse eggs: effects of microinjected inositol 1,4,5-trisphosphate. *Devl Biol.* **133**, 296–304.

Lee, S.H., Ahuja, K.K., Gilbert, D.J. & Whittingham, D. (1988) The appearance of glycoconjugates associated with cortical granule release during mouse fertilization. *Development* **102**, 595–604.

Le Guen, P., Crozet, N., Huneau, D. & Gall, L. (1989) Distribution and role of microfilaments during early events of sheep fertilization. *Gamete Res.* **22**, 411–425.

Longo, F.J. (1987) Actin-plasma membrane associations in mouse eggs and oocytes. *J. exp. Zool.* **243**, 299–309.

Longo, F.J. & Chen, D.Y. (1985) Development of cortical polarity in mouse eggs: involvement of the meiotic apparatus. *Devl Biol.* **107**, 382–394.

Maro, B., Johnson, M.H., Pickering, S.J. & Flach, G. (1984) Mechanism of polar body formation in the mouse oocytes: an interaction between the chromosomes, the cytoskeleton and the plasma membrane. *J. Embryol. exp. Morph.* **92**, 11–32.

Miyazaki, S. (1988) Inositol 1,4,5-trisphosphate induced calcium release and GTP-binding protein mediated periodic calcium rises in golden hamster eggs. *J. Cell Biol.* **106**, 354–353.

Miyazaki, S. (1990) Cell signalling at fertilization of hamster eggs. *J. Reprod. Fert., Suppl.* **42**, 163–175.

Miyazaki, S., Hashimoto, N., Yoshimoto, Y., Kishimoto, T., Igusa, Y. Hiramoto, Y. (1986) Temporal and spatial dynamics of the periodic increase in intracellular free calcium at fertilization of golden hamster eggs. *Devl Biol.* **118**, 259–287.

Moor, R.M. & Warnes, G.M. (1978) Regulation of oocyte maturation in mammals. In *Control of Ovulation*, pp. 159–176. Eds D. B. Crighton, G. R. Foxcroft, N. B. Haynes & G. E. Lamming. Butterworth Scientific, London.

Nicosia, S.V., Wolf, D.P. & Inoue, M. (1977) Cortical Granule distribution and cell surface characteristics in mouse eggs. *Devl Biol.* **57**, 56–74.

Okada, A., Yanagimachi, R. & Yanagimachi, H. (1986) Development of a cortical granule-free area of cortex and the perivitelline space in the hamster oocyte during maturation and following ovulation. *J. Submicrosc. Cytol.* **18**, 233–247.

Reima, I. & Lehtonen, E. (1985) Localization of non erythroid spectrin and actin in mouse oocytes and preimplantation embryos. *Differentiation* **30**, 68–75.

Ross, C.A., Meldolesi, J., Milner, T.A., Satoh, T., Supattapone, S. & Snyder, S. (1989) Inositol 1,4,5-trisphosphate receptor localized to endoplasmic reticulum in cerebellar Purkinje neurons. *Nature, Lond.* **339**, 468–470.

Sathananthan, A.H. & Trounson, A.O. (1982a) Ultrastructural observations on cortical granules in human follicular oocytes cultured *in vitro*. *Gamete Res.* **5**, 191–198.

Sathananthan, A.H. & Trounson, A.O. (1982b) Ultrastructure of cortical granule release and zona interaction in monospermic and polyspermic ova fertilized in vitro. *Gamete Res.* **6**, 225–234.

Schalkoff, M.E., Oskowitz, S.P. & Powers, R.D. (1989) Ultrastructural observations of human and mouse oocytes treated with cryopreservatives. *Biol. Reprod.* **40**, 379–393.

Schmell, E.D., Gulyas, B.J. & Hedrick, J.L. (1983) Egg surface changes during fertilization and the molecular mechanism of the block to polyspermy. In *Mechanism and Control of Animal Fertilization*,
pp. 365–413. Ed. J. F. Hartmann. Academic Press, New York.

Steinhardt, R.A., Epel, D., Carroll, E.J. & Yanagimachi, R. (1974) Is calcium ionophore a universal activator for unfertilized eggs. *Nature, Lond.* **252**, 41–43.

Stice, C.L. & Robl, J.M. (1989) A rabbit soluble sperm factor microinjected into mammalian oocytes causes oocyte activation. *Biol. Reprod., Suppl.* **1**, 54, Abstr. 21.

Swann, K. & Whitaker, M.J. (1990) Second messengers at fertilization in sea-urchin eggs. *J. Reprod. Fert., Suppl.* **42**, 141–153.

Szollosi, D., Calcarco, P. & Donahue, R.P. (1972) Absence of centrioles in the first and second meiotic spindles of mouse oocytes. *J. Cell Sci.* **11**, 521–541.

Turner, P.R., Jaffe, L.A. & Fein, A. (1986) Regulation of cortical granule exocytosis in sea urchin eggs by inositol 1,4,5-trisphosphate and GTP-binding protein. *J. Cell Biol.* **102**, 70–76.

van Blerkom, J. & Bell, H. (1986) Regulation of development in the fully grown mouse oocyte: chromosome mediated temporal and spatial differentiation of the cytoplasm and plasma membrane. *J. Embryol. exp. Morphol.* **93**, 213–238.

van Blerkom, J. & Runner, M.N. (1984) A cytoplasmic reorganisation provides mitochondria needed for resumption of arrested meiosis in the mouse oocyte. *Am. J. Anat.* **171**, 335–355.

Volpe, P., Krause, K-H., Hashimoto, S., Zorzato, F., Pozzan, T., Meldolesi, J. & Lew, D.P. (1988) Calciosome, a cytoplasmic organelle: the inositol 1,4,5-trisphosphate-sensitive Ca^{2+} store of non-muscle cells. *Proc. natn. Acad. Sci. USA* **85**, 1091–1095.

Wall, R.J., Pursel, V.G., Hammer, R.E. & Brinster, R.L. (1985) Development of porcine ova that were centrifuged to permit visualization of pronuclei and nuclei. *Biol. Reprod.* **32**, 645–651.

Warnes, G.M., Moor, R.M. & Johnson, M.H. (1977) Changes in protein synthesis during maturation of sheep oocytes *in vivo* and *in vitro*. *J. Reprod. Fert.* **49**, 331–335.

Wassarman, P.M. (1983) Oogenesis: synthetic events in the developing mammalian egg. In *Mechanism and Control of Animal Fertilization*, pp. 1–54. Ed. J. F. Hartmann. Academic Press, New York.

Whitaker, M.J. & Baker, P.F. (1983) Calcium-dependent exocytosis in an in vitro secretory granule plasma membrane preparation from sea urchin eggs and the effects of some inhibitors of cytoskeletal function. *Proc. R. Soc. B* **218**, 397–413.

Yanagimachi, R. (1988) Sperm-egg fusion. In *Current Topics in Membranes and Transport*, vol. 32, pp. 3–43. Academic Press, London.

Zamboni, L. (1970) Ultrastructure of mammalian oocytes and ova. *Biol. Reprod.* **10**, 125–149.

Zamboni, L., Paterson, H. & Jones, M. (1976) Loss of cortical granules in mouse ova activated in vivo by electrical shock. *Anat. Rec.* **147**, 95–101.

SECOND MESSENGER TARGETS
AND THE
ONSET OF DEVELOPMENT

Chairman
M. Johnson

J. Reprod. Fert., Suppl. **42** (1990), 191–197

Inracellular free calcium and the first cell cycle of the sea-urchin embryo (*Lytechinus pictus*)

R. A. Steinhardt

Department of Molecular and Cell Biology, 391 Life Science Addition, University of California, Berkeley, CA 94720, USA

Keywords: calcium; nuclear envelope; CaM kinase; mitosis; sea-urchin

Introduction

As first shown in the sea-urchin egg, activation of development by fertilization and by partheno-genetic agents depends upon increases in intracellular free calcium (Steinhardt & Epel, 1974; Steinhardt *et al.*, 1977; Zucker & Steinhardt, 1978; Poenie *et al.*, 1985). Until recently it has not been possible to go beyond the earliest events of activation and examine the possible role of calcium later in the cell cycle. With the advent of better reporters for the low levels of calcium found in cells, several workers have implicated changes in intracellular free calcium as possible signals in the regulation of several stages of mitosis in both animal and plant cells (Wolniak *et al.*, 1983; Hepler, 1985; Keith *et al.*, 1985; Poenie *et al.*, 1985; Ratan *et al.*, 1986; Wolniak & Bart, 1986; Poenie *et al.*, 1986; Poenie & Steinhardt, 1987). While calcium signals have been associated with all the major structural transitions in mitosis, the analysis of their regulatory role in our laboratory has proceeded furthermost in the case of nuclear envelope breakdown (NEB). Evidence has been presented which specifically implicates transient increases in intracellular free calcium ($[Ca^{2+}]_i$) in the timing of nuclear envelope breakdown in the sea-urchin embryo. It has been demonstrated that a calcium transient immediately precedes NEB in sea-urchin embryos and that buffering with EGTA or BAPTA will prevent NEB (Steinhardt & Alderton, 1988; Twigg *et al.*, 1988). Additionally, premature calcium rises can trigger early NEB, provided there has been an adequate period of protein synthesis (Steinhardt & Alderton, 1988; Twigg *et al.*, 1988). Parallel results have been obtained in similar experiments on early division cycles in the sand dollar embryo (Silver, 1989). In this brief review, I will discuss our evidence implicating calcium in regulation of the first cell cycle in the embryo of the sea urchin, *Lytechinus pictus*, and discuss some more recent data pointing to a possible target for the rise in free intracellular calcium triggering nuclear envelope breakdown. The work reviewed here is heavily dependent on the efforts of my collaborators, Janet Alderton, Celia Baitinger, Martin Poenie, Howard Schulman, and Roger Tsien, but I, not they, am responsible for any errors in this summary.

Changes in $[Ca^{2+}]_i$ during the first cell cycle in the sea-urchin embryo

At fertilization there is the first large calcium transient activating the process of cellularization (Steinhardt *et al.*, 1977; Whitaker & Steinhardt, 1982; Swann & Whitaker, 1990). This transient elevation of $[Ca^{2+}]_i$ reaches an average value of 2 μM and takes a few minutes to level off completely (Poenie *et al.*, 1985). We have reason to believe that the real peak concentrations reached are more than 2 μM locally since the average value assumes equal distribution.

The fluorescent chelator fura-2 has made it possible to follow $[Ca^{2+}]_i$ at resting levels and beyond the large peak associated with fertilization (Poenie *et al.*, 1985; Grynkiwicz *et al.*, 1985). There are several peaks of $[Ca^{2+}]_i$ associated with mitotic transitions that are usually detectable with fura-2. The first of these is a rise previously associated with pronuclear migration (Poenie *et al.*, 1985). In more recent experiments Janet Alderton has been able to separate that early peak from pronuclear migration and has shown that it is associated with pronuclear fusion (Fig. 1a). The appearance of the peaks that follow is more variable, although the average values of $[Ca^{2+}]_i$ attained are quite reproducible. Figure 1(b) shows the continuation of the record of Fig. 1(a) and illustrates changes in $[Ca^{2+}]_i$ seen at NEB, the onset of anaphase and cytokinesis.

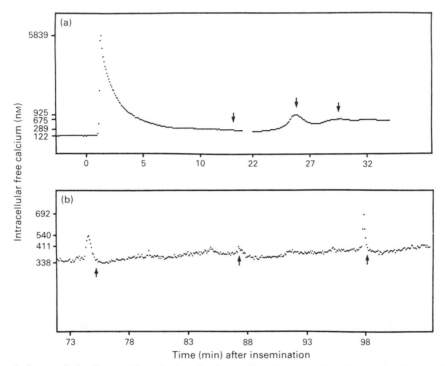

Fig. 1. Intracellular free calcium during the first cell cycle. **(a)** A fura-2 record of intracellular free calcium after fertilization of an *L. pictus* egg. After a 5 μM peak transient at fertilization, $[Ca^{2+}]_i$ changes were followed through pronuclear migration, pronuclear fusion and the establishment of a bipolar spindle. The first arrow marks the end of pronuclear migration with the male and female pronucleus adjacent. The second arrow marks pronuclear fusion. The third arrow marks the establishment of the bipolar spindle. Visual observations were made continuously in red light while the light at 500–530 nm was collected for calcium measurements. See Steinhardt & Alderton (1988) for methods. Experiment conducted at 18°C. **(b)** A continuation of the fura-2 record after fertilization started in (a). The first arrow marks the completion of nuclear envelope breakdown. The second arrow marks the onset of anaphase. The third arrow marks the process of cytokinesis.

Changes in $[Ca^{2+}]_i$ just before nuclear envelope breakdown

It is often difficult to detect rises in $[Ca^{2+}]_i$ in embryos against a high fluorescent background, most likely due to various degrees of compartmentalization of fura-2. However, the large transient occurring just before NEB after ammonia activation is always quite prominent (Poenie *et al.*, 1985; Steinhardt & Alderton, 1988). Figure 2 illustrates the change in $[Ca^{2+}]_i$ following activation with a 15-min pulse of 15 mM-ammonium chloride. About 60 min after the start of the ammonia pulse a large transient rise in $[Ca^{2+}]_i$ abruptly precedes nuclear envelope breakdown.

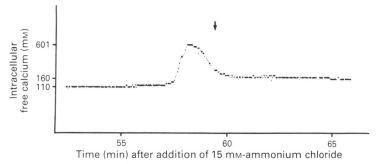

Fig. 2. A fura-2 record of intracellular free calcium after activation of an *L. pictus* egg with a 15-min treatment with 15 mM-ammonium chloride in sea water at pH 8. The arrow marks the completion of nuclear envelope breakdown.

The effects of buffering $[Ca^{2+}]_i$

It is necessary to manipulate $[Ca^{2+}]_i$ to test its possible function as an essential signal. This involves the injection of chelators since the changes in free calcium are dependent on intracellular stores in sea-urchin embryos (Poenie *et al.*, 1985). By injecting calcium–chelator buffer solutions along with the indicator fura-2 it was possible to prevent the transient increase in $[Ca^{2+}]_i$ immediately preceding NEB and block both nuclear envelope breakdown following ammonia activation or fertilization and block further progress of mitosis. Figure 3 illustrates that correlation showing that blocking the rise in free calcium will stop the progress of mitosis in *L. pictus* embryos just before NEB following fertilization. In both fertilization and ammonia activation NEB was observed within 1–3 min following the first calcium rise occurring more than 40 min after activation. Figure 3 follows $[Ca^{2+}]_i$ after fertilization which was watched continuously from the time of injection of the blocking buffer until $[Ca^{2+}]_i$ eventually overcame the buffering effects of injected EGTA ([ethylenebis{oxyethylenenitrilo}]tetraacetic acid) and recovered to the level which triggers NEB. Table 1 summarizes 13 experiments in which buffer solutions were injected to test the hypothesis that the calcium peak is essential for NEB. Keeping $[Ca^{2+}]_i$ at or below 270 nM with EGTA prevented NEB (see also Fig. 3). To control for possible toxic effects of organic acids, we used another chelator, nitrolotriacetic acid, which is relatively ineffective at binding calcium; this had no effect on NEB. To control for possible effects of pH we injected bis(aminophenoxy)ethane N,N'-tetraacetic acid [BAPTA] (Tsien, 1980) instead of EGTA. BAPTA was roughly as effective at blocking NEB. Since EGTA or BAPTA might block by binding a heavy metal such as zinc, we applied 10 μM-TPEN (Steinhardt *et al.*, 1977), N,N,N'-tetrakis(2-pyridylmethyl)ethylenediamine, in a separate test, and found that NEB proceeded normally in 30 embryos observed continuously. As seen in Table 1, low concentrations of EGTA or BAPTA were ineffective. This threshold of about 0·2–0·3 mM of chelator also implies that the block is induced by binding calcium, not a heavy metal.

The best evidence that the block is most probably due to calcium buffering follows from an additional observation on the nature of the block. Figure 3 and Table 1 shows that the EGTA or BAPTA block is temporary, inducing an average delay of 52 ± 4 min ($n = 8$). In 3 earlier experiments, which were not followed all the way to eventual NEB, the block lasted the entire period of observation (42–60 min). In Exps 2, 4 and 6, $[Ca^{2+}]_i$ was monitored continuously until the block of NEB was overcome at 47, 55 and 58 min, respectively. The values for $[Ca^{2+}]_i$ increased gradually, reaching 540 nM, 620 nM and 541 nM respectively at the time of NEB. Apparently EGTA loses its effectiveness at buffering calcium in the embryo with time: it might become loaded from calcium stores, or by extracellular calcium entry. Another possibility is that EGTA has been sequestered or lost from the cytoplasm so that its effective concentration is too low to buffer calcium. A similar phenomenon might be responsible for the lack of effect of EGTA injections on the timing of cell

Table 1. Effect of buffer injections on nuclear envelope breakdown in *L. pictus* eggs

Exp.	Chelator conc. in cell after injection (mM)	Baseline $[Ca^{2+}]i$ after injection (nM)	$[Ca^{2+}]i$ at time of control NEB (nM)	Delay in NEB from controls (min)	$[Ca^{2+}]i$ at time of NEB experimentals (nM)
1	0·1 EGTA	—	—	0	
2	0·2 EGTA	156	251	55	540
3	0·2 EGTA	176	—	45	
4	0·3 EGTA	128	261	47	622
5	0·3 EGTA	—	—	47	
6	1·0 EGTA	116	160	58	541
7	0·2 BAPTA	123	—	0	
8	0·6 BAPTA	144	166	31	
9	0·7 BAPTA	132	144	69	
10	1·2 BAPTA	—	—	65	
11	0·5 NTA	135	506	0	506
12	1·2 NTA	215	593	0	593
13	1·5 NTA	—	—	0	

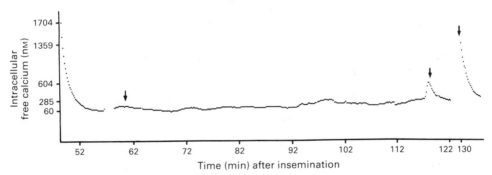

Fig. 3. A fura-2 record of intracellular free calcium after injection of blocking buffer (80 mM-EGTA, 160 mM-potassium gluconate, 8 mM-Hepes, 48 mM-$CaCl_2$, 3·2 mM-$MgCl_2$, pH 7·4). First peak marks the injection artefact. The first arrow marks the time of nuclear envelope breakdown in control uninjected eggs. The second arrow marks the natural recovery of $[Ca^{2+}]_i$ levels to threshold for NEB and the completion of NEB. The third arrow marks the injection of rescue buffer without dye (80 mM-EGTA, 160 mM-potassium gluconate, 8 mM-Hepes, 73 mM-$CaCl_2$, 1·3 mM-$MgCl_2$, pH 7·4) to show that the original fura-2 is still reporting cytoplasmic free calcium.

division in *Xenopus* embryos (Baker & Warner, 1972). However, if EGTA can become ineffective with time, how can we be sure that there is enough active fura-2 to report accurately the free calcium concentration? In 6 additional experiments eggs injected with fura-2 in the usual manner before activation were reinjected 1–2 h later with rescue buffer (without additional dye) preset to higher calcium concentrations. In every case the cytoplasmic calcium, as reported by the fura-2 previously injected, reached the micromolar levels normally seen when the fura-2 is injected at the same time as the buffer. Figure 3 illustrates this point. At the last arrow a reinjection of rescue buffer (without additional dye) allows the levels of free calcium to reach micromolar levels. We concluded that there is sufficient dye to report accurately the free calcium levels in the cytoplasm at the end of these experiments.

Rescue and advancement of nuclear envelope breakdown

It should be possible to overcome the EGTA block by subsequent reinjections of a rescue buffer solution preset to higher calcium concentrations. Normally NEB is observed visually within 3 min after the peak $[Ca^{2+}]_i$ transient preceding it. In the rescue by reinjection experiments the interval is slightly longer. Rescue by reinjection was successful in 4 of 5 experiments with NEB occurring at an average 10 ± 2.16 min after reinjection. In one case reinjection with rescue buffer failed to shorten significantly the period of the block for no apparent reason. We suspect that this one anomaly may have resulted from an injury due to a poor injection. We did 10 additional experiments to see whether it was possible to advance the time of NEB by injection with rescue buffer 46–71 min after insemination to induce an artificial calcium rise early. In 9 of these experiments NEB followed within 3 min of the injection, advancing the time of NEB by as much as 44 min for the earliest injection and advancing NEB the 12 min remaining to the time of the control NEB for the latest injection done at 71 min after insemination. In one case the injection had no effect, with both control and experimental NEBs occurring within 1 min of each other. The experience with the injections with blocking buffer was entirely different. With blocking buffer the calcium entry associated with the penetration of the injection pipette did not trigger an early NEB in spite of the momentarily high levels of $[Ca^{2+}]_i$. The only difference between blocking buffer and rescue buffer is the amount of added calcium. The calculated free calcium for the composition of blocking buffer is 10^{-7} M and 4×10^{-7} for the rescue buffer (see Fig. 3 legend for compositions). Since the egg is at a higher ionic strength than the solutions for which we know the binding constants for EGTA (Martell & Smith, 1974), we have found free calcium values to be slightly higher than those predicted by calculation. The difference in free calcium between blocking buffer and rescue buffer is enough to trigger NEB and closely matches the levels that correlate with normal NEB in the non-buffer-injected egg.

A target for intracellular free calcium signals

The effects of injected calcium and calcium buffers suggest that, at least for nuclear evelope breakdown, calcium signals play an essential regulatory role. This conclusion forces us to try to identify possible targets for the calcium transients. One possible target of the increased intracellular calcium which may mediate mitotic events is the multifunctional calcium- and calmodulin-dependent protein kinase also referred to as calcium/calmodulin-dependent protein kinase [CaM kinase] (Poenie & Steinhardt, 1987). This enzyme is present in a wide variety of tissues and species and has been shown to phosphorylate a broad range of substrates *in vitro* (see Schulman & Lou, 1989, for review). As purified from rat forebrain, where it is particularly abundant, the multifunctional CaM kinase is composed of a major alpha subunit and two minor subunits, beta and beta′. All of the subunits bind calmodulin and have catalytic activity, based on their ability to undergo autophosphorylation in a calcium/calmodulin dependent manner. One especially interesting feature is the ability of the kinase to become independent of the continued presence of calcium/calmodulin once a level of 2–3 mol P per holoenzyme is achieved (Miller & Kennedy, 1986). Presumably, if the right balance of phosphorylation and dephosphorylation occurs, the activating effect of a calcium pulse can be prolonged, although this effect has not yet been demonstrated in any biological situation. Purification of a calcium- and calmodulin-dependent protein kinase with properties similar to those of the rat brain kinase has been reported for the egg of *L. pictus* (Chou & Rebhun, 1986).

The action of inhibitory synthetic peptides on nuclear envelope breakdown

The sequence and functional domains of the multifunctional kinase from rat brain have been determined. Both subunits of CaM kinase contain an 'autoinhibitory domain' which is not similar to the autoinhibitory sequences of other kinases (Schulman & Lou, 1989). Two peptides corresponding to a portion of the 'autoinhibitory' domain of the a subunit of the brain CaM kinase (CaM-K-(284-302) and CaM-K-(273-302)) have been shown to inhibit the Ca/CaM-dependent phosphorylation of 'autocamtide II' (a specific peptide substrate for the CaM kinase) as well as the autophosphorylation of the rat brain kinase *in vitro* (Hanson *et al.*, 1989). CaM-K-(273-302) is the more potent inhibitor, inhibiting the phosphorylation of autocamtide II by the rat brain kinase with an IC_{50} of approximately 1 μM, while the IC_{50} for inhibition of the Ca/CaM dependent phosphorylation of autocamtide II by CaM-K-(284-302) is more than an order of magnitude higher. These peptides are likely to be specific inhibitors of the multifunctional CaM kinase and proved to be useful tools to test the involvement of a multifunctional CaM kinase in nuclear mitotic events. The inhibitory effects of these peptides have been tested by microinjection into the eggs of *L. pictus* during the first cell division (R. A. Steinhardt, J. Alderton, C. Baitinger & H. Schulman, unpublished data).

Microinjection of CaM-K-(273-302) to levels corresponding to estimated intracellular concentrations of 20–42 μM (0·52–1·1% of the cell volume) before fertilization invariably delayed NEB (22/22 cells injected); delays ranging from 19 to 88 min in duration occurred. Three of these delays could be characterized as blocks of NEB since these eggs were not monitored after delays of 88 min. Although there was characteristically a delay of a few minutes before pronuclear fusion, most of the delay occurred after the bipolar spindle was established in every case. To make sure that the delays really occurred before the stage of nuclear envelope breakdown, we injected 5 cells after the bipolar spindle was established. In each case, a substantive delay occurred. The duration of the delay in NEB was in most instances related to the amount of peptide injected, with the highest concentrations usually giving the longest delays. Significant delays occurred at the lowest concentration of CaM-K-(273-302) injected, corresponding to 0·52% of the cell volume and an estimated intracellular concentration of 20 μM peptide. The pattern of fluctuations in intracellular free calcium was checked in 3 of the injected eggs; peptide-injected eggs showed a normal pattern of fluctuations in intracellular free calcium at the appropriate times compared to control cells, up to and including the peak which normally occurs just before nuclear envelope breakdown.

As a control for the effect of injecting synthetic peptides, we microinjected the very weak inhibitor CaM-K-(284-302). Injection of CaM-K-(284-302) to estimated intracellular concentrations of 54–108 μM had, in 6 of 7 cases, no effect on the timing of onset of nuclear envelope breakdown; NEB occurred in synchrony with uninjected controls. In one case, in which an estimated intracellular concentration of 74 μM was reached, a 9-min delay occurred. At higher concentrations, corresponding to very large injection volumes (over 4% of the cell volume), nuclear envelope breakdown was delayed between 11 and 27 min (3/4 cases) or proceeded normally (1 case).

In our experiments to be reported in detail elsewhere, extracts of the egg cytoplasm of *L. pictus* phosphorylated an endogenous alpha CaM kinase-like peptide of M_r 56 000 in a calcium/calmodulin manner and this phosphorylation was inhibited by CaM-K-(273-302) but not by CaM-K-(284-302) (C. Baitinger personal communication).

The action of antibodies to Ca/CaM kinase on NEB

When a monoclonal antibody directed against the multifunctional Ca/CaM kinase beta subunit of rat brain was microinjected into eggs before fertilization, mitosis was arrested just before NEB without any delays in earlier events (J. Alderton, C. Baitinger & H. Schulman, personal communication). Effective intracellular concentrations of this antibody were in the range of 7–100 nM. At 7 nM there was a 30-min delay. At 14 nM and above there was a complete block ($n = 12$). This antibody was able to precipitate the alpha-like peptide of M_r 56 000 in sea-urchin egg homogenates that was phosphorylated in a calcium/calmodulin-dependent manner. Two different antibodies against the rat brain alpha subunit had no inhibitory effects in the range tested, 20–260 nM, and did not react with proteins in the sea-urchin egg extracts or homogenates ($n = 14$, $n = 10$).

Conclusions

In this brief review I have tried to summarize our evidence implicating intracellular free calcium in regulating the first division cycle of the sea-urchin embryo beyond the well known activating release of $[Ca^{2+}]_i$ at fertilization. Transient elevations of $[Ca^{2+}]_i$ precede several stages of mitosis in the first cell division of the sea-urchin embryo. At this point our analysis has been focussed on nuclear envelope breakdown (NEB). Blocking the rise by buffering calcium can arrest mitosis before NEB and artificial increases of $[Ca^{2+}]_i$ can advance the timing of normal NEB. A synthetic inhibitory peptide CaM-K-(273-302) specific to CaM kinase will also arrest mitosis just before NEB. Monoclonal antibodies directed against the beta subunit of rat brain CaM kinase also block NEB and precipitate a peptide of M_r 56 000 which is similar to the alpha subunit of rat brain CaM kinase and which is phosphorylated in a calcium- and calmodulin-dependent manner. Apart from extending this analysis to other stages of mitosis and other cell types, we would next like to try to identify the targets of CaM kinase involved in the timing of nuclear envelope breakdown.

The work in my laboratory is supported by N.I.H. grant GM39374.

References

Baker, P.F. & Warner, A.E. (1972) Intracellular calcium and cell cleavage in early embryos. *J. Cell Biol.* **53**, 579–581.

Chou, Y.H. & Rebhun, L.I. (1986) Purification and characterization of a sea urchin egg Ca^{2+}-calmodulin-dependent kinase with myosin light chain phosphorylating properties. *J. biol. Chem.* **261**, 5389–5395.

Grynkiwicz, G., Poenie, M. & Tsien, R.Y. (1985) A new generation of calcium indicators with greatly improved fluorescence properties. *J. biol. Chem.* **260**, 3440–3450.

Hanson, P., Kapiloff, M.S., Lou, L.L., Rosenenfeld, M.G. & Schulman, H. (1989) Expression of the multifunctional CaM kinase clone and mutational analysis of its autoregulation. *Neuron* **3**, 59–70.

Hepler, P.K. (1985) Calcium restriction prolongs metaphase in dividing *Tradescantia* stamen hairs. *J. Cell Biol.* **100**, 1363–1368.

Keith, C.H., Ratan, R., Maxfield, F.R., Baer, A. & Shelanski, M.L. (1985) Local cytoplasmic gradients in living mitotic cells. *Nature, Lond.* **316**, 848–850.

Martell, A.E. & Smith, R.M. (1974) *Critical Stability Constants*. Plenum, London.

Miller, S.G. & Kennedy, M.B. (1986) Regulation of brain type II Ca^{2+}/calmodulin dependent protein kinase by autophosphorylation: Ca^{2+}-triggered molecular switch. *Cell* **44**, 861–870.

Poenie, M. & Steinhardt, R.A. (1987) The dynamics of calcium during mitosis. In *Calcium and Cell Function*, vol. 7, pp. 133–157. Ed. W. Y. Cheung. Academic Press, New York.

Poenie, M., Alderton, J., Tsien, R.Y. & Steinhardt, R.A. (1985) Changes in free calcium levels with stages of the cell cycle. *Nature, Lond.* **315**, 147–149.

Poenie, M., Alderton, J., Steinhardt, R.A. & Tsien, R. (1986) Calcium rises abruptly and briefly throughout the cell at the onset of anaphase. *Science, NY* **233**, 886–889.

Ratan, R., Shelanski, M.L. & Maxfield, F.R.(1986) Transition from metaphase to anaphase is accompanied by local changes in cytoplasmic free calcium in PtK2 kidney epithelial cells. *Proc. natn. Acad. Sci. USA* **83**, 5136–5140.

Schulman, H. & Lou, L.L. (1989) Multifunctional Ca^{2+}/calmodulin-dependent protein kinase: domain structure and regulation. *Trends in Biochem. Sci.* **14**, 62–66.

Silver, R.B. (1989) Nuclear evelope breakdown and mitosis is inhibited by microinjection of calcium buffers in a calcium-reversible fashion and by antagonists of intracellular Ca^{2+} channels. *Devl Biol.* **131**, 11–26.

Steinhardt, R.A. & Alderton, J. (1988) Intracellular free calcium rise triggers nuclear envelope breakdown in the sea urchin embryo. *Nature, Lond.* **332**, 364–366.

Steinhardt, R.A. & Epel, D. (1974) Activation of sea urchin eggs by a calcium ionophore. *Proc. natn. Acad. Sci. USA* **71**, 1915–1919.

Steinhardt, R.A., Zucker, R. & Schatten, G. (1977) Intracellular calcium release at fertilization in the sea urchin egg. *Devl Biol.* **58**, 185–196.

Swann, K. & Whitaker, M.J. (1990) Second messengers at fertilization in sea-urchin eggs. *J. Reprod. Fert., Suppl.* **42**, 141–153.

Tsien, R.Y. (1980) New calcium indicators and buffers with high selectivity against magnesium and protons. *Biochemistry, NY* **19**, 2396–2404.

Twigg, J., Patel, R. & Whitaker, M. (1988) Translational control of IP3-induced chromatin condensation during the early cell cycles of sea urchin embryos. *Nature, Lond.* **332**, 366–368.

Whitaker, M.J. & Steinhardt, R.A. (1982) Ionic regulation of egg activation. *Q. Rev. Biophys.* **15**, 593–666.

Wolniak, S.M. & Bart, K.M. (1986) The buffering of calcium with Quin2 reversibly forestalls anaphase onset in stamen hair cells of *Tradescantia*. *Eur. J. Cell Biol.* **39**, 273–277.

Wolniak, S.M., Hepler, P.K. & Jackson, W.T. (1983) Ionic changes in the mitotic apparatus at the metaphase/anaphase transition. *J. Cell Biol.* **96**, 598–605.

Zucker, R. & Steinhardt, R.A. (1978) Intracellular calcium and the mechanisms of parthenogenetic activation of the sea urchin egg. *Devl Biol.* **65**, 285–295.

J. Reprod. Fert., Suppl. **42** (1990), 199–204

Printed in Great Britain
© 1990 Journals of Reproduction & Fertility Ltd

Cell cycle control proteins are second messenger targets at fertilization in sea-urchin eggs

Michael J. Whitaker

Department of Physiology, University College London, Gower Street, London WC1E 6BT, UK

Keywords: calcium; cyclin; cell cycle; fertilization; phosphorylation; cell messengers

Introduction

Two ionic signals start the cell cycle at fertilization

Eggs generally pause at a specific point in the cell division cycle as they wait to be fertilized. Sea-urchin eggs stop their cell division cycle after completing meiosis. The fertilizing spermatozoon triggers resumption of the cycle and at 30 min after fertilization the zygote undergoes its first round of DNA synthesis. The signals that start the cell cycle are a transient increase in intracellular free calcium concentration (Ca_i) and a sustained increase in intracellular pH (pH_i) (Whitaker & Steinhardt, 1982). The two ionic signals at fertilization are generated by the phosphoinositide messengers inositol trisphosphate ($InsP_3$) and diacylglycerol (Whitaker, 1989; Swann & Whitaker, 1990).

The primary ionic signal is the Ca_i transient: the pH_i increase is the consequence of the Ca_i increase (Whitaker & Steinhardt, 1982; Swann & Whitaker, 1990). The Ca_i signal triggers the cell division cycle to continue by targetting cell cycle control proteins (Whitaker & Patel, 1990).

Cell cycle control proteins

Most of what we know about the molecular mechanisms of cell cycle control comes from work on the yeast cell division cycle. A large number of mutants with defective cell division cycles have been identified. It turns out that defects in cell cycle control genes lead to cell cycle arrest at specific points in the cell cycle. We can conclude that there are specific *cell cycle control points* in the yeast cell cycle and that progress through these control points is controlled by specific *cell cycle control proteins* (Nurse & Thuriaux, 1980; MacNeill & Nurse, 1989). The cell cycle control points are at START, just before the beginning of DNA synthesis, mitosis ENTRY, just before the onset of mitosis, and mitosis EXIT, at the metaphase/anaphase transition. These control points may be common to all eukaryotic cell cycles (Whitaker & Patel, 1990). Of the various genes specifying cell cycle control proteins in yeast, two have been shown to have their counterparts in eggs, oocytes and mammalian somatic cells: they are cdc2 and cdc13. The former (Nurse & Bissett, 1981) codes for a phosphoprotein, $pp34^{cdc2}$ that is tyrosine phosphorylated in late G1 (probably at START) and dephosphorylated at mitosis ENTRY (Draetta & Beach, 1988; Lee *et al.*, 1988; Gould & Nurse, 1989; Moreno *et al.*, 1988; Morla *et al.*, 1989). The pattern of cell cycle-related phosphorylation of pp34 is very similar in yeast, frog and starfish oocytes and in somatic cells (Hunt, 1989). The latter, cdc13, is a gene coding for the yeast homologue (Solomon *et al.*, 1988; Goebl & Byers, 1988) of a cell cycle protein, cyclin, that was first identified in clam oocytes and sea urchin embryos (Rosenthal *et al.*, 1980; Evans *et al.*, 1983). Cyclins are synthesized continuously throughout the cell cycle, but undergo an episode of destruction during mitosis.

There is good reason to think that pp34 and cyclin are pivotal cell cycle control proteins, not only because they are essential for progression through the yeast cell cycle, but also because they are the major component of a cytoplasmic activity known as MPF (maturation/mitosis promoting factor). MPF is found in the cytoplasm of cells as they pass mitosis ENTRY. It will induce pre-mature mitosis onset in interphase cells when microinjected (Wasserman & Smith, 1978; Masui & Clarke, 1979; Kishimoto *et al.*, 1982). MPF probably consists largely of dephosphorylated pp34 and phosphorylated cyclin (Dunphy *et al.*, 1988; Gautier *et al.*, 1988, 1989; Labbe *et al.*, 1989a, b; Draetta *et al.*, 1989; Meijer *et al.*, 1989). Entry into mitosis is driven by dephosphorylation of pp34 and phosphorylation of the cyclin component of the pp34/cyclin oligomer and exit from mitosis is due to the destruction of phosphorylated cyclin (Pondaven *et al.*, 1990; Whitaker & Patel, 1990).

We are interested in the links between the dual ionic signals that restart the cell cycle at fertiliz-ation and their targets, the cell cycle control proteins pp34 and cyclin.

Cyclin and pH_i signal

One consequence of the increase in pH_i at fertilization in sea-urchin eggs is a marked increase in the rate of protein synthesis (Grainger *et al.*, 1979). The increase is best understood as the removal of a brake set in the egg after maturation (Whitaker & Steinhardt, 1982; Woodland, 1990). The cyto-plasmic pH of the unfertilized sea-urchin egg (pH 6·7) results in unusually low rates of protein synthesis. The rate returns to normal at fertilization. Sea-urchin eggs contain undetectable levels of cyclin (T. Hunt, unpublished). The pH signal at fertilization triggers cyclin accumulation by stimulating protein synthesis (Evans *et al.*, 1983). The pH_i signal at fertilization is a consequence of the Ca_i transient (Whitaker & Steinhardt, 1982; Swann & Whitaker, 1990). We can induce a pH_i increase that is independent of a calcium transient by treating eggs with a weak base, such as ammonia, or the phorbol ester PMA (phorbol myristate acetate). Ammonia causes cytoplasmic alkalinization by diffusing into the egg and taking up protons (Winkler & Grainger, 1978); PMA causes a calcium-independent cytoplasmic alkalinization by stimulating the sodium–hydrogen anti-porter *via* protein kinase C (Swann & Whitaker, 1985). A pH_i increase alone is sufficient to stimu-late cyclin synthesis (Patel *et al.*, 1989a; Whitaker & Patel, 1990), indicating that one element needed to restart the cell cycle at fertilization is provided by the pH_i signal.

Cyclin synthesis alone is not sufficient to restart the cell cycle in sea-urchin eggs

Cyclin mRNA injected into immature frog oocytes will induce maturation (meiosis onset) (Swenson *et al.*, 1986). Cyclin mRNA is also a necessary and sufficient stimulus for nuclear condensation/decondensation cycles in a cell-free cell cycle system (Murray & Kirschner, 1989). These observations suggest that mitosis onset may be driven solely by cyclin accumulation (Alberts *et al.*, 1989; Murray, 1989). The corollary is that cyclin accumulation driven by the pH_i signal should cause mitosis onset in sea urchin eggs. It does not.

It has been known for some time that a pH_i signal alone will not restart the cell cycle in unferti-lized sea-urchin eggs (Epel *et al.*, 1974). Cyclin accumulates to high levels in eggs stimulated with the pH_i signal (Whitaker & Patel, 1990), but neither DNA synthesis (Epel *et al.*, 1974; Whitaker & Steinhardt, 1981) nor mitosis onset occur, even after several hours (Patel *et al.*, 1989b; Whitaker & Patel, 1990). These data indicate that the cell cycle in early sea-urchin embryos is not driven by cyclin alone; a similar conclusion has been reached for the yeast cell cycle, the timing of which is unaltered by overexpression of the cdc13 yeast cyclin gene (Enoch & Nurse, 1990). The sea-urchin experiments also demonstrate that the Ca_i signal plays a direct part in restarting the cell cycle at fertilization, as well as providing the indirect stimulus to cyclin synthesis by causing the pH_i increase. One direct consequence of the calcium transient at fertilization is the phosphorylation of the other key cell cycle control protein, pp34.

pp34 and Ca_i signal

The pp34 complex immunoprecipitated by an antibody directed against a pp34 consensus (PSTAIR) sequence is phosphorylated immediately after fertilization (Patel *et al.*, 1989a). The phosphorylation is also induced by the parthenogenetic activator A23187, a calcium ionophore, and requires only the Ca_i signal, since it occurs even when the pH_i signal is suppressed (Patel *et al.*, 1989a, b). In yeast and in mammalian somatic cells, pp34 is phosphorylated in G1, probably at the START cell cycle control point that governs entry into S phase (Draetta & Beach, 1988; Lee *et al.*, 1988). In yeast, pp34 is required to pass START (Nurse & Bissett, 1981), and so it is likely that the phosphorylation of pp34 controls entry into S phase. We have no direct evidence to support this idea for sea-urchin embryos, only the indirect evidence that parthenogenetic agents that restart the cell cycle (and induce DNA synthesis) also cause phosphorylation of pp34 (Patel *et al.*, 1989a, b).

Ammonia activation

Activating eggs with ammonia illustrates this point quite well. At low concentrations, ammonia treatment increases pH_i and induces cyclin synthesis, but, as indicated above, does not restart the cell cycle. Only at higher concentrations is ammonia an effective parthenogenetic agent (Epel *et al.*, 1974). At these higher concentrations, ammonia mimics certain aspects of the Ca_i signal, as well as increasing pH_i (Zucker *et al.*, 1978; Whitaker & Steinhardt, 1981). Concentrations of ammonia that induce DNA synthesis and restart the cell cycle also induce a rapid phosphorylation of pp34, while lower concentrations that induce only the pH_i increase (Whitaker & Steinhardt, 1981) and cyclin synthesis do not (Whitaker & Patel, 1990).

pp34, cyclin, Ca_i and mitosis onset

Cyclin and pp34 together form the complex that is activated at the mitosis ENTRY cell cycle control point to stimulate nuclear envelope breakdown and chromatin condensation (Hunt, 1989). Activation of the complex involves the dephosphorylation of pp34 and the conjugate phosphorylation of cyclin (Hunt, 1989; Meijer *et al.*, 1989; Gautier *et al.*, 1989; Whitaker & Patel, 1990; Pondaven *et al.*, 1990). Besides pp34 and cyclin, there is a third essential ingredient for mitosis onset in sea-urchin eggs, i.e. a Ca_i transient that occurs just before nuclear envelope breakdown (Poenie *et al.*, 1985; Steinhardt, 1990; Whitaker & Patel, 1990). Mitosis onset can be delayed or prevented by microinjecting calcium chelators or advanced by microinjecting calcium or the phosphoinositide messenger $InsP_3$ (Steinhardt & Alderton, 1988; Twigg *et al.*, 1988). We have suggested that the mitosis ENTRY Ca_i transient triggers the dephosphorylation of pp34; so far, we have shown only that blocking the transient prevents the conjugate phosphorylation of cyclin (Whitaker & Patel, 1990).

Targets of the fertilization Ca_i signal

The Ca_i signal at fertilization targets at least 2 cell cycle control proteins, pp34 and cyclin (Fig. 1). It activates an unknown kinase to phosphorylate pp34 and indirectly stimulates cyclin synthesis by activating the Na^+/H^+ antiporter to increase pH_i. It seems very likely that this is how the dual ionic signals at fertilization restart the cell division cycle. Our conclusion is based as much on the close analogies between the cell cycles of yeast, embryos and mammalian cells (Whitaker & Patel, 1990) as it is on our experiments with sea-urchin eggs and embryos. We have no direct proof, in fact, that either pp34 phosphorylation/dephosphorylation or cyclin synthesis are essential for mitosis onset in sea-urchin embryos, although the correlation between cell cycle re-initiation and pp34 phosphorylation (discussed above) and the fact that mitosis onset in sea-urchin embryos requires a period of protein synthesis (Wagenaar, 1983; Twigg *et al.*, 1988) both strongly suggest that this is so. On the other hand, there is good direct evidence, discussed above, from experiments on sea-urchin

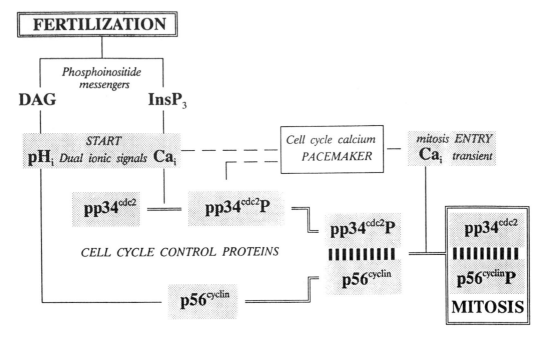

Fig. 1. The dual ionic signals at fertilization and their cell cycle targets. The Ca_i and pH_i signals are generated by the phosphoinositide second messengers. The Ca_i signal targets p34^{cdc2}, leading to its phosphorylation. The pH_i signal stimulates the synthesis of p56^{cdc13} (cyclin). In sea urchins (Whitaker & Patel, 1990) and in yeast (Enoch & Nurse, 1990), the activation of pp34 at START is required for it to participate at mitosis ENTRY. This may come about because only phosphorylated pp34 can bind to cyclin; cyclin is itself phosphorylated by pp34 when pp34 is dephosphorylated as a result of the mitosis ENTRY Ca_i transient. The fertilization Ca_i transient also resets the cell cycle calcium oscillator (possibly *via* phosphorylation of pp34).

embryos that a second cell cycle Ca_i signal is the immediate stimulus to mitosis onset (Steinhardt, 1990; Whitaker & Patel, 1990).

Cell cycle calcium transients

We do not know how this second Ca_i signal is generated. An attractive possibility would be that it is triggered by cyclin accumulation. This is not the case: the mitosis ENTRY Ca_i transient is independent of protein synthesis and cyclin synthesis itself does not stimulate the transient in the absence of a fertilization Ca_i signal (Patel *et al.*, 1989b). The second cell cycle Ca_i transient must in some way arise out of the first. If we look again at ammonia-activated eggs, we find a mitosis ENTRY Ca_i transient (Steinhardt & Alderton, 1988; Patel *et al.*, 1989b; Steinhardt, 1990): ammonia treatment mimics the fertilization Ca_i transient in this respect, too. A common feature of both the fertilization Ca_i transient and ammonia activation is the phosphorylation of pp34. It is reasonable to suppose that there may be a link between pp34 and the mechanism that generates cell cycle Ca_i transients (Picard *et al.*, 1990; Doree *et al.*, 1990; Whitaker & Patel, 1990).

The fertilization Ca_i transient in the sea-urchin egg restarts the cell division cycle by targetting the cell cycle control proteins pp34^{cdc2} and cyclin. It is a specific and well-understood example of the cell cycle Ca_i transients that may govern cell cycle transitions in somatic cells, as well as in eggs and oocytes (Whitaker & Patel, 1990).

This work was supported by the Wellcome Trust and the Royal Society.

References

Alberts, B., Bray, D., Lewis, J. & Watson, J.D. (1989) *The Molecular Biology of the Cell*. Garland, New York.

Dorée, M., Cavadore, J.-C. & Picard, A. (1990) Facts and hypotheses of calcium regulation of MPF activity during meiotic regulation of starfish oocytes. *J. Reprod. Fert., Suppl.* **42**, 135–140.

Draetta, G. & Beach, D. (1988) Activation of cdc2 protein kinase during mitosis in human cells: cell cycle-dependent phosphorylation and subunit re-arrangement. *Cell* **54**, 17–26.

Draetta, G., Luca, F., Westendorf, J., Brizuela, L., Ruderman, J. & Beach, D. (1989) cdc2 is complexed with both cyclin A and B: evidence for inactivation of MPF by proteolysis. *Cell* **56**, 829–838.

Dunphy, W.G., Brizuela, L., Beach, D. & Newport, J. (1988) The Xenopus cdc2 protein is a component of MPF, a cytoplasmic regulator of mitosis. *Cell* **54**, 423–431.

Enoch, T. & Nurse, P. (1990) Mutation of fission yeast cell cycle control genes abolishes dependence of mitosis on DNA replication. *Cell* **60**, 665–673.

Epel, D., Steinhardt, R.A., Humphreys, T. & Mazia, D. (1974) An analysis of the partial metabolic derepression of the sea urchin egg by ammonia: the existence of independent pathways. *Devl Biol.* **40**, 245–255.

Evans, T., Rosenthal, E.T., Youngbloom, J., Distel, D. & Hunt, T. (1983) Cyclin: A protein specified by maternal mRNA in sea urchin eggs that is destroyed at each cleavage division. *Cell* **33**, 389–396.

Gautier, J., Norbury, C., Lokha, M., Nurse, P. & Maller, J. (1988) Purified maturation-promoting factor contains the product of a *Xenopus* homolog of the fission yeast cell cycle control gene cdc2+. *Cell* **54**, 433–439.

Gautier, J., Matsukawa, T., Nurse, P. & Maller, J. (1989) Dephosphorylation and activation of *Xenopus* p34^cdc2 protein kinase during the cell cycle. *Nature, Lond.* **339**, 626–629.

Goebl, M. & Byers, B. (1988) Cyclin in fission yeast. *Cell* **54**, 739–740.

Gould, K. & Nurse, P. (1989) Tyrosine phosphorylation of the fission yeast cdc2^1 protein kinase regulates entry into mitosis. *Nature, Lond.* **342**, 39–45.

Grainger, J.L., Winkler, M.M., Shen, S.S. & Steinhardt, R.A. (1979) Intracellular pH controls protein synthesis rate in sea urchin eggs and early embryos. *Devl Biol.* **68**, 396–406.

Hunt, T. (1989) Maturation promoting factor, cyclin and the control of M-phase. *Curr. Opinion Cell Biol.* **1**, 268–278.

Kishimoto, T., Kuriyama, R., Kondo, H. & Kanatani, H. (1982) Generality of the action of various maturation-promoting factors. *Expl Cell Res.* **137**, 121–126.

Labbe, J., Picard, A., Peaucellier, G., Cavadore, J-C., Nurse, P. & Doree, M. (1989a) Purification of MPF from starfish: identification as the H1 histone kinase p34^cdc2 and a possible mechanism for its periodic activation. *Cell* **57**, 253–263.

Labbe, J., Capony, J-P., Caput, D., Cavadore, J-C., Derancourt, J., Kaghad, M., Lelias, J-M., Picard, A. & Doree, M. (1989b) MPF from starfish oocytes at first meiotic metaphase is a heterodimer containing one molecule of cdc2 and one molecule of cyclin B. *EMBO J.* **8**, 3053–3058.

Lee, M.G., Norbury, C.J., Spurr, N.K. & Nurse, P. (1988) Regulated expression and phosphorylation of a possible mammalian cell cycle control protein. *Nature, Lond.* **333**, 676–679.

MacNeill, S.A. & Nurse, P. (1989) Genetic interactions in the control of mitosis in fission yeast. *Curr. Genet.* **16**, 1–6.

Masui, Y. & Clarke, H.J. (1979) Oocyte maturation. *Int. Rev. Cytol.* **86**, 129–196.

Meijer, L., Arion, D., Golsteyn, R., Pines, J., Brizuela, L., Hunt, T. & Beach, D. (1989) Cyclin is a component of the sea urchin egg M-phase specific histone H1 kinase. *EMBO J.* **8**, 2275–2282.

Moreno, S., Hayles, J. & Nurse, P. (1988) Regulation of p34^cdc2 protein kinase during mitosis. *Cell* **58**, 361–372.

Morla, A.Q., Draetta, G., Beach, D. & Wang, J.Y.J. (1989) Reversible tyrosine phosphorylation of *cdc2*: dephosphorylation accompanies activation during entry into mitosis. *Cell* **58**, 193–203.

Murray, A. (1989) The cell cycle as a *cdc2* cycle. *Nature, Lond.* **342**, 14–15.

Murray, A.W. & Kirschner, M.W. (1989) Cyclin synthesis drives the early embryonic cell cycle. *Nature, Lond.* **339**, 275–280.

Nurse, P. & Bissett, Y. (1981) Gene required in G1 for commitment to cell cycle and in G2 for control of mitosis in fusion yeast. *Nature, Lond.* **292**, 558–560.

Nurse, P. & Thuriaux, P. (1980) Regulatory genes controlling mitosis in the fusion yeast *Schizosaccharomyces pombe*. *Genetics, Princeton* **96**, 627–637.

Patel, R., Twigg, J., Sheppard, B. & Whitaker, M.J. (1989a) Calcium, cyclin and cell cycle control in sea urchin embryos. In *Developmental Biology* (UCLA Symp. No. 125), pp. 21–35. Eds E. Davidson, J. Ruderman & J. Posakony. A. R. Liss, New York.

Patel, R., Twigg, J., Crossley, I., Golsteyn, R. & Whitaker, M.J. (1989b) Calcium-induced chromatin condensation and cyclin phosphorylation during chromatin condensation cycles in ammonia-activated sea urchin eggs. *J. Cell Sci., Suppl.* **12**, 129–144.

Picard, A., Cavadore, J-C., Lor, P., Parnango, J-C., Oeda, C. & Doree, M. (1990) Microinjecting a peptide sequence conserved in p34^cdc2 homologues induces a transient increase of free calcium in starfish and *Xenopus* oocytes. *Science, NY* **247**, 327–329.

Poenie, M., Alderton, J., Tsien, R.Y. & Steinhardt, R.A. (1985) Changes of free calcium levels with stages of the cell division cycle. *Nature, Lond.* **315**, 147–149.

Pondaven, P., Meijer, L. & Beach, D. (1990) Activation of M-phase specific histone H1 kinase by modification of the phosphorylation of its p34^cdc2 and cyclin components. *Genes Devel.* **4**, 9–17.

Rosenthal, E.T., Hunt, T. & Ruderman, J.V. (1980) Selective translation of mRNA controls the pattern of protein synthesis during early development of the surf clam, *Spisula solidissima*. *Cell* **20**, 487–492.

Solomon, M., Booher, R., Kirschner, M. & Beach, D. (1988) Cyclin in fission yeast. *Cell* **54**, 738–739.

Steinhardt, R.A. & Alderton, J. (1988) Intracellular free calciums rise triggers nuclear envelope breakdown in the sea urchin embryo. *Nature, Lond.* **332**, 364–366.

Steinhardt, R.A. (1990) Intracellular free calcium and the first cell cycle of the sea-urchin embryo (*Lytechinus pictus*). *J. Reprod. Fert., Suppl.* **42**, 191–197.

Swann, K. & Whitaker, M.J. (1985) Phorbol ester stimulates the sodium-hydrogen exchange of sea urchin eggs. *Nature, Lond.* **314**, 274–277.

Swann, K. & Whitaker, M.J. (1990) Second messengers at fertilization in sea-urchin eggs. *J. Reprod. Fert., Suppl.* **42**, 141–153.

Swenson, K.I., Farell, K.M. & Ruderman, J.V. (1986) The clam embryo protein cyclin A induces entry into M phase and the resumption of meiosis in *Xenopus* oocytes. *Cell* **47**, 861–870.

Twigg, J., Patel, R. & Whitaker, M.J. (1988) Translational control of $InsP_3$-induced chromatin condensation during the early cell cycles of sea urchin embryos. *Nature, Lond.* **332**, 366–369.

Wagenaar, E.B. (1983) The timing of the synthesis of proteins required for mitosis in the cell cycle of the sea urchin embryo. *Expl Cell Res.* **144**, 393–403.

Wasserman, W.J. & Smith, L.D. (1978) The cyclic behaviour of a cytoplasmic factor controlling nuclear membrane breakdown. *J. Cell Biol.* **78**, R15–R22.

Whitaker, M.J. (1989) Phosphoinositide messengers in eggs and oocytes. In *Inositol Lipids and Cellular Signalling*, pp. 459–483. Eds R. H. Michell, C. P. Downes & A. Drummond. Academic Press, New York.

Whitaker, M.J. & Patel, R. (1990) Calcium and cell cycle control. *Development* **108**, 525–542.

Whitaker, M.J. & Steinhardt, R.A. (1981) The relation between the increase in reduced nicotinamide nucleotides and the initiation and maintenance of DNA synthesis in the egg of the sea urchin *Lytechinus pictus*. *Cell* **25**, 95–103.

Whitaker, M.J. & Steinhardt, R.A. (1982) Ionic regulation of egg activation. *Q. Rev. Biophys.* **15**, 593–666.

Winkler, M.M. & Grainger, J.L. (1978) Mechanism of action of NH_4Cl and other weak bases in the activation of sea urchin eggs. *Nature, Lond.* **273**, 236–238.

Woodland, H.R. (1990) Regulation of protein synthesis in early amphibian development. *J. Reprod. Fert., Suppl.* **42**, 215–224.

Zucker, R.S., Steinhardt, R.A. & Winkler, M.M. (1978) Intracellular calcium and the mechanism of parthenogenetic activation of sea urchin eggs. *Devl Biol.* **65**, 285–295.

J. Reprod. Fert., Suppl. **42** (1990), 205–213

Cell cycle control in early mouse development

Josie McConnell

Department of Anatomy, University of Cambridge, Downing Street, Cambridge CB2 3DY, UK

Summary. Recent advances in the understanding of the molecular basis of cell cycle control, particularly that of mitotic control, are reviewed with respect to what is known about cell cycle control in early mouse embryos. The behaviour of the murine homologue of cdc2$^+$, a component of Maturation Promotion Factor (MPF), is described at these early stages.

Keywords: cdc2$^+$; MPF; cell cycle regulation; preimplantation mouse embryo

Introduction

The preimplantation mouse embryo does not at first sight appear to be an obvious system in which to study the control mechanisms operating in cell cycle regulation; the paucity of embryonic material precludes biochemical purification and analysis of factors involved in mitotic control. Also the murine system lacks cell cycle mutants which have been so useful in other systems such as yeast (Nurse, 1985; Hayles & Nurse, 1986) for defining the gene products which are essential for controlling passage through the cell cycle.

The mouse system does, however, have distinct advantages over other more extensively studied embryonic systems such as those of *Xenopus* and sea urchins. In common with other more extensively studied embryonic systems, early cleavage in the mouse embryo is not accompanied by cell growth, as is the case in most cell culture cell lines, and therefore the analysis of cell cycle control can be carried out without consideration of the complicating factors involved in the regulation of cell growth. The mouse embryo also has the unique advantage of relatively long cell cycles. This property is shown in Fig. 1; by the time the *Xenopus* embryo has developed to several million cells the mouse embryo is only midway through the 2nd cell cycle. Such long cell cycles allow the precise description of cellular events, such as the beginning and end of DNA synthesis. Against this background it is also possible to manipulate the cycle either by administering drugs or by microinjection of molecular probes such as antibodies, antisense oligonulcotides, or competing peptide. Given the lengthy cell cycle times it is possible to monitor carefully the effects of perturbing the system by these molecular probes, both at the cellular and molecular level.

Recent data (Lokha *et al.*, 1988; Gautier *et al.*, 1990) have shown that maturation promotion factor (MPF) which has been shown to be responsible for driving cells into mitosis is composed principally of two components. In *Xenopus* these two components have molecular weights of 32 000 and 45 000 and in other systems such as that of *Spisula* similar results have been obtained (Draetta *et al.*, 1989). From studies using antibodies it has become clear that the component of M_r 32 000 corresponds to the product of the cdc2$^+$ gene in yeast. Genetic and molecular analyses have shown that this gene product plays a pivotal role in control of the cell cycle (Lee & Nurse, 1987). In yeast it appears to be required at two points in the cell cycle, first during G_1 at a point known as start, and subsequently to entry into mitosis. The M_r 45 000 component of MPF has been identified as being homologous to 'cyclin' (Gautier *et al.*, 1990), a protein which was first described in the sea urchin (Evans *et al.*, 1983), but has subsequently been investigated in other systems and which appears to accumulate during each cell cycle, being abruptly destroyed as cells exit from mitosis. The mechanism of regulation of the activity of the MPF is still not entirely clear, but it is certain that phosphorylation plays an important part in the activation and function of this complex (Lee *et al.*, 1988; Moreno *et al.*, 1989). Recently, delicate mutational analysis has demonstrated that the exchange of a single tyrosine residue for a phenylalanine in the cdc2$^+$ protein in yeast seriously perturbs correct control of mitosis in this system (Gould & Nurse, 1989).

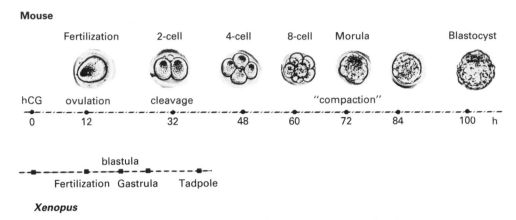

Fig. 1. Comparison of the timing of mouse and *Xenopus* development.

As discussed previously both classical biochemical and genetic studies are difficult in the mouse system. It is, however, relatively simple to apply a purely phenomenological approach to identify proteins which may be important in cell cycle control. Such an approach consists of observing the behaviour of proteins as the cell progresses through the cell cycle—any proteins which undergo changes coincident with a pivotal point in the cell cycle (e.g. begining of DNA synthesis, or entry into mitosis) may be candidates for gene products involved in regulation of the cell cycle.

In early mouse development several newly synthesized proteins appear to be modified in a cell cycle-dependent fashion. One set of proteins which migrates at M_r 35 000 shows a dramatic change in levels of phosphorylation as synchronized populations of embryos enter and exit from the first and subsequent mitoses. Recent data have demonstrated that this group of proteins does not correspond to the murine homologue of cdc2$^+$. Additionally, studies using carefully timed groups of embryos have shown that the modifications occurring to these proteins are temporally quite different from modifications occurring to the cdc2$^+$ homologue in mice.

This short paper summarizes some purely descriptive work which has been performed in the early mouse embryo, and describes some recent work using antibodies to one component of MPF, i.e. the product of the cdc2$^+$ gene.

Materials and Methods

Recovery and handling of embryos. Follicular development was promoted in 3–4-week-old female mice (either MF1 strain, Laboratory Animal Centre, Cambridge University; or C57BL/10 × CBA F1, bred in the laboratory) by injecting 5 i.u. pregnant mares' serum gonadotrophin (Folligon, Intervet). Ovulation was induced by administering 5 i.u. human chorionic gonadotrophin (hCG; Chorulon, Intervet) 48 h later. Females were paired overnight with CFLP males (Interfauna) and those with a vaginal plug the following morning were retained. Embryos were recovered from the oviducts at 24 h after hCG as fertilized 1-cell zygotes, or, when 2-, 3- or 4-cell embryos were required, were flushed at 44–48 h after hCG with Medium 2 containing 4 mg BSA/ml (M2 + BSA; Fulton & Whittingham, 1978). This medium was used for all manipulations at atmospheric CO_2. For culture, embryos were placed in modified T6 medium (Howlett *et al.*, 1988) under oil in Sterilin tissue culture dishes pre-equilibrated at 37°C in 5% CO_2. All manipulations were carried out on a Wild M5 dissecting microscope fitted with a heated stage and adjacent hot pad to prevent cooling.

In-vitro fertilization. In-vitro fertilization was performed as described by Howlett & Bolton (1985).

One-dimensional SDS-polyacrylamide gel electrophoresis. Embryos were cultured for 1 h (for one-dimensional analysis) or 2 h (for two-dimensional analysis) in a dilution of 3 μl [^{35}S]methionine (1000–1400 Ci mmol^{-1}: Amersham International) in 50 μl Medium T6 + BSA. Embryos were washed three times with protein-free M2 medium and placed in 10 μl double-strength SDS sample buffer (Laemmli, 1970), boiled for 2 min and stored at −70°C. Proteins were separated on 10% SDS-polyacrylamide gels as described by Flach *et al.* (1982), 10 embryos being applied to each lane to facilitate comparative analysis. After electrophoresis, gels were dried, autoradiographed and exposed for 1–3 days to preflashed Fuji X-ray film before autoradiography at −70°C.

Antibody generation. The antibody used throughout this work was raised against a 15-amino acid peptide, represented using the single amino acid letter code by EGVPSTAIREISLLKE. This region of the protein is conserved between humans, *S. pombe* and *S. cerevisiae* and spans amino acids 42–57 in the human homologue of cdc2$^+$. Peptide conjugation, antibody production and affinity purification of this antibody were performed exactly as described by Simanis & Nurse (1986).

Results

Initial studies of the M_r 35 000 'complex' in early mouse embryos

Before fertilization the mouse oocyte is arrested in second meiotic metaphase. After fertilization pronuclei form and migrate centrally before syngamy. Division to 2 cells occurs approximately 18–20 h after insemination. Progress through this first cell cycle is independent of any transcription from the embryonic genome (Flach *et al.*, 1982), but does depend on translation of maternally inherited mRNA templates. If translation is inhibited then this first cell division will not occur. By comparison of the patterns of the [^{35}S]methionine-labelled proteins obtained when unfertilized or 2-cell embryos are labelled *in vivo* with the patterns obtained when the mRNA from these stages is extracted and translated in an in-vitro translation system, it is clear that certain mRNAs which are present in eggs are more efficiently translated after fertilization (compare panels A and B with C and D, Fig. 2). The most striking example of this sort of regulation occurs with a group of proteins which are arrowed and have a molecular weight of approximately 35 000 (Braude *et al.*, 1979). Further analysis of these rapidly synthesized proteins which migrate at M_r 35 000 (Flach *et al.*, 1982) has demonstrated that their synthesis decreases markedly as the zygotic genome is activated at the end of the second cell cycle; after this point their synthesis is barely detectable.

Early studies by H. M. Pratt and M. Goddard (unpublished) demonstrated that, although this complex of M_r 35 000 was only synthesized abundantly during the first 2 cell cycles of mouse development, the protein synthesized from this template at these early stages was extremely stable (Fig. 3). Three different sorts of embryo were analysed: (i) embryos which blocked at the 2-cell stage (B2), (ii) those that were cultured continuously in α-amanitin from the 1-cell stage (αA), and (iii) non-blocking embryos which developed normally to morulae (F$_1$). Embryos from each group were pulse-labelled with [^{3}H]methionine for 2 h at the beginning of the second cell cycle. Radiolabelled methionine was then 'chased' out and the embryos were cultured in non-radioactive medium. At timed intervals after this labelling, 32, 46 and 66 h, equal numbers of embryos (20) were collected, lysed and analysed by SDS-gel electrophoresis and autoradiography. From the data presented in Fig. 3, it is clear that the complex of M_r 35 000 which is abundantly synthesized in the first and second cycles and is indicated by an asterisk, is extremely stable and that no detectable

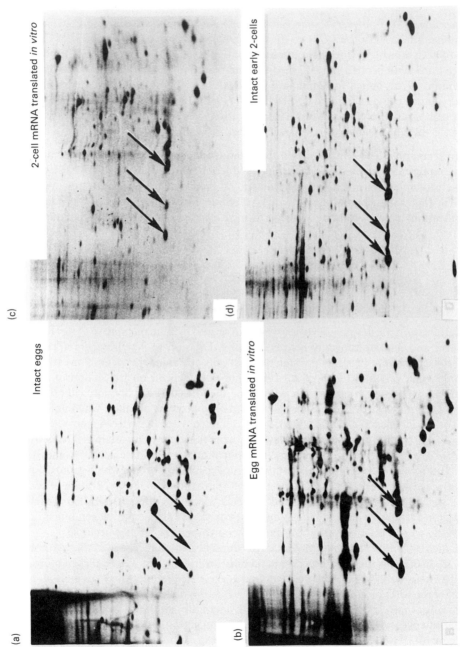

Fig. 2. Two-dimensional protein patterns of intact eggs and 2-cells compared with extracted mRNA translated in a cell-free extract. (After Braude *et al.*, 1979.)

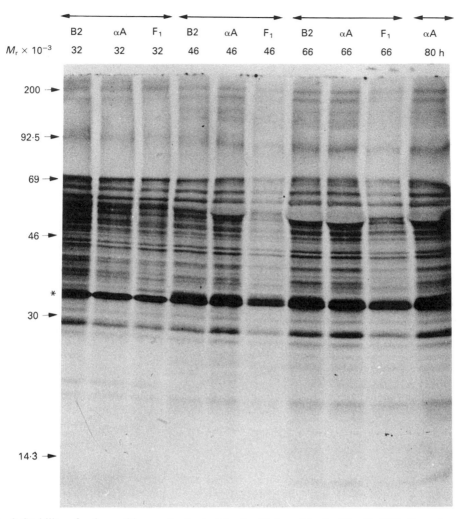

Fig. 3. Stability of polypeptides synthesized at the 1-cell stage, blocked 2-cells (B2), F_1 embryos cultured continuously in α-amanitin from the 1 cell stage (αA) and F_1 embryos (F_1) were pulsed with [³H]methionine for 2 h until 32 h after hCG, washed and incubated in unlabelled methionine (100 mM) and then analysed at the times indicated.

degradation of this protein occurs over extensive time periods, or during the time before the formation of the morula.

Modification of the M_r 35 000 complex in a cell cycle-dependent fashion

In several systems periodic behaviour of certain proteins has been observed. The most striking is that of 'cyclins' (Evans *et al.*, 1983). Protein synthesis is required for transition through the first cell cycle in mice. Further investigations were undertaken to determine whether any newly synthesized proteins were modified in a cell cycle-dependent fashion. Synchronized groups of embryos were sampled at timed intervals after insemination, labelled for 1 h with [³⁵S]methionine and analysed using SDS-gel electrophoresis and autoradiography. The results of such an experiment are shown in Fig. 4. It can be seen that the M_r 35 000 complex does appear to change mobility at a time which is coincident with entry into M phase, 17–18 h after insemination, and that this protein complex returns

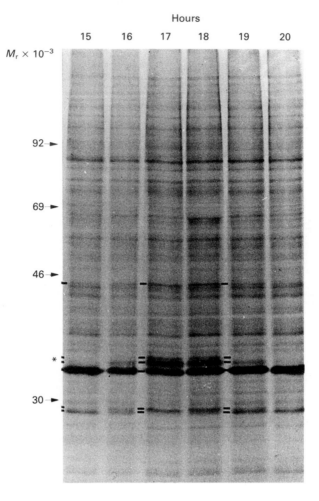

Fig. 4. Pattern of protein synthesis changes during first mitosis: one-dimensional gel showing pattern of [^{35}S]methionine-labelled proteins synthesized during a 1-h labelling period beginning at the time indicated after fertilization.

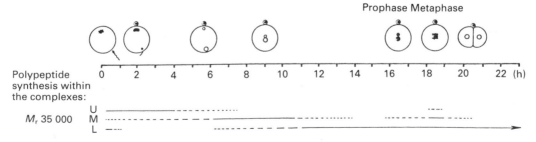

Fig. 5. Schematic representation of the behaviour of the M_r 35 000 complex during the first cell cycle.

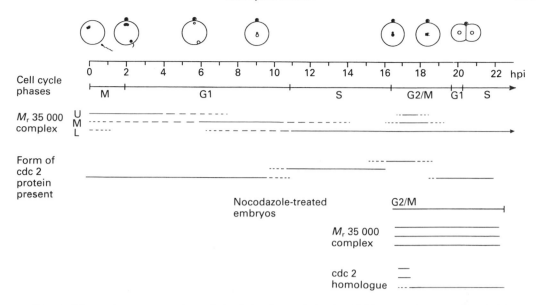

Fig. 6. Schematic representation of the behaviour of the M_r 35 000 complex and the cdc2[+] homologue during the first cell cycle of mouse development. (After McConnell & Lee, 1989.)

to its faster migrating form as the cells exit from mitosis, at 19–20 h. Additional work on this complex (Howlett, 1986) has shown that the alteration in mobility seen on entry into mitosis is due to phosphorylation and that the M_r 35 000 complex appears to be in its upper or highly phosphorylated state in unfertilized eggs which are arrested in M phase. Further pulse–chase experiments have demonstrated that the M_r 35 000 complex is reversibly phosphorylated on entry and exit from subsequent mitosis. A schematic representation of the behaviour of the complex is shown in Fig. 5.

Is the M_r 35 000 complex equivalent to any previously described cell cycle gene product?

The gene product of the cdc2[+] gene has been shown by genetic analysis to play a pivotal role in the control of the cell cycle. The human homologue of this gene has been cloned (Lee & Nurse, 1987) and antibodies have been generated against a 15-amino acid synthetic peptide which corresponds to a highly conserved region of the molecule. Antibodies reacting with this synthetic peptide cross-react with material from mouse cell lines (Lee *et al.*, 1988), and it has previously been shown that cdc2[+]-like proteins are phosphorylated at particular points in the cell cycle. The similarity in molecular weight, and the modification by phosphorylation suggested that the M_r 35 000 complex and the cdc2[+] homologue in mice might be the same protein. Experiments undertaken to test this hypothesis are described by McConnell & Lee (1989). In summary it appears that the cdc2[+] homologue in mouse embryos is not equivalent to the M_r 35 000 complex and furthermore the phosphorylation events occurring to the M_r 35 000 complex are exactly the reverse of those occurring to the cdc2[+] homologue with respect to the cell cycle timing. A schematic representation of the data presented by McConnell & Lee (1989) is shown in Fig. 6.

Discussion

The information presented in this article shows that the M_r 35 000 complex is not equivalent to the murine homologue of the cdc2[+] protein. This is not surprising in the light of recent results: data from experiments with *Xenopus* cell-free extracts (Murray & Kirshner, 1989) indicate that synthesis of cdc2$^+$ is not required for entry into M phase and that it is the synthesis of cyclin alone which is required for entry into mitosis. There is mounting evidence that it is not the synthesis of cdc2$^+$ protein which controls its activity but post-translational modifications (phosphorylation) which cause its activation (Lee *et al.*, 1988; Gould & Nurse, 1989).

Except for the molecular weight, it therefore seems that the cdc2$^+$ molecule is quite different from the M_r 35 000 complex. The M_r 35 000 complex is abundantly synthesized, whereas the cdc2$^+$ homologue does not appear to be synthesized in the early stages of mouse development. All attempts to immunoprecipitate newly synthesized cdc2$^+$ material from the early mouse embryo have been unsuccessful (J. McConnell, unpublished data). Additionally, as shown by McConnell & Lee (1989) the phosphorylation events occurring to the cdc2$^+$ molecule appear to be exactly the reverse of those occurring to the M_r 35 000 complex at timed points during the first cell cycle of mouse development.

More detailed investigation of the timing and phosphorylation events occurring to the murine homologue of the cdc2$^+$ protein are required, and phosphoamino acid analysis plus peptide mapping is being performed on ^{32}P-labelled cdc2$^+$ protein and M_r 35 000 complex isolated at particular points in the cell cycle. It is probably worth noting that from Western blot analysis (McConnell & Lee, 1989) the cdc2$^+$ molecule undergoes two phosphorylation events which cause an alteration in the mobility of this protein; the first occurs on entry into S phase, the second in G_2/M before mitosis. It is satisfactory to note that these times exactly coincide with the points in the cell cycle in yeast where the cdc2$^+$ product is required.

We are currently attempting to perturb the behaviour of the M_r 35 000 protein complex by injecting peptides which are homologous to conserved regions of the cdc2$^+$ molecule. Such approaches have yielded valuable information in other systems (Labbe *et al.*, 1989) but as yet we have not been able to establish a link between cdc2$^+$ and the M_r 35 000 complex, but it is hoped that these more defined types of analysis will establish whether there is some connection.

A murine homologue of the cyclin gene has not yet been isolated, and attempts to identify a possible candidate by injecting antisense oligonucleotides corresponding to a conserved sequence in all cyclins into early mouse embryos has not resulted in the prevention of synthesis of a particular protein as analysed on 2D-gels (unpublished data). There may be several explanations for this phenomenon. Firstly codon usage may be different in mouse embryo, or cyclin may be synthesized at such low levels in these early cell cycles that inhibition of its synthesis is not detected. The latter explanation seems unlikely since no morphological effects were observed in the injected embryos. The isolation of cDNA clones encoding embryonic mouse cyclins may help in the design of more specific probes. It would seem unlikely the the M_r 35 000 protein complex is the murine equivalent of the cyclin type molecules which have been documented in other systems. For although the M_r 35 000 complex is rapidly synthesized after fertilization it is not destroyed as cells exit from mitosis. The available evidence from *Xenopus* (Murray & Kirschner, 1989) and other systems indicates that the destruction of cyclin is an absolute requirement for exit from M phase. In conclusion, no proof is yet available to suggest that the M_r 35 000 complex of proteins is involved in control of the cell cycle; it may be the case that the modifications of this complex occur as a result of some alterations in other critical molecules, e.g. cdc2$^+$ or cyclin. The use of more defined molecular probes may help to answer this question. Finally, it is worth pointing out that control of the cell cycle in early mammalian embryos may be somewhat different from that operating in more commonly studied systems like those of *Xenopus* and *Spisula*. The former has long cell cycles with an extended G_1 phase whereas the latter have very short cell cycles which are composed almost exclusively of S and M phases. It would therefore seem worth pursuing the mechanisms operating in the control of the mammalian cell cycle, since the control mechanism may differ from those operating in more rapidly dividing externally fertilised creatures.

I thank L. Campbell, L. Clayton, S. Pickering and M. H. Johnson for advice and help in the preparation of this manuscript.

References

Braude, P.R., Pelham, H., Flack, G. & Lobatto, R. (1979) Post-translational control in the early mouse embryo. *Nature, Lond.* **282**, 102–105.

Draetta, G., Luca, F., Westendorf, J., Brizuela, L., Ruderman, J. & Beach, D. (1989) cdc2⁺ protein kinase is complexed with both cyclin A and B: evidence for proteolytic inactivation of MPF. *Cell* **56**, 829–838.

Evans, T., Rosenthal, E.T., Youngbloom, J., Distel, D. & Hunt, T. (1983) Cyclin: a protein specified by maternal mRNA in sea urchin eggs that is destroyed at each cleavage division. *Cell* **33**, 389–396.

Flach, G., Johnson, M.H., Braude, P.R., Taylor, R.S. & Bolton, V.N. (1982) The transition from maternal to embryonic control in the two cell mouse embryo. *EMBO J.* **1**, 681–686.

Fulton, B.P. & Whittingham, D.G. (1978) Activation of mammalian oocytes by intracellular injection of calcium. *Nature, Lond.* **273**, 149–151.

Gautier, J., Minshull, J., Lokha, M.J., Hunt, T. & Maller, J.L. (1990) Cyclin is a component of Maturation Promoting Factor from Xenopus. *Cell* **60**, 487–494.

Gould, K.L. & Nurse, P. (1989) Tyrosine phosphorylation of the fission yeast cdc2⁺ protein kinase regulates entry into mitosis. *Nature, Lond.* **342**, 39–45.

Hayles, J. & Nurse, P. (1986) Cell cycle regulation in yeast. *J. Cell Sci. Suppl.* **4**, 155–170.

Howlett, S.K. (1986) A set of proteins showing cell cycle-dependent modification in the early mouse embryo. *Cell* **45**, 387–396.

Howlett, S.K. & Bolton, V.N. (1985) Sequence and regulation of morphological and molecular events during the first cell cycle of mouse embryogenesis. *J. Embryol. exp. Morph.* **87**, 175–206.

Howlett, S.K., Barton, S. & Surani, M.A.H. (1988) Nuclear cytoplasmic interactions following nuclear transplantation in mouse embryos. *Development* **101**, 915–925.

Labbe, J.C., Picard, A., Peaucellier, G., Cavadore, J.C., Nurse, P. & Doree, M. (1989) Purification of MPF from starfish: identification as the H1 histone kinase p34cdc2 and a possible mechanism for its periodic activation. *Cell* **57**, 253–263.

Laemmli, U.K. (1970) Cleavage of structural proteins during the assembly of the head of bacteriophage T4. *Nature, Lond.* **227**, 680–685.

Lee, M.G. & Nurse, P. (1987) Complementation used to clone a human homologue of the fission yeast cell cycle control gene cdc2. *Nature, Lond.* **327**, 31–35.

Lee, M.G., Norbury, C.J., Spurr, N.K. & Nurse, P. (1988) Regulated expression and phosphorylation of a possible mammalian cell-cycle control protein. *Nature, Lond.* **333**, 676–679.

Lokha, M.J., Hayes, M.K. & Maller, J.L. (1988) Purification of maturation-promoting factor, an intracellular regulator of early mitotic events. *Proc. natn. Acad. Sci. USA* **85**, 3009–3013.

McConnell, J. & Lee, M. (1989) Presence of cdc2⁺-like proteins in the preimplantation mouse embryo. *Development* **107**, 481–489.

Moreno, S., Hayles, J. & Nurse, P. (1989) Regulation of p34 cdc2 protein kinase during mitosis. *Cell* **58**, 361 372.

Murray, A.W. & Kirschner, M.W. (1989) Cyclin synthesis drives the early embryonic cell cycle. *Nature, Lond.* **339**, 275–279.

Nurse, P. (1985) Cell cycle control genes in yeast. *Trends in Genetics* **1**, 51–55.

Simanis, V. & Nurse, P. (1986) The cell cycle control gene cdc2⁺ of fusion yeast encodes a protein kinase potentially regulated by phosphorylation. *Cell* **45**, 261–268.

J. Reprod. Fert., Suppl. **42** (1990), 215–224

Regulation of protein synthesis in early amphibian development

H. R. Woodland

Department of Biological Sciences, University of Warwick, Coventry CV4 7AL, UK

Keywords: protein synthesis; amphibians; development translational control

Introduction

The early development of all organisms is characterized by changing patterns of protein synthesis superimposed on very marked changes in the overall rate of protein synthesis. In general there is a very considerable increase in the overall rate of protein synthesis in the period from oocyte maturation to organogenesis, abrupt changes being most dramatically seen in organisms where there is a dormant phase of development, as in sea urchins. After maturation the unfertilized eggs are retained in the gonad pending their release to the sea, and their rate of protein synthesis is extremely low. Fertilization then leads to a very rapid mobilization of the protein synthetic apparatus, so that about 25% of ribosomes are engaged in protein synthesis within 2 h (Goustin & Wilt, 1981). Although considerable research effort has been directed at sea-urchin dormancy, in its extreme form the phenomenon is relatively unusual, and it is commoner to see a more-or-less continuous increase from oogenesis onwards. This is really what happens in sea urchins, if one ignores the dormancy period (e.g. Goustin & Wilt, 1981). It is this kind of pattern that is found in *Xenopus*, as illustrated by the pattern of ribosome incorporation into polysomes during development (Fig. 1). A larger scale view of early stages in this pattern is presented in Fig. 2.

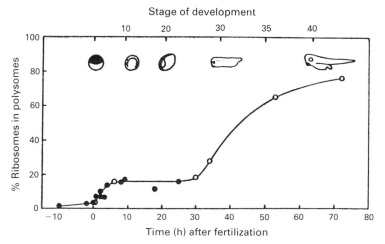

Fig. 1. Mobilization of ribosomes in *Xenopus* embryos: − 10 h is the time at which progesterone sets in motion the maturation and ovulation of the oocyte, which passes to the exterior and is fertilized at 0 h. (From Woodland, 1974.)

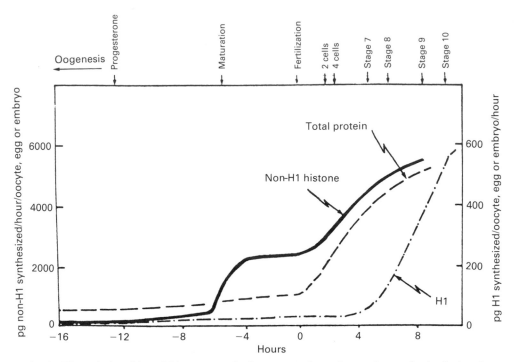

Fig. 2. The relationship of histone synthetic rates and total protein synthesis during late oogenesis (a period of several months) and early development up to the 30 000-cell stage. The total protein synthesis rate is presented on an arbitrary scale and represents the polysome content. Stage 7 is the very early blastula and stage 10 the early gastrula. Transcription of mRNA begins at stage $8\frac{1}{2}$. (From Woodland, 1980.)

Since later embryos are not unusually active in protein synthesis, the first point that emerges from Figs 1 and 2 is that the rates of protein synthesis are unusually low from the oocyte to the neurula stage. Indeed the rates of synthesis in the large oocyte are so low that it almost seems dormant! But it would be unreasonable to view it in this light, since a similarly low proportion of ribosomes are engaged in protein synthesis throughout oogenesis, even though there are much smaller numbers of ribosomes in its early stages (Taylor & Smith, 1985). There is never a dip in the rate of protein synthesis and therefore there is no dormant phase, nor is there an abrupt increase in rate at fertilization; rather there is a modest increase of about 50–100% during maturation (whether it is abrupt or gradual is not known) and then a progressive increase through cleavage. In considering the significance of these changes in rate it is important to know whether the synthesis of all proteins varies independently or if there are much larger groupings behaving as regulatory classes. This is in turn very important when one comes to consider the mechanisms that bring about the changes in rates.

Qualitative and quantitative changes in protein synthesis during early development

Changes in protein synthesis during oocyte maturation

Ballantine *et al.* (1979) made a global analysis of protein synthesis during maturation using two-dimensional gel electrophoresis. Some proteins clearly increase their rate of synthesis, some decrease or disappear. If there were groups of mRNAs which acted as simple regulatory classes they might be revealed by comparing the incorporation of precursor into many proteins; classes might increase or decrease by constant factors. No such groups were detected; rather the proteins formed a continuum (except for those that became undetectable, and so could be called a class). This analysis has several limitations, for while it excludes the existence of the simplest kind of regulatory classes associated with the increase in protein synthesis, it certainly does not mean that they do not exist in a more complex form. Further, if there were several dozen simple regulatory classes, experimental error would probably ensure that only a continuum was discerned. Lastly, this kind of analysis is restricted to the kind of proteins that are resolved on the sort of two-dimensional gels used. We will see that histones, which they do not resolve, do seem to provide a regulatory class (see below).

Other studies have selected individual proteins or a small family of proteins for investigation. The main family studied to date has been the histones, and individual proteins have been selected for a variety of ways, including screening for mRNAs present in untranslated ribonucleoprotein particles (RNPs) in oocytes.

Histones have been very extensively studied during early amphibian development (Woodland, 1980, 1982). All four nucleosomal histones (Adamson & Woodland, 1974, 1977; Woodland & Adamson, 1977) and H1 (Flynn & Woodland, 1980; Van Dongen *et al.*, 1983) are synthesized at a low rate during oogenesis, using part of a large pool of mRNA molecules. This yields a large pool of stored histones that is used to assemble nuclei during cleavage. At maturation the nucleosomal histones are synthesized about 50 times faster, thus behaving like a single regulatory class. The H1 histones do not increase in rate of synthesis until the mid-blastula stage, indicating that even though this kind of message shares sequence motifs, like the conserved 3′ stem/loop structure, with the other histone mRNAs, it is nevertheless differently regulated. This suggests that other sequences must be involved in the regulation of histone mRNA translation.

The two-dimensional gel analyses of a number of authors indicated that a variety of mRNAs, like core histones, were mobilized from a stored form during maturation. To obtain the mRNAs encoding such proteins, Dworkin & Dworkin-Rastl (1985) screened a cDNA library for mRNA sequences present in the post-ribosomal supernatant of oocytes. Of 18 such mRNAs, they showed that 13 became much more intensively translated by the 16-cell stage and 4 were mobilized later. Many of these RNAs are of unknown function, but D7 is especially interesting because its destruction with oligonucleotides leads to a delay in the time course of maturation. Another (G10) has been used to analyse binding proteins, which might repress its translation in the oocyte, and polyadenylation, which seems to be involved in its translational activation (see below).

One mRNA that shows a particularly dramatic activation during maturation is the transcript of the proto-oncogene c-*mos*. Persuasive evidence was obtained that initiation of translation of the c-*mos* RNA was the trigger that set the events of maturation in train (Sagata *et al.*, 1988, 1989a). Beyond this possible role it is now clear that c-*mos* is necessary to maintain the matured oocyte (that is the unfertilized egg) in the metaphase state (Watanabe *et al.*, 1989; Sagata *et al.*, 1989b). It would be very interesting to examine the synthesis of the c-*mos* product in those oocytes that fail to undergo maturation after treatment with maturation-inducing hormones *in vitro* or *in vivo*. This is because, in spite of failing to complete maturation by germinal vesicle breakdown, they still increase histone synthesis via translational control (Adamson & Woodland, 1977).

There are also proteins whose synthesis ceases during maturation. These include some of the ribosomal proteins (Pierandrei-Amaldi *et al.*, 1982). Since rRNA synthesis also ceases at this time feedback control suggests itself as a possible mechanism. This is unlikely to be the case because later in development translation is reactivated normally in anucleolate embryos, which make no rRNA (Pierandrei-Amaldi *et al.*, 1985). Further, in oocytes large amounts of injected L1 ribosomal protein mRNA (Baum *et al.*, 1988) or L1 mRNA made in embryos on injected genes (Pierandrei-Amaldi *et al.*, 1988) are both translated to produce excess L1 protein, which is then degraded. In the oocyte, therefore, regulation may be at the protein stability and also RNA splicing and stability levels, but it is not translational (Pierandrei-Amaldi *et al.*, 1988).

c-*mos*, whose translational activation at fertilization was discussed above, is also an mRNA whose product ceases to be detectable during very early development; in this case at fertilization (Sagata *et al.*, 1989b). However, this is primarily because the protein is degraded by a Ca^{2+}-activated protease, calpain (Watanabe *et al.*, 1989) and it is not known whether its translation ceases at this time. If translational control was absent, then inhibition of calpain (e.g. by calstatin) in the zygote or at early cleavage stages should produce the same effect as injecting cytostatic factor or large amounts of c-*mos* RNA into cleaving blastomeres.

Translation control at blastula stages

A number of stored maternal mRNAs are not activated until the blastula stage. The first discovered was H1 histone (Woodland *et al.*, 1979; Flynn & Woodland, 1980), which is made at a low rate in the egg and accelerates in synthesis during cleavage, much later than the core nucleosomal histones (Fig. 2). Just why the synthesis of H1 is largely delayed is unclear, given that the oocyte contains stored H1 protein (Van Dongen *et al.*, 1983). Further mRNAs which exhibit this behaviour are those encoding fibronectin (Lee *et al.*, 1984) and nuclear lamins (Stick & Hausen, 1985). Lamin L_{111} is synthesized and stored in oocytes to form a pool for nuclear assembly during cleavage. The translation of L_{III} is reactivated at MBT, and L_I appears for the first time at MBT, also through translational control. This system seems to present a very favourable opportunity for analysing this kind of translational control.

Lastly, three proteins recognizable as spots on two-dimensional gels were shown, by analysis of androgenetic haploid hybrids, to be translationally activated at the blastula stage (Woodland & Ballantine, 1980).

Translational control related to the cell cycle

In a number of marine invertebrates the rise and fall in the synthesis of a small number of abundant cell-cycle-related polypeptides is a particularly obvious feature of the early cleavage cycles. Key proteins in this category are the cyclins, which seem to activate MPF and thus drive cells into the M-phase. This is an extensive and active area of current research, which will not be reviewed here. Cyclins have now been shown to show the expected translational control in *Xenopus*. A particularly exciting feature of this work is that the cyclins show their cyclical translational activation in a cell-free system (Minshull *et al.*, 1989). This system is currently unfractionated, but if its refinement is possible it might be possible to dissect the control system in detail.

Mechanism of translational control

Initial agents instigating translational control events

Much of the discussion above centres around the events of maturation, which are instigated by hormonal action. The mechanism has been discussed by Smith (1975, 1989). It seems that gonado-trophins stimulate cells of the follicle to produce steroid hormone, probably progesterone, in a transcription-dependent process. This progesterone must then act on the surface of the oocyte; intracellular injection of progesterone is ineffective in provoking maturation, and when coupled to large molecules it can evoke maturation without entering the cell (Baulieu *et al.*, 1978). This is a most unusual way for a steroid hormone to act, since steroids normally penetrate cells and interact with intracellular receptors that bind directly to specific batteries of genes. In support of a novel mechanism in maturation it is found that in the oocyte progesterone action does not require the nucleus at all (Smith, 1975; Adamson & Woodland, 1977), suggesting that a different kind of receptor must certainly be involved. It may be that this is located in the plasma membrane, and thus it may operate through intracellular second messengers in a process more like that used by peptide hormones. Indeed, insulin and insulin-like growth factor are also capable of inducing maturation (Maller & Koontz, 1981).

The triggers for later translational control events are unknown, except in a general way for the cell cycle-related changes. In the case of fibronectin, which switches on at the mid-blastula transition, it is clear that whatever is involved it is not a DNA replication-counting mechanism, as is true for the mid-blastula transition itself, since fibronectin turns on in activated unfertilized eggs (Lee *et al.*, 1984).

Overall rates of protein synthesis

From what has been said above it will be apparent that overall changes in protein synthetic rates are, at least to some extent, an amalgam of independent components. It is therefore worth asking if there is any evidence at all for overall controls on protein synthesis in amphibian embryos. As yet there is no simple answer to this question, but two kinds of information are relevant. The first concerns measurements of protein synthetic efficiency, the second relates to information on the translation of injected mRNAs.

Direct measurements of ribosome transit rates along mRNAs have been reported by Richter *et al.* (1982). They found no increase in elongation rate on endogenous mRNAs during maturation (although there was a 2-fold increase on injected globin mRNA, but curiously not on those for zein or ovalbumin, whose proteins are translocated across the endoplasmic reticulum, or on adenovirus protein IX mRNA). In themselves elongation rates can have no direct effect on protein synthetic rates, but rather the latter is regulated solely by polypeptide initiation frequency. In an absence of changes in initiation frequency polysome sizes are proportional to the rate of elongation. Since elongation rates are unchanged at maturation (Richter *et al.*, 1982), as is the polysome size (Woodland, 1974; Richter *et al.*, 1982), it follows that the rate of initiation is also constant. Thus the 2-fold increase in the rate of protein synthesis must primarily result from the translation of a larger number of mRNAs. This conclusion fits with the observation of Richter *et al.* (1982) that in short-term [^{35}S]methionine incorporation studies the labelling of polysomal nascent peptides doubles in amount during maturation, and also the observation that the number of polysomes increases (Woodland, 1974). The likely cause of the increase in mRNA utilization could either be that repressing agents ('masking' proteins) are removed from many RNAs, or that positive control factors make mRNAs translatable (e.g. by enabling ribosome binding). Evidence in favour of the former view is that sea-urchin histone mRNAs are translated equally efficiently when injected into the oocyte and the egg, although the endogenous histones increase synthesis 50-fold (Woodland & Wilt, 1980). This experiment needs repeating with *Xenopus* mRNAs. Additional evidence is considered below.

If the increase in protein synthesis at maturation, and indeed through early development, is simply a matter of unrepressed mRNA availability, it would be anticipated that further injected RNA molecules would increase the overall rate of protein synthesis. This was first properly tested by Laskey *et al.* (1977), who showed that injecting large amounts of globin mRNA into oocytes did not increase the overall rate of protein synthesis; rather there was competition between the injected and endogenous mRNAs such that endogenous protein synthesis was reduced. This result has been confirmed by various later authors (e.g. Asselbergs *et al.*, 1979) and the phenomenon has also been shown to occur in fertilized sea-urchin eggs (Colin & Hille, 1986; Hille *et al.*, 1990). However, spare translational capacity is not always absent since half-grown *Xenopus* oocytes will increase protein synthesis when injected with globin mRNA (Taylor *et al.*, 1985). It has also been reported that mRNAs which will be translated on membrane-bound polysomes do not compete for the translational machinery with injected or endogenous mRNAs that are translated on cytosolic polysomes (Richter & Smith, 1981). Part of the reason for this may be that the oocyte has limited endoplasmic reticulum, and for this reason limited capacity to translate secretory mRNAs. However, competition for a limiting component must apply to most messages since most oocyte and egg proteins are destined for the cytosol and many experiments suggest that their translation proceeds efficiently. Moreover, small and large amounts of injected globin mRNA are translated on the same sized polysomes (Lingrel & Woodland, 1974), and so the competition between injected and endogenous mRNAs cannot be for a component that acts at or after ribosome binding during the initiation of protein synthesis, since competition would then decrease mean polysome size. Lingrel & Woodland (1974) termed this component a 'pre-initiation' factor. It could be an mRNA-binding protein that permits translation (examples of such proteins are the proteins of cap-binding complex, CBP1, eIF4A, eIF4B and eIF4F; see below).

Richter & Smith (1981) made an important observation that must be taken into account when interpreting these competition experiments. This was that when large amounts of mRNA were injected, over 95% was rapidly destroyed. Since competition occurred in these experiments the only viable interpretation is that competition is a once and for all event and it is hard to avoid the conclusion that it is for a stabilizing factor. If this is so, then there should be degradation of endogenous sequences as well, but this has not been tested. In addition the stored mRNA should be in a distinct non-degradable, non-competable pool. This interpretation also implies that the mRNA injection experiments tell us little about the regulatory properties of the translational machinery.

A little after this report, using our own colony of frogs, Drummond et al. (1985a, b) reported that a variety of natural and synthetic mRNAs were only degraded to the 50% level, and that this value did not depend on the amount of mRNA injected. Since then the original laboratory has reported that they later found considerable variability in the amounts of mRNA degraded (from 25% to 97·5%) and attribute the variability to the properties of oocytes from different frogs. If this is so, it would be important to make a detailed comparison of stability and competition in these different kinds of oocytes.

Figure 1 emphasizes that there is a progressive and considerable increase in protein synthesis, depending solely on translational control up to MBT, when mRNA transcription begins. At oocyte and egg stages there is little if any spare translational capacity and one imagines this holds true through cleavage. In addition there is no change in polysome size, and hence probably in initiation frequency. Thus the pre-initiation component must increase in availability as development proceeds, presumably accompanied by the commensurate release of stored mRNA molecules from the sequestered maternal pool. Other components of translation may also increase during early development. For example the content of tRNA is very low per total ribosome in the oocyte (about 1 total tRNA/ribosome rather than 20:1; Woodland, 1974). Since protein synthesis is efficient there must be sufficient tRNA, and of course only about 1% of the ribosomes are present in polysomes. The very intense tRNA synthesis commencing at the mid-blastula transition (Brown & Littna, 1966) must make good this deficiency.

The nature of the rate limiting component has recently been investigated by Audet et al. (1987). The effect of a variety of initiation factors on translation of endogenous oocyte proteins was tested. The factors eIF-2, eIF-3, eIF-4B, eIF-4D and eIF-5 all had no effect, but eIF-4A stimulated protein synthesis 2-fold. Since it had no effect on in-vitro matured oocytes it was argued that active eIF-4A availability controlled the overall rate of protein synthesis in oocytes and that its increase led to the 2-fold increase occurring during maturation. Another component of the same cap-binding complex as eIF-4A, eIF-4F is apparently inhibited in translationally inactive cell-free systems made from sea-urchin eggs. This inhibition is relieved by addition of eIF-4F (Huang et al., 1987; Hille et al., 1990). These results are not inconsistent with the hypothesis of Lingrel & Woodland (1974) that a 'pre-initiation' factor is rate limiting for mRNA translation in the frog oocyte, since eIF-4A is part of the cap-binding complex which forms a pre-initiation complex necessary for 40S subunit binding.

However, there are problems in fitting the proposed role of eIF-4A in limiting exogenous mRNA translation with the measurement of Audet et al. (1987) of the stability of their injected mRNA. No matter how much globin RNA was injected only a threshold level of 4 ng remained stable, even though competition with endogenous sequences occurred when the larger amounts were injected. This might be taken to imply that, once formed, the cap-binding complex on the injected mRNA was non-exchangeable; however, this is inconsistent with the observation that the translation of a first globin mRNA can be suppressed by competition from a second mRNA, injected later (Richter & Smith, 1981). The only alternative viable hypothesis seems to be that eIF-4A has a second role in stabilizing mRNA, but this possibility has yet to be tested. It would correlate with the role of the cap itself in stabilizing mRNA.

RNA-binding proteins which repress the translation of mRNAs and the role of polyadenylation

The evidence that tentatively suggests that there is a sequestered untranslated pool of mRNAs in the maternal pool has been reviewed above. This pool would include some mRNAs, like histones, which are also represented among the translated mRNAs, and others which are not (e.g. lamin L_1 and c-*mos*). The most likely mechanism for repression of a variety of mRNAs that are capable of release from repression at different times, is binding to protein repressors. These proteins could both prevent translation and stabilize the mRNAs. The data summarized suggest that the binding of these proteins would have to be very stable, little exchange occurring *in vivo* over periods of many hours or days.

The protein composition of the mRNA particles of ovary has been examined by several authors (review Richter, 1988). Some proteins are common to other tissues and some are ovary-specific. The important point that concerns us is whether they have any role in repression of translation. Richter & Smith (1984) reconstituted these proteins onto globin mRNA *in vitro* and showed that they caused about 70% repression of translation of the globin mRNA when it was injected into oocytes. It is not certain which proteins produced the effect. However, independently Kick *et al.* (1987) showed that a single, purified oocyte protein of M_r 60 000 could produce the same kind of repression (see Sommerville, 1990). This protein probably binds to the poly(A) tail of mRNA. It is very interesting that the repression of translation is sensitive to phosphorylation. There are therefore two phosphoproteins present in mRNPs (both oocyte-specific) as well as protein kinase activity, and treatment of reconstituted and native RNPs with phosphatase renders them translatable. Since oocyte maturation is well known to be associated with, indeed driven by, phosphorylation events, the possibility that phosphorylation/dephosphorylation is involved in translational regulation is particularly attractive (see Sommerville, 1990).

A word of caution is necessary here, since globin mRNA is not normally found in oocytes and is translated efficiently when injected into them. If the results of Kick *et al.* (1987) are biologically meaningful they fit with the view that the repressing proteins are all bound to stored mRNAs in a non-exchangeable form; they also beg the question of whether globin mRNA would enter the non-translated pool if it were actually synthesized in the oocyte.

The conclusion that translational control may be brought about by poly(A)-binding proteins, like the M_r 60 000 protein described above, correlates with many observations on a variety of systems, showing that the behaviour of poly(A) tails correlates with changes in translation. In general embryos show a positive correlation between the presence of a poly(A) tail and translation. This is particularly well shown in embryos of the surf-clam, *Spisula*, in which before fertilization most maternal mRNAs are poly(A)$^-$ and untranslated. They enter both poly(A)$^+$ and translated classes on fertilization (Rosenthal *et al.*, 1982). Evidence of a similar kind exists for various embryos, including *Xenopus* (Sturgess *et al.*, 1980; Dworkin & Dworkin-Rastl, 1985; McGrew *et al.*, 1989). In other systems direct evidence that poly(A) tails are important in translation has been reported by Jacobson & Favreau (1983), who showed that pure poly(A) reduced the in-vitro translation of poly(A)$^+$, but not poly(A)$^-$, mRNAs, and also by Sachs & Davis (1989) using yeast mutants. For *Xenopus*, Deshpande *et al.* (1979) and Drummond *et al.* (1985b) have shown a correlation between poly(A) tail presence or length and efficiency of translation in *Xenopus* oocytes. However, the most solid evidence for an involvement of polyadenylation in such control has been obtained in a study of a single cloned mRNA species, G10.

If we are to understand the role of phenomena like the binding of message-specific proteins it will be invaluable to study individual cloned molecules which reproduce control phenomena when injected into eggs or developing embryos. This has now been shown to be possible with at least one mRNA, G10. This was originally isolated as an mRNA predominantly present as free RNP particles in oocytes (Dworkin & Dworkin-Rastl, 1985), and was later shown to move into polysomes after maturation (McGrew *et al.*, 1989). This behaviour is reproduced by injected SP6 transcripts of G10, provided that they have a normal poly(A) tail (McGrew *et al.*, 1989). Swiderski & Richter (1988) have studied the proteins bound to untranslated injected G10 transcripts in oocytes. Some of these polypeptides are not found bound to globin mRNA, which is an mRNA that substantially enters polysomes. These proteins are good candidates for repressors of translation.

The injected G10 transcripts become polysomal during maturation, a process that is accompanied by a doubling in the length of their poly(A) tails. Lengthening the poly(A) tail to the same extent *in vitro* before injection is not sufficient to cause G10 translation in oocytes (surprisingly, yet more A residues are added on maturation). Since it was also found that blockage of the A addition process by cordycepin prevents G10 incorporation into polysomes at maturation it was concluded that it is the process of polyadenylation itself that is essential for increased translation during maturation. The sequences necessary for increased polyadenylation (AAUAAA and UUUUUUAU) are common to several mRNAs mobilized during maturation, suggesting that this mechanism may be common to many, if not all rRNAs that are activated at this time. The core nucleosomal histone mRNAs must of course be an exception because when they are mobilized their short poly(A) tails are removed (Ballantine & Woodland, 1985). It is doubtful whether there is any causal relationship between these two events, since histone H1 mRNA is also depolyadenylated at this time (Ruderman *et al.*, 1979), but its translation is not activated until much later (see above). Further work is needed to establish whether histones are the only exception to this requirement for a poly(A) tail for translation through maturation. Cytoskeletal actin is a molecule well worth further study since it seems to show a decreased polyadenylation and translation in the oocyte/egg transition, although this is not coincident with maturation (Sturgess *et al.*, 1980). Certainly, the general rule is emerging that lengthening of poly(A) tails is needed for translational mobilization of non-histone mRNAs and decrease prevents it. How this fits with the observation that proteins binding to poly(A) tails inhibit translation is unclear.

Conclusions

If nothing else, this review serves to emphasize that translational control in amphibian development is still largely a mysterious process as regards mechanism and even the range of proteins affected remains unclear. However, certain of the mechanisms involved are currently emerging. The increase in synthesis of some, although certainly not all, proteins at maturation seems to involve the lengthening of their poly(A) tails. The histones clearly increase synthesis by another mechanism. It is possible that these two phenomena are the sole cause of the overall increase in protein synthesis at maturation, and depolyadenylation may also control some of the proteins that decrease at this time, both by reducing mRNA translatabilty and stability. It is these kinds of processes which are likely to be the most important in producing the overall changes in rate of protein synthesis, although other factors (like perhaps active eIF-4A availability) may also need to increase to permit the overall increase in rate to occur. It should be stressed that this increase at maturation is small compared to that which translational control brings about during cleavage and the mechanism for this increase is unknown. Certainly it will require the increased availability of yet more translational machinery.

The reasons for the prevalence of translational control mechanisms in early development lie in the extremely unfavourable gene dosage in the gigantic cells involved. This has been discussed in detail by Woodland (1982). In amphibians those proteins affected by translational control whose function is known affect general cellular functions. Translational control may also affect proteins causing cell differentiation, since in *Drosophila* it brings about, for example, the translation of the *dorsal⁺* gene product, which then establishes the dorso-ventral axis (Steward *et al.*, 1988). The emerging unity of developmental mechanisms in diverse animals suggests that such phenomena might therefore also occur in amphibians.

References

Adamson, E.D. & Woodland, H.R. (1974) Histone synthesis in early amphibian development: histone synthesis and DNA synthesis are not co-ordinated. *J. molec. Biol.* **88**, 263–285.

Adamson, E.D. & Woodland, H.R. (1977) Changes in the rate of histone synthesis during oocyte maturation and very early development of *Xenopus laevis. Devl Biol.* **57**, 136–147.

Asselbergs, F.A.M., Van Venrooij, W.J. & Bloemendal, H. (1979) Messenger RNA competition in living *Xenopus* oocytes. *Eur. J. Biochem.* **94**, 249–254.

Audet, R.G., Goodchild, J. & Richter, J.D. (1987) Eukaryotic initiation factor 4a stimulates translation in microinjected *Xenopus* oocytes. *Devl Biol.* **121**, 58–68.

Ballantine, J.E.M. & Woodland, H.R. (1985) Polyadenylation of histone mRNA in *Xenopus* oocytes and embryos. *FEBS Letters* **180**, 224–228.

Ballantine, J.E.M., Woodland, H.R. & Sturgess, E.A. (1979) Changes in protein synthesis during the development of *Xenopus laevis. J. Embryol. exp. Morph.* **51**, 137–153.

Baulieu, E.E., Godeau, F., Schorderet, M. & Schorderet-Slatkine, S. (1978) Steroid-induced meiotic division in *Xenopus laevis* oocytes: surface and calcium. *Nature, Lond.* **275**, 593–598.

Baum, E.Z., Hyman, L.E. & Wormington, W.M. (1988) Post-translational control of ribosomal protein L1 accumulation in *Xenopus* oocytes. *Devl Biol.* **126**, 141–149.

Brown, D.D. & Littna, E. (1966) Synthesis and accumulation of low molecular weight RNA during embryogenesis of *Xenopus laevis. J. molec. Biol.* **20**, 95–112.

Colin, A.M. & Hille, M.B. (1986) Injected mRNA does not increase protein synthesis in unfertilized, fertilized, or ammonia-activated sea urchin eggs. *Devl Biol.* **115**, 184–192.

Deshpande, A.K., Chatterjee, B. & Roy, A.K. (1979) Translation and stability of rat liver messenger RNA for α_{2u}-globulin in *Xenopus* oocytes. *J. biol. Chem.* **254**, 8937–8942.

Drummond, D.R., Armstrong, J. & Colman, A. (1985a) Stability and movement of mRNAs and their encoded proteins in *Xenopus* oocytes. *J. Cell Biol.* **100**, 1148–1156.

Drummond, D.R., Armstrong, J. & Colman, A. (1985b) The effect of capping and polyadenylation on the stability, movement and translation of synthetic mRNAs in *Xenopus* oocytes. *Nucleic Acids Res.* **13**, 7375–7394.

Dworkin, M.B. & Dworkin-Rastl, E. (1985) Changes in RNA titers and polyadenylation during oogenesis and oocyte maturation in *Xenopus laevis. Devl Biol.* **112**, 451–459.

Flynn, J.M. & Woodland, H.R. (1980) The synthesis of histone H1 during amphibian development. *Devl Biol.* **75**, 222–230.

Goustin, A.S. & Wilt, F.H. (1981) Protein synthesis, polyribosomes, and peptide elongation in early development of *Strongylocentrotus purpuratus. Devl Biol.* **82**, 32–40.

Hille, M.B., Dholakia, J.N., Wahba, A., Fanning, E., Stimler L., Xu, Z. & Yablonka-Reuveni, Z. (1990) In-vivo and in-vitro evidence supporting co-regulation of translation in sea-urchin eggs by polypeptide initiation factors, pH optimization, and mRNAs. *J. Reprod. Fert., Suppl.* **42**, 235–248.

Huang, W.I., Hansen, L.H., Merrick, W.C. & Jagus, R. (1987) Inhibitor of eukaryotic initiation factor 4F activity in unfertilized sea urchin eggs. *Proc. natn Acad. Sci. USA* **84**, 6359–6363.

Jacobson, A. & Favreau, M. (1983) Possible involvement of poly(A) in protein synthesis. *Nucleic Acids Res.* **11**, 6353–6368.

Kick, D., Barrett, P., Cummings, A. & Sommerville, J. (1987) Phosphorylation of a 60 kDa polypeptide from *Xenopus* oocytes blocks RNA translation. *Nucleic Acids Res.* **15**, 4099–4109.

Laskey, R.A., Mills, A.D., Gurdon, J.B. & Partington, G.A. (1977) Protein synthesis in oocytes of Xenopus laevis is not regulated by the supply of messenger RNA. *Cell* **11**, 345–351.

Lee, G., Hynes, R. & Kirschner, M. (1984) Temporal and spatial regulation of fibronectin in early Xenopus development. *Cell* **36**, 729–740.

Lingrel, J.B. & Woodland, H.R. (1974) Initiation does not limit the rate of histone synthesis in message injected *Xenopus* oocytes. *Eur. J. Biochem.* **47**, 47–56.

Maller, J.L. & Koontz, J.W. (1981) A study of the induction of cell division in amphibian oocytes by insulin. *Devl Biol.* **85**, 309–316.

Minshull, J., Blow, J.J. & Hunt, T. (1989) Translation of cyclin mRNA is necessary for extracts of activated Xenopus eggs to enter mitosis. *Cell* **56**, 947–956.

McGrew, L.L., Dworkin-Rastl, E., Dworkin, M.B. & Richter, J.D. (1989) Poly(A) elongation during Xenopus oocyte maturation is required for translational recruitment and is mediated by a short sequence element. *Genes & Dev.* **3**, 803–815.

Pierandrei-Amaldi, P., Campioni, N., Beccari, E., Bozzoni, I. & Amaldi, F. (1982) Expression of ribosomal protein genes in Xenopus laevis development. *Cell* **30**, 163–171.

Pierandrei-Amaldi, P., Beccari, E., Bozzoni, I. & Amaldi, F. (1985) Ribosomal protein production in normal and anucleolate Xenopus embryos: regulation at the posttranscriptional and translational levels. *Cell* **42**, 317–323.

Pierandrei-Amaldi, P., Bozzoni, I. & Cardinali, B. (1988) Expression of the gene for ribosomal protein L1 in *Xenopus* embryos: alteration of the gene dosage by microinjection. *Genes & Dev.* **3**, 23–31.

Richter, J.D. (1988) Information relay from gene to protein: the mRNP connection. *Trends in Biochem. Sci.* **13**, 483–486.

Richter, J.D. & Smith, L.D. (1981) Differential captivity for translation and lack of competition between mRNAs that segregate to free and membrane-bound polysomes. *Cell* **27**, 183–191.

Richter, J.D. & Smith, L.D. (1984) Reversible inhibition of translation by *Xenopus* oocyte-specific proteins. *Nature, Lond.* **309**, 378–380.

Richter, J.D., Wasserman, W.J. & Smith, L.D. (1982) The mechanism for increased protein synthesis during *Xenopus* oocyte maturation. *Devl Biol.* **89**, 159–167.

Rosenthal, E.T., Tansey, T.R. & Ruderman, J.V. (1982) Sequence-specific adenylations and deadenylations accompany changes in the translation of maternal mRNA after fertilization of *Spisula* oocytes. *J. molec. Biol.* **166**, 309–327.

Ruderman, J.V., Woodland, H.R. & Sturgess, E.A. (1979) Modulations of histone messenger RNA during the early development of *Xenopus laevis*. *Devl Biol.* **71**, 71–82.

Sachs, A.B. & Davis, R.W. (1989) The poly(A) binding protein is required for poly(A) shortening and 60S subunit-dependent translation initiation. *Cell* **58**, 857–867.

Sagata, N., Oskarsson, M., Copeland, T., Brumbaugh, J. & Vande Woude, G.F. (1988) Function of c-*mos* proto-oncogene product in meiotic maturation in *Xenopus* oocytes. *Nature, Lond.* **335**, 519–525.

Sagata, N., Daar, I., Oskarsson, M., Showalter, S.D. & Vande Woude, G.F. (1989a) The product of the *mos* proto-oncogene as a candidate "initiator" for oocyte maturation. *Science, NY* **245**, 643–646.

Sagata, N., Watanabe, N., Vande Woude, G.F. & Ikawa, Y. (1989b) The c-*mos* proto-oncogene product is a cytostatic factor responsible for meiotic arrest in vertebrate eggs. *Nature, Lond.* **342**, 512–518.

Smith, L.D. (1975) Molecular events during oocyte maturation. In *Biochemistry of Animal Development*, vol. III, pp. 1–46. Ed. R. Weber. Academic Press, New York.

Smith, L.D. (1989) The induction of oocyte maturation: membrane signalling events and regulation of the cell cycle. *Development* **107**, 685–699.

Sommerville, J. (1990) RNA-binding phosphoproteins and the regulation of maternal mRNA in *Xenopus*. *J. Reprod. Fert., Suppl.* **42**, 225–233.

Steward, R., Zusman, S.B., Huang, L.H. & Schedl, P. (1988) The *dorsal* protein is distributed in a gradient in early Drosophila embryos. *Cell* **55**, 487–495.

Stick, R. & Hausen, P. (1985) Changes in the nuclear lamina composition during early development of Xenopus laevis. *Cell* **41**, 191–200.

Sturgess, E.A., Ballantine, J.E.M., Woodland, H.R., Mohun, P.R., Lane, C.D. & Dimitriadis, G.J. (1980) Actin synthesis during the early development of *Xenopus laevis*. *J. Embryol. exp. Morph.* **58**, 303–320.

Swiderski, R.E. & Richter, J.D. (1988) Photocrosslinking of proteins to maternal mRNA in *Xenopus* oocytes. *Devl Biol.* **128**, 349–358.

Taylor, M.A. & Smith, L.D. (1985) Quantitative changes in protein synthesis during oogenesis in *Xenopus laevis*. *Devl Biol.* **110**, 230–237.

Taylor, M.A., Johnson, A.D. & Smith, L.D. (1985) Growing *Xenopus* oocytes have spare translational capacity. *Proc. natn. Acad. Sci. USA* **82**, 6586–6589.

Van Dongen, W.M.A.M., Moorman, A.F.M. & Destrée, O.H.J. (1983) The accumulation of the maternal pool of histone H1 during oogenesis of *Xenopus laevis*. *Cell Differentiation* **12**, 257–264.

Watanabe, N., Vande Woude, G.F., Ikawa, Y. & Sagata, N. (1989) Specific proteolysis of the c-*mos* proto-oncogene product by calpain on fertilization of *Xenopus* eggs. *Nature, Lond.* **342**, 505–511.

Woodland, H.R. (1974) Changes in the polysome content of developing *Xenopus laevis* embryos. *Devl Biol.* **40**, 90–101.

Woodland, H.R. (1980) Histone synthesis during the development of *Xenopus*. *FEBS Lett.* **121**, 1–7.

Woodland, H.R. (1982) The translational control phase of early development. *Bio. Sci. Rep.* **2**, 471–491.

Woodland, H.R. & Adamson, E.D. (1977) The synthesis and storage of histones during the oogenesis and early development of *Xenopus laevis*. *Devl Biol.* **57**, 118–135.

Woodland, H.R. & Ballantine, J.E.M. (1980) Paternal gene expression in developing hybrid embryos of *Xenopus laevis* and *Xenopus borealis*. *J. Embryol. exp. Morph.* **60**, 359–372.

Woodland, H.R. & Wilt, F.H. (1980) The stability and translation of sea urchin histone mRNA injected into *Xenopus laevis* eggs and developing embryos. *Devl Biol.* **75**, 214–221.

Woodland, H.R., Flynn, J.M. & Wyllie, A.J. (1979) Utilization of stored mRNA in *Xenopus* embryos and its replacement by newly synthesized transcripts:histone H1 synthesis using interspecies hybrids. *Cell* **18**, 165–171.

J. Reprod. Fert., Suppl. **42** (1990), 225–233

RNA-binding phosphoproteins and the regulation of maternal mRNA in *Xenopus*

J. Sommerville

Department of Biology, Bute Medical Buildings, University of St Andrews, St Andrews, Fife KY16 9TS, UK

Keywords: phosphoproteins; maternal mRNA; *Xenopus*; oocytes

Maternal mRNA

In amphibians, an extended oogenesis is required for the accumulation of enough gene products, such as messenger RNA, ribosomes, transfer RNA, translation factors, to permit the early stages of embryogenesis to proceed in the absence of gene transcription (see review by Davidson, 1986). However, problems associated with their storage and ordered interaction require that these different components are synthesized sequentially during different stages of oogenesis. Eventually, many of the products accumulated over several months of intensive genetic activity are used up in the first several hours after fertilization.

During oogenesis of *Xenopus*, mRNA sequences are accumulated to a pool size of about 2×10^{11} molecules/oocyte. This pool size is established relatively early in oocyte growth, before the onset of vitellogenesis, and is maintained at this level through the remainder of oogenesis and into early embryogenesis (Golden *et al.*, 1980; see Fig. 1). Thus the stored mRNA supplies the early embryo with maternal mRNA to satisfy all of the demands for protein synthesis before zygotic transcription gets under way at mid-blastula (Newport & Kirschner, 1982). Calculations of the maximum rates of production of mRNA molecules from single-copy genes in oocytes indicate that the first few months of oogenesis are required for the accumulation levels observed (Sommerville, 1977; Perlman & Rosbash, 1978) and studies on the ultrastructure of lampbrush chromosome loops confirm that the maximum density of transcription complexes occurs in previtellogenic oocytes (Hill & Macgregor, 1980). In spite of a relatively high degree of stability of maternal mRNA (Ford *et al.*, 1977), transcription continues through vitellogenesis, mostly to maintain the massive pool of mRNA molecules that has already accumulated. In contrast to mRNA, the bulk of ribosomes are formed during vitellogenesis, reaching a maximum of 10^{12} ribosomes/oocyte by the end of oocyte growth (Dixon & Ford, 1982; see Fig. 1). Of the massive pools of mRNA and ribosomes, less than 2% of each interact to form polysomes during the later stages of oogenesis (Woodland, 1974; see Fig. 1).

Within this general scheme, the individual mRNA species encoding Vg1 (Melton, 1987) and c-*mos* (Sagata *et al.*, 1988) proteins do indeed reach their maximum levels at previtellogenesis. However, others such as the mRNA for cyclin (Minshull *et al.*, 1989) and the c-*myc* protein (Taylor *et al.*, 1986) appear to peak nearer to mid-oogenesis. Contrary to the general scheme, mRNAs encoding TFIIIA (Ginsberg *et al.*, 1984) and enolase (Segil *et al.*, 1988) actually decrease in amount through oogenesis. A common feature that emerges is that many of the mRNA species stable through oogenesis, yet degraded after translation in early embryogenesis, contain 3′ non-coding AU-rich sequences with the common motif AUUUA. Such sequences appear to be responsible for a block in mRNA translation in oocytes (Kruys *et al.*, 1989) and are elsewhere associated with transcript instability (Shaw & Kamen, 1986). On the other hand, activation of translation at oocyte maturation is associated with extension of the poly(A) tail in a specific subset of maternal mRNA molecules (Dworkin & Dworkin-Rastl, 1985; Dworkin *et al.*, 1985). Sequence elements required for this extension are also located in the 3′ non-coding region. In addition to the

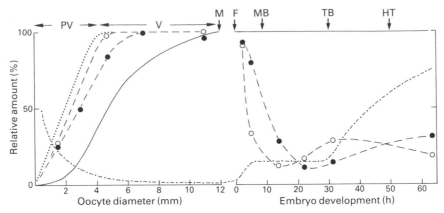

Fig. 1. Changes in pool sizes of RNP particles during oogenesis and early embryogenesis of *Xenopus laevis*. Relative amounts plotted are: mRNA molecules as estimated from poly(A) titration (· · · ·; Golden *et al.*, 1980); mRNP-bound casein kinase II activity (O– – –O; unpublished observations); non-translating mRNP particles as assayed by immunoblotting with anti-pp56 (●– – –●; unpublished observations); ribosomes as measured by absorbance in sucrose gradients (——; Dixon & Ford, 1982); ribosomes in polysomes as measured by absorbance in gradients containing high salt and sodium deoxycholate (–·–·–; Woodland, 1974; unpublished observations). (PV) and (V) indicate the extents of previtellogenesis and vitellogenesis, respectively. The timing of fertilization (F), maturation (M), mid-blastula (MB), tail-bud stage (TB) and hatching tadpole (HT) are indicated by arrows.

conventional AAUAAA sequence necessary for nuclear polyadenylation, a second, maturation-specific UUUUUAU sequence has been identified in certain maternal mRNA molecules (McGrew *et al.*, 1989). Both sequence elements appear to be necessary for a cytoplasmic poly(A) activity which occurs at maturation (Fox *et al.*, 1989). Thus the 3′ non-coding region may contain several sequences which influence stability and translation of particular mRNA molecules.

It is the purpose in this article to emphasize the role of RNA-binding proteins in stabilizing mRNA sequences, blocking their translation during oogenesis and permitting their selective activation in response to cues at maturation and fertilization. Nevertheless, it should be noted that evidence exists for alternative mechanisms based on RNA secondary structures. For instance, simultaneous expression of sense and antisense transcripts for basic fibroblast growth factor may lead to the formation *in vivo* of hybrid molecules, and extensive modification and destruction of the sense transcripts, in this instance at meiosis (Kimelman & Kirschner, 1989).

mRNA-bound proteins

Maternal mRNA exists in a complex with specific proteins as ribonucleoprotein (RNP) particles. Ribosome-free mRNP particles have an average protein:RNA mass ratio of 4:1 (Darnbrough & Ford, 1981; Richter & Smith, 1983; Cummings & Sommerville, 1988). Most of the protein mass is comprised of a few polypeptides in the M_r range of 50 000–60 000 (Darnbrough & Ford, 1981; Fig. 2a). Salt-washing and u.v. cross-linking experiments show that the polypeptides most tightly bound to polyadenylated mRNA have M_r values of 56 000 and 60 000 (Cummings & Sommerville, 1988; J. LaRovere & J. Sommerville, unpublished observations; Fig. 2a). These two polypeptides appear to be associated with all size classes of mRNP particle and it can be calculated from buoyant density and sedimentation studies that the average molecular ratio of each polypeptide to mRNA is 10:1 (Darnbrough & Ford, 1981; Kick *et al.*, 1987; Cummings & Sommerville, 1988). Whereas the M_r 56 000 and 60 000 polypeptides bind to sequences along much of the mRNA molecule, the poly(A) tail appears to be bound by a polypeptide of M_r 70 000 (J. LaRovere & J. Sommerville, unpublished observations; see Fig. 2a) presumably similar to that described as the poly(A)-binding protein in many other cell types (Sachs *et al.*, 1986).

Another characteristic of the M_r 56 000 and 60 000 polypeptides is that, after in-vivo phospho-labelling of previtellogenic oocytes or in-vitro phospholabelling of their isolated mRNP particles, these are seen to be the cell components most heavily phosphorylated (Dearsly *et al.*, 1985; Cummings & Sommerville, 1988; see Fig. 2a). These phosphoproteins, referred to henceforth as pp56 and pp60, are acidic polypeptides which are phosphorylated primarily at serine residues by an RNP-bound enzyme of the casein kinase II type (J. LaRovere, A. Cummings & J. Sommerville, unpublished observations).

Although the mRNA-bound phosphoproteins pp56 and pp60 are immunologically distinct to polyclonal antibodies, they are remarkably similar, nevertheless, in structural features such as range of charged isoforms, protease digestion patterns and relative location of phosphoamino acid residues (Cummings *et al.*, 1989). An explanation for this apparent paradox is that pp56 and pp60 are variants of the same protein, their individuality arising from differential processing of a common RNA transcript (see Lorenz & Richter, 1985) or from differential secondary modification of a common polypeptide (see Cummings *et al.*, 1989).

Non-translation of mRNP particles

The consistent presence of large amounts of pp56 and pp60 in non-polysomal mRNP particles suggests that their reversible phosphorylation may be instrumental in regulating the availability of mRNA for translation. Early experiments showed that mRNA extracted from mRNP particles could be translated efficiently *in vitro* (Darnbrough & Ford, 1976) and that reconstitution of complexes formed by adding a mixture of mRNP proteins to purified mRNA led to blocking of translation (Richter & Smith, 1984). With the isolation of individual phosphoproteins, the importance of their phosphorylation to translation could be tested. In complexes formed between pp60 and rabbit globin mRNA, it was shown that tight interaction and non-translation in cell-free systems are achieved only as long as phosphorylation of pp60 is maintained (Kick *et al.*, 1987). Furthermore, microinjection into mid-oogenic oocytes of potent inhibitors of the mRNP-bound protein kinase, such as heparin or haemin, stimulates the rate of endogenous protein synthesis by a factor of two to three (J. LaRovere, A. Cummings & J. Sommerville, unpublished observations). This stimulation appears to be due to mobilization of stored mRNA into polysomes rather than to an increase in the translational efficiency of pre-existent polysomes. In-vitro and in-vivo experiments therefore point to the equation of phosphorylation of pp56/60 with translation repression and dephosphorylation of pp56/60 with translation activation. If this is true, changes in the phosphorylated status of mRNP particles should be apparent at times in development when mRNA is being accumulated and again when the bulk of maternal mRNA is released for translation.

Developmental changes in mRNP phosphoproteins

Changes in the quantity and composition of stored mRNP particles during oogenesis and early embryogenesis have been followed by immunoassay of the mRNA-bound phosphoproteins and by enzyme assay of the mRNP-bound protein kinase (A. Cummings, J. LaRovere & J. Sommerville, unpublished observations). The amounts of pp56/60, the total level of their phosphorylation and the activity of mRNP-bound protein kinase all increase roughly in proportion to the total amount of mRNA accumulated at early oogenesis (see Fig. 1). These levels then remain constant from mid-oogenesis to the end of oocyte growth. After fertilization, pp56 and pp60 persist in mRNP particles, but are no longer phosphorylated, either *in vivo* or *in vitro* (see Fig. 2c). Slightly later,

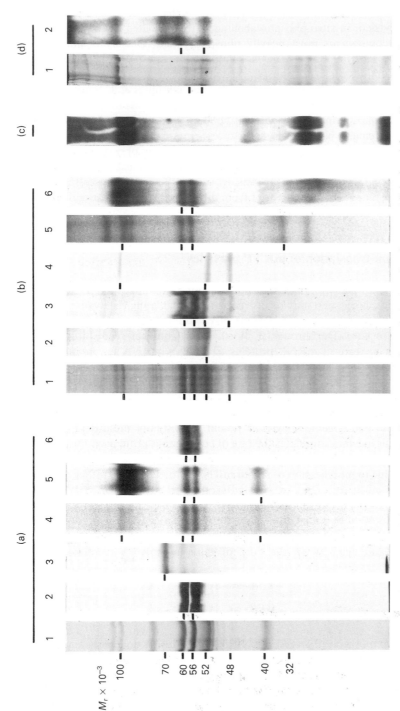

Fig. 2. Proteins of mRNP particles (a), mRNP–ribosome complexes (b & c) and polysomes (d) isolated from *Xenopus laevis* oocytes and embryos. Polypeptides are separated by SDS–PAGE and relative molecular mass is shown. **(a)** mRNP particles (60S region of glycerol gradients) from previtellogenic oocytes: Track 1, total protein; Track 2, protein selectively bound to oligo (dT)-cellulose; Track 3, protein selectively bound to poly(A)-Sepharose; Track 4, autoradiograph after phospholabelling *in vivo*; Track 5, autoradiograph after phospholabelling *in vitro*; Track 6, as Track 5 but after phospholabelling the particles were u.v. cross-linked, denatured in 0·5% SDS, selectively bound to oligo(dT)-cellulose and eluted by treatment with ribonuclease. **(b)** mRNP–ribosome complexes (80–90S region of glycerol gradients) from early vitellogenic oocytes. Track 1, total protein; Track 2, protein selectively bound to poly(U)-Sepharose and eluted with low-salt buffer; Track 3, protein further eluted with 0·5% SDS; Track 4, protein selectively bound to heparin–Sepharose CL-6B and eluted with 0·2 M-KCl; Track 5, autoradiograph after phospholabelling *in vivo*; Track 6, autoradiograph after phospholabelling *in vitro*. **(c)** mRNP–ribosome complexes from early cleavage stage embryos labelled *in vivo*, autoradiograph shown. **(d)** Polysomes (120S region of glycerol gradients containing 0·35 M-KCl) from hatched embryos homogenized in a buffer containing 0·5% sodium deoxycholate. Track 1, total protein; Track 2, autoradiograph after phospholabelling *in vitro*.

between early cleavage and gastrulation, the level of mRNP-bound protein kinase activity drops by a factor of seven (see Fig. 1). Loss of phosphorylation in mRNP particles immediately after fertilization may be due to the increase in both protein phosphatase activity and amounts of casein kinase II inhibitors, observed to occur towards the end of oogenesis and into early embryogenesis (A. Cummings, J. LaRovere & J. Sommerville, unpublished observations). All of the changes to mRNP particles occur through the period of early development associated with the formation of polysomes and with the translation of most of the maternal mRNA species (Woodland, 1974; Dworkin *et al.*, 1985).

Zygotic transcription is initiated at mid-blastula (Newport & Kirschner, 1982) and is followed at the tail-bud stage by a further increase in polysome formation (Woodland, 1974; Woodland *et al.*, 1979; see Fig. 1). During this period there is a doubling in the level of mRNP-bound protein kinase activity and a new, but smaller, pool of stored mRNP becomes established (A. Cummings, J. LaRovere & J. Sommerville, unpublished observations). It is important to note that pp56 and pp60 persist as constituents of mRNP particles throughout development and are detected in all cell types tested, including culture cells derived from metamorphosing animals and from adult tissues (unpublished observations). Therefore, these phosphoproteins can not be considered to be 'oocyte-specific' (see Darnbrough & Ford, 1981; Richter & Smith, 1983); rather they are 'oocyte-abundant', reflecting the large store of mRNA molecules in oocytes. Together with their associated protein kinase, pp56 and pp60 appear to be constitutive components of mRNP particles, wherever their occurrence.

In addition to changes seen in the quantity and composition of mRNP particles, changes are seen in their cellular location and in their interaction with other subcellular components as oogenesis progresses. The location of mRNP particles *in situ* has been followed by immunostaining sectioned ovary with antibodies directed against pp56 and pp60 (J. LaRovere & J. Sommerville, unpublished observations). For instance, changes occur in the distribution of pp56 at the early stages of oogenesis. Starting from a fairly even distribution throughout the cytoplasm of pre-vitellogenic oocytes, by early vitellogenesis this phosphoprotein, and presumably bound mRNA molecules, become concentrated in a broad zone around the outside of the nucleus. A similar transition from homogeneous to perinuclear location has been described previously for poly-adenylated mRNA sequences, as detected by in-situ hybridization (Capco & Jeffrey, 1982). An example of localization of a specific mRNA is provided by the Vg1 message which is uniformly distributed in previtellogenic oocytes and is translocated to the vegetal pole by mid-oogenesis (Melton, 1987). But even in this instance, perinuclear localization tends to occur as an intermediate step. These observations imply that maternal mRNA, probably by virtue of bound proteins, interacts with structural elements in the cell to enable migration and eventual localization within the oocyte.

Clues as to the mechanisms involved in changing cellular distributions of maternal mRNA molecules may come from studies on the sedimentation behaviour of mRNP particles. Whereas mRNP particles isolated from previtellogenic oocytes show a heterogeneous size distribution of 40–120S (Darnbrough & Ford, 1981; Cummings & Sommerville, 1988; see Fig. 3a), by mid-oogenesis the particles become mostly focussed around the 80S ribosome peak (Cummings & Sommerville, 1988; see Fig. 3b). Evidence has been presented that this change represents dissolution of mRNP aggregates and a specific interaction of single mRNP particles with single ribosomes to form non-translating complexes (Cummings & Sommerville, 1988). Treatment of the original homogenates with high salt and sodium deoxycholate results in the dissolution of mRNP aggregates and release of bound mRNP particles from ribosomes to yield free particles which sediment at 20–40S (A. Cummings, J. LaRovere & J. Sommerville, unpublished observations; see Fig. 3c). It may not be a coincidence that perinuclear localization of mRNP particles coincides with the onset of ribosome production and the formation of mRNP and ribosome complexes. One further factor required for interaction would be the cytoskeleton to provide a network on which assembly, distribution and storage of translation complexes could occur.

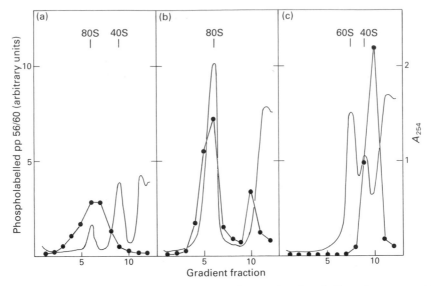

Fig. 3. Sedimentation properties of mRNP phosphoproteins. Previtellogenic oocytes (a) and early vitellogenic oocytes (b, c) were labelled *in vivo* and, after homogenization of sets of 400 oocytes, low-speed supernatants were separated on glycerol gradients. In (c), the homogenate was treated with 0·5% sodium deoxycholate and the gradient contained 0·35 M-KCl; in (a) and (b) the gradient contained 0·05 M-KCl. Sedimentation values of the main absorbance peaks (———) are indicated. Amounts of phospholabelled pp56 plus pp60 (●———●) are derived from densitometric scanning of autoradiographs after SDS–PAGE of gradient fractions.

The role of translation factors

Although pp56 and pp60 are the major RNA-binding proteins contained in the mRNP particles, other proteins occur with regularity. Most of the additional proteins also can be shown to have RNA-binding activity (Dearsly *et al.*, 1985; Cummings & Sommerville, 1988) and some can readily be detected and identified through their patterns of phosphorylation (unpublished observations). Studies on a range of different organisms indicate that most of the eukaryotic translation factors and ancillary enzymes have a natural affinity for RNA and can be isolated in forms bound to mRNP particles, ribosomes or polysomes (see review by Ryazanov *et al.*, 1987). These observations have added support to the original hypothesis of *omnia mecum porto* (Spirin, 1978), i.e. that RNA carries with it those proteins which are eventually required for its expression. As applied to amphibian oocytes, maternal mRNA would be expected to sequester translation initiation factors before ribosome production and the mRNP–ribosome complex would be expected to bind translation elongation factors before polysome formation.

In addition to RNA-binding properties, translation factors are also found to be associated with structural elements of the cytoplasm (Howe & Hershey, 1984). Thus the non-random distribution of maternal mRNA in oocytes may be achieved by an RNA–protein factor–cytoskeleton or an RNA–protein factor-membrane association. Within this scheme translation factors may act, not only as determinants for the assembly of mRNP particles into ribosome-containing complexes, but also for the distribution of such complexes throughout the cytoplasm and for the eventual activation of their translation.

Proteins from mRNP–ribosome complexes have been examined for their resemblance to known translation elongation factors. Separation on columns of heparin–Sepharose (Goldstein & Safer, 1979) reveals polypeptides which can be identified as the elongation factors EF-1α (M_r 52 000) and EF-2 (M_r 100 000) (unpublished results; see Fig. 2b). An additional bound polypeptide in material from early vitellogenic oocytes is the tRNA-storage protein p48 (Denis & Le Maire, 1983) which has been shown to have structural and functional homology to EF-1α (Mattaj *et al.*, 1987; Viel *et al.*, 1987). Whereas EF-1α is not phosphorylated *in vivo* in the mRNP–ribosome complex, EF-2 exists mostly in a phosphorylated form (unpublished results). It is interesting that in mammalian cell systems phosphorylation of EF-2 is associated not only with tight-binding to ribosomes, but also with direct inhibition of translation (Nairn & Palfrey, 1987; Ryazanov *et al.*, 1988). Therefore, secondary modification of translation elongation factors represents an additional level at which translation can be blocked in oocytes.

In-vitro phosphorylation of mRNP–ribosome complexes reveals an additional group of polypeptides with M_r values of 75 000–100 000 which label to very high specific activity (Cummings & Sommerville, 1988; Cummings *et al.*, 1989; see Fig. 2b). The identity of these polypeptides is not known, but various characteristics suggest that they may be aminoacyl tRNA synthctases which are retained in the mRNP–ribosome complex in conditions of low salt.

Protein synthesis at oocyte maturation increases approximately 2-fold (Wasserman *et al.*, 1982) and alteration of translation factors is relevant to this transition. An apparent depletion of the cap-binding translation factor eIF-4A in full-grown oocytes has been reported and its supplementation by microinjection of purified eIF-4A leads to a 2-fold increase in translation, thus mimicking the increase seen at maturation (Audet *et al.*, 1987). Recently, complexes have been isolated from full-grown oocytes which contain polypeptides of M_r 30 000 (p30), 36 000 (p36) and 47 000 (p47); p30 being homologous to EF-1β and p47 being homologous to EF-1γ (Bellé *et al.*, 1989). Since phosphorylation of p47 (EF-1γ) by the p34^{cdc2} protein kinase occurs *in vivo* at oocyte maturation and p30 (EF-1β) and p36 are substrates *in vitro* for casein kinase II (Bellé *et al.*, 1989), a role is suggested for phosphorylation of elongation factors to regulate translation at this stage and perhaps continuing on into early development.

Due to the aggregation of RNP particles in oocytes, polysomes are difficult to obtain in a pure state without resort to treatment with detergents and high salt. Furthermore, polysome number does not increase through oogenesis and so they become increasingly minor components as the oocyte grows (see Fig. 1). However, in embryos, especially after hatching, polysomes become abundant and the presence of mRNP proteins and translation factors can more critically be assessed. In contrast to oocyte mRNP–ribosome complexes, embryonic polysomes show no evidence of tightly-bound phosphorylated EF-2 (unpublished observations; see Fig. 2d). Phospho-labelled polypeptides of M_r 52 000, 60 000, 66 000 and 125 000 are detected. It is not known whether the M_r 52 000 component is a phosphorylated form of EF-1α, but the 60 000 component can be shown by immunoblotting to be pp60, and pp56 can also be shown to be present (unpublished results). Therefore, even in active polysome fractions, pp56 and pp60 may be retained as minor components of mRNP. The differences from translationally-blocked mRNP are that, in polysomes, pp56 and pp60 are present at much lower amounts per particle and are not phospholabelled *in vivo* (unpublished results). Nevertheless, the potential for regulating translation by phosphorylation of mRNP-associated proteins remains a feature throughout early development.

I thank Alison Cummings and Joan LaRovere for their contribution to the work described in this report.

References

Audet, R.G., Goodchild, J. & Richter, J.D. (1987) Eukaryotic initiation factor 4A stimulates translation in microinjected *Xenopus* oocytes. *Devl Biol.* **121**, 58–68.

Bellé, R., Derancourt, J., Poulhe, R., Capony, J.-P., Ozon, R. & Mulner-Lorillon, O. (1989) A purified complex from *Xenopus* oocytes contains a p47 pro-

tein an in vivo substrate of MPF, and a p30 protein respectively homologous to elongation factors EF-1γ and EF-1β. *FEBS Lett.* **255**, 101–104.

Capco, D.G. & Jeffrey, W.R. (1982) Transient locations of messenger RNA in *Xenopus laevis* oocytes. *Devl Biol.* **82**, 1–12.

Cummings, A. & Sommerville, J. (1988) Protein kinase activity associated with stored messenger ribonucleoprotein particles of *Xenopus* oocytes. *J. Cell Biol.* **107**, 45–46.

Cummings, A., Barrett, P. & Sommerville, J. (1989) Multiple modification in the phosphoproteins bound to stored messenger RNA in *Xenopus* oocytes. *Biochim. Biophys. Acta* **1014**, 319–326.

Darnbrough, C.H. & Ford, P.J. (1976) Cell free translation of messenger RNA from oocytes of *Xenopus laevis*. *Devl Biol* **50**, 285–301.

Darnbrough, C.H. & Ford, P.J. (1981) Identification in *Xenopus laevis* of a class of oocyte-specific proteins bound to messenger RNA. *Eur. J. Biochem.* **113**, 415–426.

Davidson, E.H. (1986) *Gene Activity in Early Development*. Academic Press, New York.

Dearsly, A.L., Johnson, R.M., Barrett, P. & Sommerville, J. (1985) Identification of a 60 kDa phosphoprotein that binds stored messenger RNA of *Xenopus* oocytes. *Eur. J. Biochem.* **150**, 95–103.

Denis, H. & Le Maire, M. (1983) Thesaurisomes, a novel kind of nucleoprotein particle. In *Subcellular Biochemistry*, Vol. 9, pp. 42–54. Ed. D. B. Roodyn. Plenum Publishing Corporation, New York.

Dixon, L.K. & Ford, P.J. (1982) Persistence of nonribosome bound 5S RNA in full-grown oocytes of *Xenopus laevis*. *Devl Biol*. **91**, 474–477.

Dworkin, M.B. & Dworkin-Rastl, E. (1985) Changes in RNA titres and polyadenylation during oogenesis and oocyte maturation in *Xenopus laevis*. *Devl Biol*. **112**, 451–457.

Dworkin, M.B., Shrutkowski, A. & Dworkin-Rastl, E. (1985) Mobilization of specific maternal RNA species into polysomes after fertilization in *Xenopus laevis*. *Proc. natn. Acad. Sci. USA* **82**, 7636–7640.

Ford, P.J., Mathieson, T. & Rosbash, M. (1977) Very long-lived messenger RNA in ovaries of *Xenopus laevis*. *Devl Biol*. **57**, 417–426.

Fox, C.A., Sheets, M.D. & Wickens, M.P. (1989) Poly(A) addition during maturation of frog oocytes: distinct nuclear and cytoplasmic activities and regulation by the sequence UUUUUAU. *Genes Dev*. **3**, 2151–2162.

Ginsberg, A.M., King, B.O. & Roeder, R.G. (1984) *Xenopus* 5S gene transcription factor, TFIIIA: Characterization of a DNA clone and measurement of RNA levels throughout development. *Cell* **39**, 479–489.

Golden, L., Schafer, U. & Rosbash, M. (1980) Accumulation of individual p(A) RNAs during oogenesis of *Xenopus laevis*. *Cell* **22**, 835–844.

Goldstein, J. & Safer, B. (1979) Use of Heparin-Sepharose for the rapid isolation of initiation and elongation factors. *Methods Enzymol*. **60**, 165–181.

Hill, R.S. & Macgregor, J.C. (1980) The development of lampbrush chromosome-type transcription in the early diplotene oocytes of *Xenopus laevis*: an electron-microscope analysis. *J. cell Sci*. **44**, 87–101.

Howe, J.G. & Hershey, J.W.B. (1984) Translation initiation factor and ribosome association with the cytoskeletal framework fraction from HeLa cells. *Cell* **37**, 85–93.

Kick, D., Barrett, P., Cummings, A. & Sommerville, J. (1987) Phosphorylation of a 60 kDa polypeptide from *Xenopus* oocytes blocks messenger RNA translation. *Nucleic Acid Res*. **15**, 4099–4109.

Kimelman, D. & Kirschner, M.W. (1989) An antisense mRNA directs the covalent modification of the transcript encoding fibroblast growth factor in *Xenopus* oocytes. *Cell* **56**, 687–696.

Kruys, V., Marinx, O., Shaw, G., Deschamps, J. & Huez, G. (1989) Translational blockade imposed by cytokine-derived UA-rich sequences. *Science, NY* **245**, 852–855.

Lorenz, L.J. & Richter, J.D. (1985) A cDNA clone for a polyadenylated RNA-binding protein of *Xenopus laevis* oocytes hybridizes to four developmentally-regulated mRNAs. *Molec. cell. Biol*. **5**, 2697–2704.

Mattaj, I.W., Coppard, N.J., Brown, R.S., Clark, B.F.C. & De Robertis, E. (1987) 42S p48—the most abundant protein in previtellogenic *Xenopus* oocytes—resembles elongation factor 1α structurally and functionally. *EMBO J*. **6**, 2409–2413.

McGrew, L.L., Dworkin-Rastl, E., Dworkin, M.B. & Richter, J.D. (1989) Poly(A) elongation during *Xenopus* oocyte maturation is required for translational recruitment and is mediated by a short sequence element. *Genes Dev*. **3**, 803–815.

Melton, D.A. (1987) Translocation of a localized maternal mRNA to the vegetal pole of *Xenopus* oocytes. *Nature, Lond*. **328**, 80–82.

Minshull, J., Blow, J.J. & Hunt, T. (1989) Translation of cyclin mRNA is necessary for extracts of activated *Xenopus* eggs to enter mitosis. *Cell* **56**, 947–956.

Nairn, A.C. & Palfrey, H.C. (1987) Identification of the major M_r 100 000 substrate for calmodulin-dependent protein kinase III in mammalian cells as elongation factor-2. *J. biol. Chem*. **262**, 17299–17303.

Newport, J. & Kirschner, M. (1982) A major developmental transition in early *Xenopus* embryos. II. Control of the onset of transcription. *Cell* **30**, 687–696.

Perlman, S. & Rosbash, M. (1978) Analysis of *Xenopus laevis* ovary and somatic cell polyadenylated RNA by molecular hybridization. *Devl Biol*. **63**, 197–212.

Richter, J.D. & Smith, L.D. (1983) Developmentally regulated RNA binding proteins during oogenesis in *Xenopus laevis*. *J. biol. Chem*. **258**, 4864–4869.

Richter, J.D. & Smith, L.D. (1984) Reversible inhibition of translation by *Xenopus* oocyte-specific proteins. *Nature, Lond*. **309**, 378–380.

Ryazanov, A.G., Ovchinikov, L.P. & Spirin, A.S. (1987) Development of structural organization of protein-synthesizing machinery from prokaryotes to eukaryotes. *Biosystems* **20**, 275–288.

Ryazanov, A.G., Shestakova, E.A. & Natapov, P.G. (1988) Phosphorylation of elongation factor 2 by EF-2 kinase affects rate of translation. *Nature, Lond*. **334**, 170–173.

Sachs, A.B., Bond, M.W. & Kornberg, R.D. (1986) A single gene from yeast for both nuclear and cytoplasmic polyadenylate-binding proteins: domain structure and expression. *Cell* **45**, 827–835.

Sagata, N., Oskarsson, M., Copeland, T., Brumbaugh, J. & Vande Woude, G.F. (1988) Function of the c-*mos* proto-oncogene product in meiotic maturation in *Xenopus* oocytes. *Nature, Lond*. **335**, 519–525.

Segil, N., Shrutkowski, A., Dworkin, M.B. & Dworkin-Rastl, E. (1988) Enolase isoenzymes in adult and developing *Xenopus laevis* and characterization of a clone enolase sequence. *Biochem. J.* **251,** 31–39.

Shaw, G, & Kamen, R. (1986) A conserved AU sequence from the 3′ untranslated region of GM-CSF mRNA mediates selective mRNA degradation. *Cell* **46,** 659–667.

Sommerville, J. (1977) Gene activity in the lampbrush chromosomes of amphibian oocytes. In *Biochemistry of Cell Differentiation II,* Vol. 15, pp. 79–156. Ed. J. Paul. University Park Press, Baltimore.

Spirin, A.S. (1978) Eukaryotic messenger RNA and informosomes. *FEBS Lett.* **88,** 15–17.

Taylor, M.V., Gusse, M., Evan, G.I., Dathan, N. & Mechali, M. (1986) *Xenopus myc* proto-oncogene during development: expression of a stable maternal mRNA uncoupled from cell division. *EMBO J.* **5,** 3563–3570.

Viel, A., Dje, M.K., Mazabraud, A., Denis, H. & Le Maire, M. (1987) Thesaurin a, the major protein of *Xenopus laevis* previtellogenic oocytes, present in the 42S particles, is homologous to elongation factor EF-1α. *FEBS Lett.* **223,** 232–236.

Wasserman, W.J., Richter, J.D. & Smith, L.D. (1982) Protein synthesis during maturation-promoting factor and progesterone-induced maturation in *Xenopus* oocytes. *Devl Biol.* **89,** 152–158.

Woodland, H.R. (1974) Changes in polysome content of developing *Xenopus laevis* embryos. *Devl Biol.* **40,** 90–101.

Woodland, H.R., Flynn, J.M. & Wyllie, A.J. (1979) Utilization of stored mRNA in *Xenopus* embryos and its replacement by newly synthesized transcripts. *Cell* **18,** 165–171.

J. Reprod. Fert., Suppl. **42** (1990), 235–248

Printed in Great Britain
© 1990 Journals of Reproduction & Fertility Ltd

In-vivo and in-vitro evidence supporting co-regulation of translation in sea-urchin eggs by polypeptide initiation factors, pH optimization, and mRNAs

Merrill B. Hille, J. N. Dholakia*, A. Wahba*, Elinor Fanning, Lynn Stimler, Zhe Xu and Zipora Yablonka-Reuveni†

*Department of Zoology NJ15, University of Washington, Seattle WA 98195, USA; and
Department of Biochemistry, The University of Mississippi Medical Center, Jackson, MS 39216, USA

Keywords: sea urchin; translational regulation; pH regulation; cell-free extracts; polypeptide initiation factors; eIF-2; GEF; eIF-2B; eIF-4

Introduction

Gene expression in eukaryotic organisms occurs in two steps: (1) transcription of genes into mRNAs that are then transported to the cytoplasm, and (2) the assembly of the mRNA with ribosomes, initiation factors, and elongation factors for the translation into the protein gene product. Regulation of gene expression can occur at many points in this process, including the start of the translation of cytoplasmic mRNAs, which is pertinent to early embryogenesis. For instance, during meiosis in animals, the translation of specific mRNAs is reprogrammed from the synthesis of proteins needed for growth to those proteins needed for the succession of rapid cleavages following fertilization (Rosenthal *et al.*, 1980; Rosenthal & Wilt, 1987; Richter, 1987). These cleavage-specific mRNAs are actually synthesized very early in oogenesis then stored in an inaccessible form (Richter, 1987). During meiosis the mRNAs for proteins used in the growth phase of oogenesis leave the polyribosome population, are deadenylated, and are eventually degraded in surf clams (Rosenthal *et al.*, 1983; Rosenthal & Ruderman, 1987), in mammals (Bachvarova *et al.*, 1985) and in amphibians (Hyman & Wormington, 1988). At the same time the mRNAs for proteins to be used during the cleavage stages are activated from the stored pool of messenger ribonucleoprotein particles (mRNPs) and are polyadenylated (Rosenthal *et al.*, 1983; Rosenthal & Ruderman, 1987). Fertilization must occur during meiosis in these animals, and there is a gradual increase in translation rates during meiosis and after fertilization.

Similarly, in echinoids the reprogramming from the translation of growth-specific mRNAs to cleavage-specific mRNAs occurs during meiosis (Grainger *et al.*, 1986); however, in these animals the translational rates are dramatically slowed during meiosis as the eggs are stored before spawning and subsequent fertilization. After sperm–egg fusion in echinoids and a subsequent transient increase in intracellular calcium and a permanent increase in intracellular pH (Steinhardt *et al.*, 1977; Shen & Steinhardt, 1978), the stored translational apparatus is rapidly activated and some of the mRNAs are polyadenylated (Slater & Slater, 1974; Wilt, 1977). By the 2-cell stage (about 1 h) there is a 20- to 25-fold increase in the numbers of ribosomes in polyribosomes actively translating messages (Infante & Nemer, 1967; Humphreys, 1971; Goustin & Wilt, 1981), and a 2-fold increase in the rate of polypeptide elongation by ribosomes (Brandis & Raff, 1978; Hille & Albers, 1979). Alkalinization of the cytoplasm of the egg is sufficient to stimulate the polypeptide initiation process and the mobilization of ribosomes onto mRNAs, while both the transient Ca²⁺ release and

†Present address: Department of Biological Structures SM20, University of Washington, Seattle, WA 98195, USA.

alkalinization are needed to change the elongation rates (Brandis & Raff, 1979; Winkler *et al.*, 1980). The synthesis of new mRNAs is not required for this post-fertilization stimulation of translation, as enucleation by chemical or physical methods does not decrease the stimulation of translation (Brachet *et al.*, 1963; Gross *et al.*, 1964; Denny & Tyler, 1964). Because polyribosomes are rapidly formed after fertilization, most of the required protein components must already exist in the unfertilized egg cytoplasm, albeit in an inactive state as described below.

We have been exploring the roles of the initiation events and of the various initiation factors in mediating the rapid rise in translation in fertilized echinoid eggs. This paper will summarize our experiments and compare observations from in-vitro nuclear-mitochondria-free lysates with experiments *in vivo*. Our experiments support the hypothesis that both mRNAs and translational initiation factors must be rapidly activated after fertilization for the rise in protein synthesis rate to occur. We suggest that the 20-fold increase in polyribosomes after fertilization can be accounted for by a 20-fold increase in mRNA availability and a simultaneous 20-fold increase in initiation activity. The 20-fold increase in initiation activity in turn could be a product of (1) a 4- or 5-fold increase in amounts of active initiation factors multiplied by (2) a 4- or 5-fold increase due to changes in the conformations the various proteins and RNAs of the translational apparatus because of the more alkaline cytoplasm of the embryo. Thus, the increase in initiation activity after fertilization can be considered as being due to the alkalinization of the cytoplasm which gives rise to both the modification of pre-existing initiation factors and to the conformational changes which move translation towards its optimum rate. The latter would be analogous to the stimulation of enzyme activities by pH changes. The post-fertilization pH of 7·4 is, after all, a more usual cytoplasmic pH than that of 6·8–7·0.

Regulation

Regulation by masked mRNAs

It is now well documented that mRNAs are masked in some form in eggs (see reviews by Raff & Showman, 1985; Rosenthal & Wilt, 1987). We know, for instance, that mRNPs in sea urchin egg lysates do not bind to active reticulocyte 43S preinitiation complexes and so cannot take part in peptide initiation (Winkler *et al.*, 1985). Also, mRNPs isolated from sea-urchin eggs under physiological conditions are not translated in reticulocyte lysates, while mRNPs subjected to centrifugal force or high salts are translated. Some proteins appear to be removed from the mRNPs by gravitational forces or ionic interactions. These proteins are inhibitory when added to translation-lysates of rabbit reticulocytes (Grainger & Winkler, 1987). Similarly, for amphibians, Richter & Smith (1984) showed that oocyte-specific proteins, when reconstituted with mRNAs *in vitro*, repress the translation of the mRNAs *in vivo* and *in vitro* (see also Richter, 1987; Woodland, 1990; Sommerville, 1990). There is therefore evidence that proteins suppress the translation of mRNAs. In addition, Mandley & Lopo (1987) have evidence of a nuclease-sensitive inhibitor of translation in sea-urchin eggs. Furthermore, we have shown that the stimulation of peptide synthesis by purified initiation factors in sea-urchin egg lysates is dependent on the addition of active globin mRNA (Colin *et al.*, 1987), which implicates mRNAs as well as initiation factors as being rate-limiting in sea urchin eggs.

Initiation factors as regulators of translation in mammals

Before presenting the roles of initiation factors in regulating translation in sea-urchin eggs and embryos, we will briefly review the well established roles that 3 initiation factors (eIF-2, GEF/eIF-2B, and eIF-4E) play in translational regulation in mammalian cells. Eukaryotic initiation factor 2 (eIF-2) forms a ternary complex with GTP and met-tRNA$_i$ (see Fig. 1). This ternary complex is tranferred to a 40S ribosomal subunit which is then competent, in the presence of eIF-4, to recognize the cap structure at the end of 5'mRNA (see Hershey *et al.*, 1986). After shuttling along the mRNA to the AUG initiation codon, the 40S preinitiation complex combines with a 60S ribosomal subunit to form an 80S initiation complex, thereby setting the stage for polypeptide chain elongation. Upon formation of the 80S initiation complex, the eIF-2-associated GTP is hydrolysed and eIF-2 is released as an inactive eIF-2·GDP binary complex (see Fig. 1) (Walton & Gill, 1975; Trachsel *et al.*, 1977; Trachsel & Staehelin, 1978; Peterson *et al.*, 1979). Regeneration of eIF-2·GTP·Met-tRNA$_i$ requires a guanine nucleotide exchange factor, GEF (also called eIF-2B), which facilitates the exchange of eIF-2-bound GDP for GTP and the recycling of active eIF-2 (Siekierka *et al.*, 1982, 1983; Panniers & Henshaw, 1983; Salimans *et al.*, 1984; Dholakia *et al.*, 1986; Dholakia & Wahba, 1989).

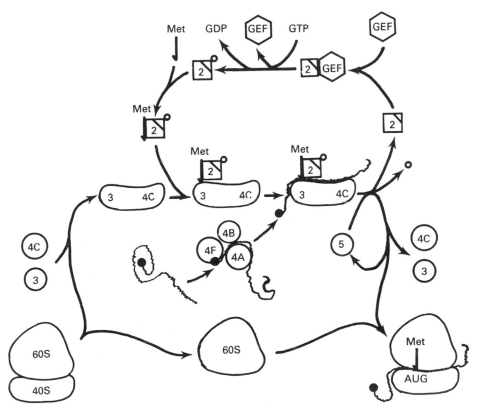

Fig. 1. Pathway of initiation of protein synthesis. Initiation factors are represented by their respective numbers except for GEF (also called eIF-2B), which is represented as GEF. GTP is represented as a small triangle on the upper right corner of eIF-2 with a circle for the γ-phosphate. GDP is represented as a triangle without the γ-phosphate. Initiation begins with the joining of the ternary complex of met-tRNA/eIF-2/GTP with the small ribosomal subunit containing eIF-3 and eIF-4C.

Regulation of polypeptide chain initiation in mammals occurs during this recycling of eIF-2·GDP. Phosphorylation of the α-subunit of eIF-2 by the haem-controlled repressor (HCR) (Farrell *et al.*, 1977; Pain, 1986) or the double-stranded RNA-induced kinase (Levin *et al.*, 1980) in mammalian cells is associated with the cessation of protein synthesis and is due to the inability of GEF to catalyse the GDP/GTP nucleotide exchange reaction on the phosphorylated protein (Siekierka *et al.*, 1982, 1984; Matts *et al.*, 1983). The correlation of eIF-2α phosphorylation and translational repression has been observed in mammalian cell lines, especially after heat shock (Ernst *et al.*, 1982; Duncan & Hershey, 1984; Scorsone *et al.*, 1987; Rowlands *et al.*, 1988), serum deprivation (Duncan & Hershey, 1985; Rowlands *et al.*, 1988), and interferon treatment followed by virus infection (Kostura & Mathews, 1989). Phosphorylation of GEF has been shown to increase translational activity (Dholakia & Wahba, 1988).

Regulation of polypeptide chain initiation also occurs during recognition of the cap structure at the 5′ end of mRNAs (Ray *et al.*, 1983). In most eukaryotes, the mRNAs are capped at the 5′ end with a terminal 7-methylguanylate. This 5′ cap is recognized by a cap-binding protein complex, eIF-4, that facilitates the transfer of mRNA to the 43S preinitiation complex. The eIF-4E protein of the complex then binds to the capped 5′ terminus of the mRNAs. As rapid phosphorylation of eIF-4E often accompanies an increase in the rates of protein synthesis (Bonneau & Sonenberg, 1987; Duncan *et al.*, 1987), phosphorylation of eIF-4E is implicated in translational regulation. These three initiation factors, eIF-2, GEF and eIF-4E, therefore have the potential to be rapidly regulated in sea-urchin eggs by phosphorylation and dephosphorylation.

Table 1. Analysis of the amounts of 40S subunits under different experimental conditions

		% A_{260} nm in 40S fraction		
		Exp. 1	Exp. 2	Exp. 3
Unfertilized eggs	Unstirred	0·8	0·7 ± 0·1†	0·4†
	Rotated	2·8 ± 0·1†	1·2	
	Rotated		1·0*	2·4 ± 0·3†*
Fertilized eggs	Rotated	2·5 ± 0·2†	2·0*	2·5 ± 0·3†*

In Exp. 1 some eggs were left in clumps in the sea water after spawning. Other eggs were rotated at 38 r.p.m. in Erlenmeyer flasks for 30–60 min, then the cultures rapidly chilled in excess buffer (80 mM-KCl, 130 mM-K(OAc), 20 mM-triethanolamine, 5 mM-MgCl$_2$, 0·1 mM-EDTA, 1 mM-dithiothreitol, pH 6·8), concentrated, and homogenized. The post-mitochondrial homogenates were centrifuged on 20–40% sucrose gradients for 15 h at 40 000 g_{av} at 4°C, and monitored at 260 nm by pumping through a Gilford recording spectrophotometer equipped with a 0·4 cm flow cell. For each centrifugation 10 A_{260} nm units of lysate were added and the absorption at 260 nm in each fraction was determined by integrating the areas under the 40S, 60S, 80S and polyribosome peaks. (One A_{260} nm unit is defined as an absorbance of 1·0 at 260 nm of 1 ml solution in a 1 cm cuvette.) In Exp. 2 the eggs were rotated for 30 min in normal sea water, then those marked * were rotated 10 min in 1·5 mM-emetine. In Exp. 3 the eggs marked * were rotated for 30–90 min in 1·5 mM-emetine.
†Duplicate or triplicate gradients.

Total amount of small ribosomal subunits does not change after the fertilization of sea-urchin eggs

To determine whether the amount of small ribosomal subunits increases after fertilization we measured by sucrose gradient analysis the percentages of ribosomes that occur as 40S subunits. Table 1 shows that, if clumps of spawned, unfertilized eggs were not stirred before preparation, they had fewer subunits than did a similar number of unfertilized eggs cultured in sea water for 30–90 min by rotation of the culture flasks. Culturing increased the amount of 40S subunits in unfertilized eggs on the average about 4-fold. Since protein synthesis is very sensitive to levels of oxygen and decreases in levels of GTP, culturing the eggs most probably increased the amounts of oxygen available to the eggs. However, when small ribosomal subunits from cultured unfertilized eggs and cultured zygotes were compared the amounts were very similar. Thus, fertilization does

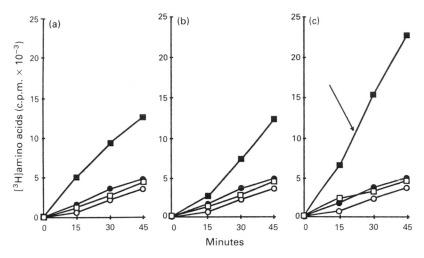

Fig. 2. Stimulation of added globin mRNA translation in egg lysates by a crude initiation factor preparation and the guanine nucleotide exchange factor, eIF-2B. The 10 μl lysates for (a), (b), and (c) contained: buffers only (○) or mRNA, 2·7 μg (●). Other additions to 10 μl lysate were: (a) crude initiation factors, 18 μg (□); the same factors plus 2·7 μg globin mRNA (■); (b) eIF-2B, 0·24 μg (□); the same factor plus 2·7 μg globin mRNA (■); (c) eIF-2B, 0·24 μg and 18 μg crude initiation factors in the absence (□) and presence of 2·7 μg globin mRNA (■). Reaction mixtures contained in 10 μl 85 mM-KCl, 1·44 mM-magnesium acetate, Hepes, pH 7·55, and 4 μCi [^{3}H]amino acids. Other conditions are as in Fig. 3. (From Colin *et al.*, 1987.)

not generate increased numbers of 40S subunits in sea urchin eggs. Any change in the initiation potential of small ribosomal subunits would, therefore, depend on increases in the activities of initiation factors GEF and/or eIF-2. We and others have evaluated the limiting capacity of translational initiation factors in sea-urchin eggs by adding the factors to egg lysates.

Initiation factors as translation regulators in sea-urchin eggs and embryos

Several specific initiation factors are deficient in egg lysates. eIF-2 was first shown to stimulate unfertilized egg lysates by Winkler *et al.* (1985). GEF stimulated translation in egg lysates in the presence of exogenous mRNA (Colin *et al.*, 1987). Also the eIF-4 complex, which contains eIF-4E, was shown to be stimulatory by Huang *et al.* (1987) and Lopo *et al.* (1988, 1989). Lysates from unfertilized eggs may also contain an inhibitor of eIF-4F activity (Huang *et al.*, 1987).

Co-operative stimulation of translation by mRNAs and initiation factors

In-vivo evidence from two studies support the co-operative stimulation of translation by mRNAs and initiation factors after fertilization. Hille *et al.* (1981) measured polyribosome characteristics in unfertilized eggs or morulae in the absence and presence of low levels of emetine that slowed but did not block elongation rates. They found that emetine did not increase the size or numbers of polyribosomes as would be expected if initiation factors were the only rate-limiting factors. These results are consistent with an interpretation that both mRNAs and initiation factors are in limited supply, or that only mRNAs are rate limiting. Colin & Hille (1986) more recently showed that active globin mRNAs injected into sea-urchin eggs do not by themselves stimulate the rates of translation in the eggs although the mRNAs are readily translated at the expense of endogenous mRNAs. Something in addition to mRNA availability therefore appears rate limiting. The logical interpretation of these in-vivo observations is that the activities of initiation factors as

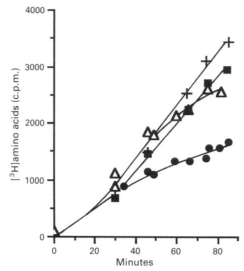

Fig. 3. Stimulation of amino acid incorporation in *L. pictus* egg lysates by eIF-2 and GEF in the presence of exogenous mRNA. Lysates were prepared from *L. pictus* eggs that were incubated for 30 min at 12°C then stopped by rapidly chilling them to -2°C in homogenization medium (HM: 300 mM-glycine, 230 mM-glycerol, 80 mM-KCl, 100 mM-potassium gluconate, 25 mM-Hepes, 2 mM-magnesium chloride, 2 mM-EGTA, pH 7·0 [This corrects a printing error in Colin *et al.*, 1987.]). The HM-washed eggs were homogenized in an equal volume of HM containing 300 U/ml of RNasin (Promega Biotec: 2800 S. Fish Hatchery Rd., Madison, WI 53711, USA), 50 μg leupeptin/ml, 0·5 mg reduced glutathione/ml and 1 mg-soybean trypsin inhibitor/ml (Colin *et al.*, 1987). Post-mitochondrial supernatants of these homogenates were stored in aliquants in liquid nitrogen and tested at the temperature appropriate for these lysates (Lopo *et al.*, 1988). Translation in the lysates was measured in 10 μl volumes at the following final concentrations: 88 mM-KCl, 68 mM-potassium gluconate, 200 mM-glycine, 155 mM-glycerol, 1·4 mM-magnesium acetate, 15 mM-creatine phosphate, 1·4 mM-ATP, 0·4 mM-GTP, 36 U-creatine phosphokinase/ml, 14 mM-Hepes, 0·1–0·4 μCi [^{3}H]amino acid mixture/ml 0·5 mM-methionine, pH 7·3–7·5. Lysate volume was 70% of the total reaction mixture with the specified reagents, mRNAs, and initiation factors contributing the remaining volume. Globin poly(A)$^{+}$ mRNA and initiation factors were prepared from rabbit reticulocytes as described by Colin *et al.* (1987) and Dholakia & Wahba (1988, 1989). The reaction was incubated at 16°C. Samples of 1·5–2 μl were removed at intervals and spotted on strips of Whatman 3MM filter paper and analysed as described by Colin *et al.* (1987). The 10 μl assays contained 1·3 μg reticulocyte poly(A)$^{+}$ mRNA, and the following factors: no factors (●), 1·26 μg eIF-2 (■), 0·183 μg GEF (△), and 1·26 μg eIF-2 and 0·183 μg GEF (+). The final pH values of the assays were 7·52 ± 0·01 as determined by a microcombination electrode at the end of each assay.

well as the availability of mRNAs are rate limiting. Similar obervations have also been made for *Xenopus* oocytes (Laskey *et al.*, 1977; Wasserman *et al.*, 1986; Richter, 1987; Patrick *et al.*, 1989; Woodland, 1990).

　　Support for a dual activation of initiation factors and mRNAs after the fertilization of sea urchin eggs comes also from our in-vitro studies showing that both mRNAs and initiation factors are required for the stimulation of sea-urchin egg lysates. Colin *et al.* (1987) found that (1) lysates prepared from *L. pictus* eggs and embryos mimic the in-vivo state since exogenous mRNAs compete with endogenous mRNAs for the limiting components in these lysates; (2) 70–80% of the translation in eggs lysates is due to new initiation as demonstrated by adding the inhibitor auritricarboxylic acid which completely blocks polypeptide initiation; (3) initiation factor GEF stimulates translation in our lysates when exogenous mRNAs were also added, but has little effect alone (Fig. 2b); and (4) a crude preparation of initiation factors stimulates translation of our lysates when

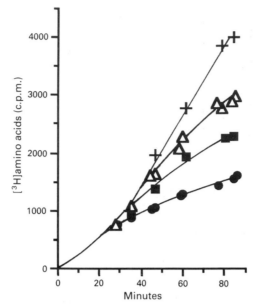

Fig. 4. Stimulation of amino acid incorporation in *L. pictus* egg lysates by eIF-4F and GEF in the presence of exogenous mRNA. The 10-µl assays contained 1·3 µg reticulocyte poly(A)$^+$ mRNA and the following factors: no factors (●), 0·15 µg eIF-4F (■), 0·183 µg GEF (△), 0·155 µg eIF-4F and 0·183 µg GEF (+). The final pH values of the assays were 7·42 ± 0·01. Methods and other conditions are as described in Fig. 3.

exogenous mRNAs are also added, but again is not by itself stimulatory (Fig. 2a; and (5) th addition of GEF and a crude preparation of initiation factors stimulates translation more th when only GEF and mRNAs are added (Fig. 2c). Thus, we can reasonably conclude that activation of both mRNAs and initiation factors is required for the observed recruitment of st mRNAs into polyribosomes after fertilization in sea urchins.

The co-operative roles of eIF-2/GEF and eIF-4F

Stimulation of egg lysates by eIF-2 and GEF are *not* additive

As described in the 'Introduction', regulation of the formation of active eIF-2·GTP·N complexes and 43S preinitiation complexes depends on an interaction of GEF with eIF eIF-2 and GEF appear to be rate-limiting in sea-urchin egg lysates, we assayed them to lysates to determine whether they could co-operate in stimulating translational rates Fig. 3, after 30 min of incubation with 1·3 µg eIF-2 and 1·3 µg globin mRNA per 10 ture, translation was stimulated to about 3 times the rate of the controls contai genously added globin mRNA. Higher concentrations of eIF-2 (1·7 µg/10 µl) did stimulation. Lower concentrations of eIF-2 were not stimulatory. In contrast, c (0·18 µg) of GEF were required for a similar stimulation of the egg lysate. The GEF and exogenous mRNA used were optimal (Colin *et al.*, 1987). The more lation of amino acid incorporation by GEF than eIF-2 may be because the ad GDP which needed to be exchanged for GTP by endogenous GEF (Fig. 3). W GEF and eIF-2 initially stimulated animo acid incorporation no more thar after 50 min the amino acid incorporation increased above that of GEF anticipated from the roles of the two factors, stimulation by either of the

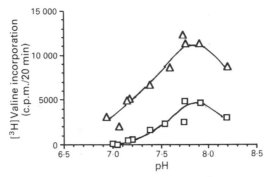

Fig. 5. Effect of pH on rates of translation in *L. pictus* lysates. Lysates were from unfertilized eggs incubated for 1·5 h at 14°C with or without phorbol myristate acetate (0·42 μM) and were prepared as described in Fig. 3. The incorporation of [³H]amino acids into precipitable proteins was measured in the lysates as in Fig. 3, but at 16·5°C. Translational rates were calculated as the slope of the incorporation of [³H]amino acids into precipitable proteins *vs* time at 30 min for lysates of unfertilized eggs (□) and eggs treated 1·5 h with phorbol myristate acetate (△).

high concentrations of eIF-2 or on catalytic amounts of the GEF as GEF recycles endogenous eIF-2. However, the stimulation by the factors was not additive. In all likelihood then, only one of the two is rate limiting in the eggs.

The stimulatory effects of eIF-4F and GEF on unfertilized egg lysates are additive

The facilitation of the binding of the active small ribosomal subunits to the 5′ end of the mRNA by eIF-4 and the facilitation of recycling of eIF-2 by GEF later in initiation (after the release of eIF-2 from the 80S mRNA initiation complexes) are two very distinct steps. We determined whether eIF-2 and eIF-4 could co-operatively boost translational rates. Figure 4 gives the kinetics for the stimulation of amino acid incorporation by eIF-4F in *L. pictus* egg lysates in the absence and presence of the optimal concentration of GEF. Both eIF-4F at 0·15 μg/10 μl lysate and GEF at 0·18 μg/10 μl lysate stimulated incorporation in the presence of 1·3 μg globin mRNAs, although the stimulation by GEF was greater. The effect of the two is nearly additive with the final slope being greater than 5-times that of the control with exogenous mRNA alone. These data are representative of three separate experiments on *L. pictus* lysates and one on *Strongylocentrotus purpuratus* lysates. We therefore conclude that not only is the ternary complex containing eIF-2 rate limiting in these lysates, but eIF-4F is too.

Quantification of translation stimulation at fertilization

Less than 1% of the ribosomes and 5% of the stored mRNA are on functional polyribosomes in unfertilized eggs. Stimulated by the post-fertilization alkalinization of the cytoplasm, ribosomes and mRNAs are recruited into polyribosomes (Epel *et al.*, 1974; Chambers, 1975; Shen & Steinhardt, 1978; Paul & Johnston, 1978; Zucker *et al.*, 1978; Winkler *et al.*, 1985). The result is a 20-fold increase in the number of ribosomes in polyribosomes by the 2-cell stage (Infante & Nemer, 1967; Humphreys, 1971; Goustin & Wilt, 1981). In addition, there is a 2-fold increase in the rate of peptide elongation after fertilization, as measured by a decrease in the time for a ribosome to transit a mRNA *in vivo* (Brandis & Raff, 1978; Hille & Albers, 1979). In total, the increase in numbers of polyribosomes and the doubling of the rate of peptide elongation on these polyribosomes, results in about a 50-fold increase in polypeptide synthesis following fertilization. This 50-fold increase is in agreement with the measurement of absolute rates of protein synthesis by Regier & Kafatos (1977). Our current goal is

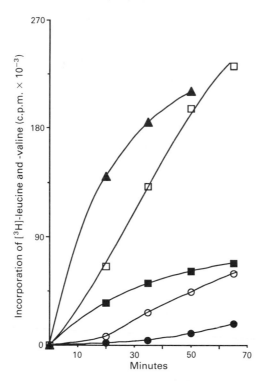

Fig. 6. Synergy of pII and initiation factors plus mRNA. The stimulation of amino acid incorporation in *L. pictus* egg and blastula lysates by initiation factors and by alkalinization was measured as in Fig. 3. The 10-μl assays of lysates from unfertilized eggs were incubated at pH 6·9 with no additions (●); at pH 7·4 with no additions (○); with 2·7 μg globin mRNA (■); with 2·7 μg globin mRNA, 0·155 μg eIF-4F and 0·183 μg GEF (□). The 10-μl assays of lysates from hatched blastulae were incubated at pH 7·4 with no additions (▲). For the description in the text the difference in translational rates were measured as the slopes of the lines between 35 and 50 min for the egg lysates and before 20 min for the lysates from blastulae. Similar conclusions are reached by comparing total incorporation of amino acids for egg lysates at 60 min or between egg and embryo lysates at 20 min.

to identify and quantify the factors responsible for the 20-fold increase in numbers of poly-ribosomes resulting from the activation of multiple components of the translational apparatus at fertilization.

Increased translational activity due to optimization of the pH of the egg cytoplasm for initiation after fertilization

The magnitude of the increased rates of peptide synthesis by alkalinization from pH 6·9 to pH 7·4 has been measured *in vitro* by Winkler & Steinhardt (1981) and by us to be 3- to 5-fold for both unfertilized and fertilized egg lysates. Plots of translational activity *versus* pH after a series of alkalinizations of lysates from eggs and of lysates from phorbol ester-activated eggs are shown in Fig. 5. The resultant bell-shaped curves are reminiscent of curves of the activities of enzymes at different pH values. We therefore propose that alkalinization *in vitro* represents instantaneous optimizations of the conformations of several or even many different proteins and RNAs rather than a specific activation of stored initiation factors or stored mRNAs. We propose further that cytoplasmic alkalinization and the subsequent conformational changes of proteins and RNAs results in a 3–5-fold increase in initiation rates at fertilization.

Current estimates of the maximum levels of stimulation by activated initiation factors after fertilization

Winkler *et al.* (1985) observed a 1·5-fold increase in translation by eIF-2, Colin *et al.* (1987) a 3-fold increase in translational rates by GEF plus globin mRNA, and Lopo *et al.* (1988) a 3-fold increase by eIF-4F. In the present paper we observe (1) that stimulation of the rate of translation by GEF and eIF-2 is not additive in *L. pictus* egg lysates, and (2) that the stimulation of *L. pictus* and *S. purpuratus* egg lysates by eIF-4F and GEF are additive with a maximum total stimulation of about 4–5-fold (measuring rate of translation or the slopes of the lines in Fig. 4 in the presence of exogenous globin mRNA). This degree of stimulation is about equal to the sum of that observed previously for GEF and eIF-4.

Can we now account for the 20-fold increase in initiation capacity or numbers of polyribosomes generated after fertilization?

First, the release of mRNPs from an inhibited state and the activation of initiation factors must be considered separately. A nearly 20-fold increase in translational activity of mRNAs is required for a 20-fold increase in the number of polyribosomes after fertilization. However, no increase in polyribosome number would be observed unless the activities of initiation factors also increased approximately 20-fold. We have demonstrated a 5-fold increase by the additive effect of two initiation factors on mRNA supplemented lysates. As a working hypothesis we propose that the total increase in the initiation of translation after fertilization could be the product of (1) an increase in the activity of initiation factors and (2) an increase in the rate of initiation caused by alkalinization from pH 6·9 to pH 7·4. Experimental support for this hypothesis is given in Fig. 6. The difference in rates of incorporation of amino acids into proteins in lysates from *L. pictus* eggs at pH 6·9 with no additions and at pH 7·4 with mRNAs and initiation factors added is about 15-fold and about half the translational activity of lysates from the blastula stage. These data clearly show that a large difference in translational activities can be attained if stimulations due to both pH and mRNA and initiation factor activities are considered.

As summarized below, the product of a 4–5-fold increase in initiation factor activity, and a 3–5-fold increase in initiation rates due to pH optimization could give the observed 20-fold increase in initiation rates required to generate polyribosomes, if simultaneously a 20-fold increase in the numbers of competent mRNAs derived from the stored mRNA pool also occurred.

(a) Rates of protein synthesis in lysates of sea-urchin eggs

		Increased translation
(1) pH effect:		
Change in pH from 7·0 to 7·4		3–5-fold
(2) Initiation factor effect:		
Addition of factors to lysates at pH 7·4:		
+mRNA + GEF or eIF-2	3-fold ⎫	4–5-fold
+mRNA + eIF-4	2-fold ⎭	
Total increase:		
pH change + eIF addition		15–20-fold
(b) In-vivo post-fertilization mRNA availability:		about 20-fold

Some unanswered questions

Major holes in our knowledge are the links between fertilization induced ionic changes of the cytoplasm and the activation of stored mRNAs and initiation factors. Grainger & Winkler (1987)

have found an inhibitory fraction that is easily dissociated by salt or physical force. Their experiments suggest that some ionic change in the egg may allow the mRNPs to be freed from the inhibitory protein (Sommerville, 1990). Other possibilities are that stored mRNAs are activated when mRNP proteins are phosphorylated or dephosphorylated (Rittschof & Traugh, 1982; Kirk *et al.*, 1987), when polyadenylation of mRNAs causes a release of the masking proteins (Galili *et al.*, 1988; Strickland *et al.*, 1988; McGrew *et al.*, 1989) or the addition of poly(A)-binding proteins (Grossi de Sa *et al.*, 1988), or when a nuclease-sensitive inhibitor is degraded (Mandley & Lopo, 1987).

Alternatively, mRNPs or initiation and elongation factors could be released from a particulate form at fertilization as are the enzymes of energetics (Isono, 1963; Aune & Epel, 1978). There is some evidence that elongation factors are activated in this manner after fertilization (Yablonka-Reuveni *et al.*, 1983; Yablonka-Reuveni & Hille, 1983).

The most likely mechanisms for the activation of the initiation factors are phosphorylation of GEF (Dholakia & Wahba, 1988) or interaction of GEF with NADPH (Wahba & Woodley, 1984; Dholakia *et al.*, 1986), dephosphorylation of eIF-2 (Farrell *et al.*, 1977; Duncan & Hershey, 1985), and phosphorylation of eIF-4E (Bonneau & Sonenberg, 1987; Duncan *et al.*, 1987). These possibilities are being actively investigated by several groups. Once we know whether these modifications occur, we will be in a position to identify the kinases and phosphatases that are activated by the second messenger cascades so elegantly described in the accompanying articles.

We thank Dr Richard Hawkins for critically reading this manuscript. These studies were supported by NSF Grant PCM-8408386 to M.B.H., NIH Grant GM 25451 to A.J.W. and a University of Washington Graduate School Research Fund to M.B.H.

References

Aune, T.M. & Epel, D. (1978) Increased intracellular pH shifts the subcellular location of G6PDH. *Cell Biol.* **79**, 164a, abstr.

Bachvarova, R., DeLeon, V., Johnson, A., Kaplan, G. & Paynton, B.V. (1985) Changes in total RNA, polyadenylated RNA, and actin mRNA during meiotic maturation of mouse oocytes. *Devl Biol.* **108**, 325–331.

Bonneau, A-M. & Sonenberg, N. (1987) Involvement of the 24-kDa Cap-binding protein in regulation of protein synthesis in mitosis. *J. biol. Chem.* **262**, 11134–11139.

Brachet, J., Deeroly, M., Ficq, A. & Quertier, J. (1963) Ribonucleic acid metabolism in unfertilized and fertilized sea urchin eggs. *Biochim. Biophys. Acta* **72**, 600–662.

Brandis, J.W. & Raff, R.A. (1978) Translation of oogenetic mRNA in sea urchin eggs and early embryos. *Devl Biol.* **67**, 99–113.

Brandis, J.W. & Raff, R.A. (1979) Elevation of protein synthesis is a complex response to fertilisation. *Nature, Lond.* **278**, 467–468.

Chambers, E.L. (1975) Na$^+$ is required for nuclear and cytoplasmic activation of sea urchin eggs by sperm and divalent ionophores. *J. Cell Biol.* **67**, 60a, abstr.

Colin, A.M. & Hille, M.B. (1986) Injected mRNA does not increase protein synthesis in unfertilized, fertilized, or ammonia-activated sea urchin eggs. *Devl Biol.* **114**, 184–192.

Colin, A.M., Brown, B.D., Dholakia, J.N., Woodley, C.L., Wahba, A.J. & Hille, M.B. (1987) Evidence for simultaneous derepression of messenger RNA and the guanine nucleotide exchange factor in fertilized sea urchin eggs. *Devl Biol.* **123**, 354–363.

Denny, P.C. & Tyler, A. (1964) Activation of protein biosynthesis in non-nucleates fragments of sea urchin eggs. *Biochem. Biophys. Res. Commun.* **14**, 245–298.

Dholakia, J.N. & Wahba, A.J. (1988) Phosphorylation of the guanine nucleotide exchange factor from rabbit reticulocytes regulates its activity in polypeptide chain initiation. *Proc. natn. Acad. Sci. USA* **85**, 51–54.

Dholakia, J.N. & Wahba, A.J. (1989) Mechanism of the nucleotide exchange reaction in eukaryotic polypeptide chain initiation. *J. biol. Chem.* **264**, 546–550.

Dholakia, J.N., Mueser, T.C., Woodley, C.L., Parkhurst, L.J. & Wahba, A.J. (1986) The association of NADPH with the guanine nucleotide exchange factor from rabbit reticulocytes: A role of pyridine dinucleotides in eukaryotic polypeptide chain initiation. *Proc. natn. Acad. Sci. USA* **83**, 6746–6750.

Duncan, R. & Hershey, J.W.B. (1984) Heat shock-induced translational alterations in HeLa cells. *J. biol. Chem.* **259**, 11882–11889.

Duncan, R. & Hershey, J.W.B. (1985) Regulation of initiation factors during translational repression caused by serum depletion. *J. biol. Chem.* **260**, 5493–5497.

Duncan, R., Milburn, S.C. & Hershey, J.W.B. (1987) Regulated phosphorylation and low abundance of HeLa cell initiation factor eIF-4F suggest a role in translational control. *J. biol. Chem.* **262**, 380–388.

Epel, D., Steinhardt, R., Humphreys, T. & Mazia, D. (1974) An analysis of the partial metabolic derepression of sea urchin eggs by ammonia: the existence of independent pathways. *Devl Biol.* **40**, 245–255.

Ernst, V., Baum, E.Z. & Reddy, P. (1982) Heat shock, protein phosphorylation, and the control of translation in rabbit reticulocytes, reticulocyte lysates, and HeLa cells. In *Heat Shock from Bacteria to Man*, pp. 215–225. Eds M. J. Schlesinger, M. Ashburner & A. Tissiers. Cold Spring Harbor Laboratory, New York.

Farrell, P.J., Balkow, K., Hunt, T., Jackson, R.J. & Trachsel, H. (1977) Phosphorylation of initiation factor eIF-2 and the control of reticulocyte protein synthesis. *Cell* **11**, 187–200.

Galili, G., Kawata, E.E., Smith, L.D. & Larkins, B.A. (1988) Role of the 3′-poly(A) sequence in translational regulation of mRNAs in *Xenopus laevis* oocytes. *J. biol. Chem.* **263**, 5764–5770.

Goustin, A.S. & Wilt, F.H. (1981) Protein synthesis, polyribosomes, and peptide elongation in early development of *Strongylocentrotus purpuratus*. *Devl Biol.* **82**, 32–40.

Grainger, J.L. & Winkler, M.M. (1987) Fertilization triggers unmasking of maternal mRNAs in sea urchin eggs. *Molec. cell. Biol.* **7**, 3947–3954.

Grainger, J.L., von Brunn, A. & Winkler, M.M. (1986) Transient synthesis of a specific set of proteins during the rapid cleavage phase of sea urchin development. *Devl Biol.* **114**, 403–415.

Gross, P.R., Malkin, L.I. & Moyer, W.A. (1964) Effects of actinomycin-D on macromolecular synthesis and early development. *Proc. natn. Acad. Sci. USA* **51**, 407–414.

Grossi de Sa, M-F., Standart, N., Martins de Sa, C., Akhayat, O., Huesca, M. & Scherrer, K. (1988) The poly(A)-binding protein facilitates *in vitro* translation of poly(A)-rich mRNA. *Eur. J. Biochem.* **176**, 521–526.

Hershey, J.W.B., Duncan, R. & Mathews, M.B. (1986) Introduction: Mechanisms of translational control. In *Current Communications in Molecular Biology: Translational Control*, pp. 1–18. Ed. M. B. Mathews. Cold Spring Harbor Laboratory, New York.

Hille, M.B. & Albers, A.A. (1979) Efficiency of protein synthesis after fertilisation of sea urchin eggs. *Nature, Lond.* **278**, 469–471.

Hille, M.B., Hall, D.C., Yablonka-Reuveni, Z., Danilchik, D. & Moon, R.T. (1981) Translational control in sea urchin eggs and embryos: initiation is rate limiting in blastula stage embryos. *Devl Biol.* **86**, 241–249.

Huang, W.-U., Hansen, L.J., Merrick, W.C. & Jagus, R. (1987) Inhibitor of eukaryotic initiation factor 4F activity in unfertilized sea urchin eggs. *Proc. natn. Acad. Sci. USA* **84**, 6359–6363.

Humphreys, T. (1971) Measurements of messenger RNA entering polysomes upon fertilization of sea urchin eggs. *Devl Biol.* **26**, 201–208.

Hyman, L.E. & Wormington, W.M. (1988) Translational inactivation of ribosomal protein mRNAs during *Xenopus* oocyte maturation. *Genes Dev.* **2**, 598–605.

Infante, A.A. & Nemer, M. (1967) Accumulation of newly synthesized RNA templates in a unique class of polyribosomes during embryogenesis. *Proc. natn. Acad. Sci. USA* **58**, 681–688.

Isono, N. (1963) Carbohydrate metabolism in sea urchin eggs IV. Intracellular localization of enzymes of pentose phosphate cycle in unfertilized and fertilized eggs. *J. Fac. Sci. Univ. Tokyo. Sec IV* **10**, 37–53.

Kirk, D., Barrett, P., Cummings, A. & Sommerville, J. (1987) Phosphorylation of a 60 kDA polypeptide from *Xenopus* oocytes blocks mRNA translation. *Nucleic Acids Res.* **15**, 4099–4109.

Kostura, M. & Mathews, M.B. (1989) Purification and activation of the double-stranded RNA-dependent eIF-2 kinase DAI. *Molec. cell. Biol.* **9**, 1576–1586.

Laskey, R.A., Mills, A.D., Gurdon, J.B. & Parington, C.A. (1977) Protein synthesis in oocytes of *Xenopus laevis* is not regulated by the supply of messenger RNA. *Cell* **11**, 345–351.

Levin, D.H., Petryshyn, R. & London, I.M. (1980) Characterization of double-stranded-RNA-activated kinase that phosphorylates α subunit of eukaryotic initiation factor 2 (eIF-2α) in reticulocyte lysates. *Proc. natn. Acad. Sci. USA* **77**, 832–836.

Lopo, A.C., MacMillan, S. & Hershey, J.W.B. (1988) Translational control in early sea urchin embryogenesis: initiation factor eIF4F stimulates protein synthesis in lysates from unfertilized eggs of *Strongylocentrotus purpuratus*. *Biochemistry, NY* **27**, 351–357.

Lopo, A.C., Lashbrook, C.C. & Hershey, J.W.B. (1989) Characterization of translational systems *in vitro* from three developmental stages of *Strongylocentrotus purpuratus*. *Biochem. J.* **258**, 553–561.

Mandley, E.N. & Lopo, A.C. (1987) Putative nuclease-sensitive control element in unfertilized eggs of the sea urchin *Lytechinus pictus*. *Biochem. Biophys. Res. Commun.* **145**, 921–926.

Matts, R.L., Levin, D.H. & London, I.M. (1983) Effect of phosphorylation of the α-subunit of eukaryotic initiation factor 2 on the function of reversing factor in the initiation of protein synthesis. *Proc. natn. Acad. Sci. USA* **80**, 2559–2563.

McGrew, L.L., Dworkin-Rastl, E., Dworkin, M.B. & Richter, J.D. (1989) Poly(A) elongation during *Xenopus* oocyte maturation is required for translational recruitment and is mediated by a short sequence element. *Genes Dev.* **3**, 803–815.

Pain, V.M. (1986) Initiation of protein synthesis in mammalian cells. *Biochem. J.* **235**, 625–637.

Panniers, R. & Henshaw, E.C. (1983) A GDP/GTP exchange factor essential for eukaryotic initiation factor 2 cycling in Ehrlich ascites tumor cells and its regulation by eukaryotic initiation factor 2 phosphorylation. *J. biol. Chem.* **258**, 7928–7934.

Patrick, T.D., Lewer, C.E. & Pain, V.M. (1989) Preparation and characterization of cell-free protein synthesis systems from oocytes and eggs of *Xenopus laevis*. *Development* **106**, 1–9.

Paul, M. & Johnston, R.N. (1978) Absence of a calcium response following ammonia activation of sea urchin eggs. *Devl Biol.* **67**, 330–335.

Peterson, D.T., Merrick, W.C. & Safer, B. (1979) Binding and release of radiolabeled eukaryotic initiation factor 2 and 3 during 80S initiation complex formation. *J. biol. Chem.* **254**, 2509–2516.

Raff, R.A. & Showman, R.M. (1985) Maternal messenger RNA: Quantitative, qualitative, and spatial control of its expression in embryos. In *Biology of Fertilization*, vol. 3, pp. 401–452. Eds C. B. Metz & A. Monroy. Academic Press, New York.

Ray, B.K., Brendler, T.G., Adya, S., Daniels-McQueen, S., Miller, J.K., Hershey, J.W.B., Grifo, J., Merrick, W.C. & Thach, R.E. (1983) Role of mRNA competition in regulating translation: Further characterization of mRNA discriminatory initiation factors. *Proc. natn. Acad. Sci. USA* **80**, 663–667.

Regier, J.C. & Kafatos, F.C. (1977) Absolute rates of protein synthesis in sea urchins with specific activity measurements of radioactive leucine and leucyl-tRNA. *Devl Biol.* **57**, 270–283.

Richter, J.D. (1987) Molecular mechanisms of translational control during the early development of *Xenopus laevis*. In *Translational Regulation of Gene Expression*, pp. 111–139. Ed. J. Ilan. Plenum Press, New York.

Richter, J.D. & Smith, L.D. (1984) Reversible inhibition of translation by Xenopus oocyte-specific proteins. *Nature, Lond.* **309**, 378–380.

Rittschof, D. & Traugh, J.A. (1982) Identification of casein kinase II and phosphorylated proteins associated with messenger ribonucleoproteins particles from reticulocytes. *Eur. J. Biochem.* **123**, 333–336.

Rosenthal, E.T. & Ruderman, J.V. (1987) Widespread changes in the translation and adenylation of maternal messenger RNAs following fertilization of *Spisula* oocytes. *Devl Biol.* **121**, 237–246.

Rosenthal, E.T. & Wilt, F. (1987) Selective messenger RNA translation in marine invertebrate oocytes, eggs and zygotes. In *Translational Regulation of Gene Expression*, pp. 87–110. Ed. J. Ilan, Plenum Press, New York.

Rosenthal, E.T., Hunt, T. & Ruderman, J.V. (1980) Selective translation of mRNA controls the pattern of protein synthesis during early development of the surf clam, *Spisula solidissima*. *Cell* **20**, 487–494.

Rosenthal, E.T., Tansey, T.R. & Ruderman, J.V. (1983) Sequence-specific adenylation and deadenylation accompanying changes in the translation of maternal messenger RNA after fertilization of *Spisula* oocytes. *J. molec. Biol.* **166**, 309–327.

Rowlands, A.G., Montine, K.S., Henshaw, E.C. & Panniers, R. (1988) Physiological stresses inhibit guanine-nucleotide-exchange factor in Ehrlich cells. *Eur. J. Biochem.* **175**, 93–99.

Salimans, M., Goumans, H., Amesz, H., Benne, R. & Voorma, H.O. (1984) Regulation of protein synthesis in eukaryotes; mode of action of eRF, an eIF-2-recycling factor from rabbit reticulocytes involved in GDP/GTP exchange. *Eur. J. Biochem.* **145**, 91–98.

Scorsone, K.A., Panniers, R., Rowlands, A.G. & Henshaw, E.C. (1987) Phosphorylation of eukaryotic initiation factor 2 during physiological stresses which affect protein synthesis. *J. biol. Chem.* **262**, 14538–14543.

Shen, S.S. & Steinhardt, R.A. (1978) Direct measurement of intracellular pH during metabolic derepression at fertilization and ammonia activation of the sea urchin egg. *Nature, Lond.* **272**, 253–255.

Siekierka, J., Mauser, L. & Ochoa, S. (1982) Mechanism of polypeptide chain initiation in eukaryotes and its control by phosphorylation of the α subunit of initiation factor 2. *Proc. natn. Acad. Sci. USA* **79**, 2537–2540.

Siekierka, J., Manne, V., Mauser, L. & Ochoa, S. (1983) Polypeptide chain initiation in eukaryotes: reversibility of the ternary complex-forming reaction. *Proc. natn. Acad. Sci. USA* **80**, 1232–1235.

Siekierka, J., Manne, V. & Ochoa, S. (1984) Mechanism of translational control by partial phosphorylation of the α subunit of eukaryotic initiation factor 2. *Proc. natn. Acad. Sci. USA* **81**, 352–356.

Slater, I. & Slater, D.W. (1974) Polyadenylation and transcription following fertilization. *Proc. natn. Acad. Sci. USA* **71**, 1103–1107.

Sommerville, J. (1990) RNA binding phosphoproteins and the regulation of maternal mRNA in *Xenopus*. *J. Reprod. Fert., Suppl.* **42**, 225–233.

Steinhardt, R.A., Zucker, R. & Schatten, G. (1977) Intracellular calcium release at fertilization in the sea urchin egg. *Devl Biol.* **58**, 185–196.

Strickland, S., Haurte, J., Belin, D., Vassalli, A., Rickles, R.J. & Vassalli, J-D. (1988) Antisense RNA directed against the 3′ noncoding region prevents dormant mRNA activation in mouse oocytes. *Science, NY* **241**, 680–684.

Trachsel, H. & Staehelin, T. (1978) Binding and release of eukaryotic initiation factor eIF-2 and GTP during protein synthesis initiation. *Proc. natn. Acad. Sci. USA* **75**, 204–208.

Trachsel, H., Erni, B., Schreier, M.H. & Staehelin, T. (1977) Initiation of mammalian protein synthesis II. The assembly of the initiation complex with purified initiation factors. *J. molec. Biol.* **116**, 755–767.

Wahba, A.J. & Woodley, C.L. (1984) Molecular aspects of development in the brine shrimp *Artemia*. *Prog. Nucleic Acid Res. molec. Biol.* **31**, 221–265.

Walton, G.M. & Gill, G.N. (1975) Nucleotide regulation of a eukaryotic protein synthesis initiation complex. *Biochim. Biophys. Acta* **390**, 231–245.

Wasserman, W.J., Penna, M.J. & Houle, J.G. (1986) The regulation of Xenopus laevis oocyte maturation. In *Gametogenesis and the Early Embryo*, pp. 111–130. Ed. J. G. Gall. A. R. Liss Inc., New York.

Wilt, F. (1977) The dynamics of maternal poly(A)-containing mRNA in fertilized sea urchin eggs. *Cell* **11**, 673–681.

Winkler, M.M. & Steinhardt, R.A. (1981) Activation of protein synthesis in a sea urchin cell free system. *Devl Biol.* **84**, 432–439.

Winkler, M.M., Steinhardt, R.A., Grainger, J.L. & Minning, L. (1980) Dual ionic controls for the activation of protein synthesis at fertilization. *Nature, Lond.* **287**, 558–560.

Winkler, M.M., Nelson, E.M., Lashbrook, C.C. & Hershey, J.W.B. (1985) Multiple levels of regulation of protein synthesis at fertilization in sea urchin eggs. *Devl Biol.* **107**, 290–300.

Woodland, H.R. (1990) Regulation of protein synthesis in early amphibian development. *J. Reprod. Fert., Suppl.* **42**, 215–224.

Yablonka-Reuveni, Z. & Hille, M.B. (1983) Isolation and distribution of elongation factor 2 in eggs and embryos of sea urchins. *Biochemistry, NY* **22**, 5205–5212.

Yablonka-Reuveni, Z., Fontaine, J.J. & Warner, A.H. (1983) Distribution of elongation factor 2 between particulate and soluble fraction of the brine shrimp *Artemia* during development. *Can. J. Biochem. Cell Biol.* **61,** 833–839.

Zucker, R.S., Steinhardt, R.A. & Winkler, M.M. (1978) Intracellular calcium release and mechanisms of parthenogenetic activation of the sea urchin egg. *Devl Biol.* **65,** 285–295.

J. Reprod. Fert., Suppl. **42** (1990), 249–254

Signal transduction during mesoderm induction in *Xenopus*

M. Whitman and D. A. Melton

*Department of Biochemistry and Molecular Biology, Harvard University, 7 Divinity Ave,
Cambridge, MA 02138, USA*

Keywords: mesoderm induction; peptide growth factor; signal transduction

Introduction

Pattern formation in the early embryo may depend on two general mechanisms for specification of cell fates: the differential localization of maternally derived determinants within the egg and inductive interactions between early embryonic cells and tissues (reviewed by Slack, 1983; Nieuwkoop *et al.*, 1985). The early *Xenopus* embryo provides a model system for examining how these two types of processes may be coupled to establish the basic body plan: the capacity to induce mesoderm is localized exclusively to blastomeres derived from the vegetal hemisphere of the egg (Nieuwkoop, 1969). In addition, information necessary for the specification of dorsal structures appears to be localized to blastomeres derived from a region of the egg (the gray crescent) specified immediately following fertilization (Black & Gerhart, 1985). In recent years, considerable progress has been made in elucidating the molecular basis for these early specification events (reviewed by Gurdon, 1987; Smith, 1989; Whitman & Melton 1989b). The identity of the mesodermal and dorsalizing inductive signals, their relationship to a possible cytoplasmic determinant, and the nature of the cellular response to mesoderm induction, both at the plasma membrane and in the nucleus, have been a focus of recent research in our laboratory.

Mesoderm induction by peptide growth factors

PGFs as inducers

Since the original observation that endodermal tissue from the vegetal region of the *Xenopus* embryo could respecify prospective ectoderm to form mesoderm, extracts from a variety of heterologous sources have been identified that can mimic endoderm in the induction of mesodermal structures (reviewed by Nieuwkoop *et al.*, 1985). More recently, Smith (1987) demonstrated that medium conditioned by a *Xenopus* tissue-culture cell line could potently induce mesoderm from prospective ectoderm (animal cap tissue), as defined by analysis of molecular markers of muscle, a mesodermal tissue, as well as histological analysis. This provided the basis for a convenient, quantitative assay for assessing the potential effect of soluble factors in specifying mesodermal tissues.

Using such an assay system, workers in several laboratories have now shown that two families of previously characterized peptide growth factors (PGFs) have the capacity to induce mesoderm: the heparin binding growth factors (FGF, HBGFs) and the transforming growth factor beta family of factors (TGFβs) (reviewed by Mercola & Stiles, 1988; Smith, 1989; Whitman & Melton, 1989a). Slack *et al.* (1987) and Kimelman & Kirschner (1987) first demonstrated that fibroblast growth factor could induce mesenchyme, muscle tissue, and possibly blood. As these mesodermal tissues were of a relatively ventro-lateral character, it was proposed that FGF was an inducer of predominantly ventral mesoderm. Kimelman & Kirschner (1987) also found that TGFβ could enhance the ability of FGF to induce muscle tissue. It was therefore suggested that the interactions between these factors might reflect the two distinct signals proposed to be required for mesodermal signalling: an initial 'mesodermalizing' signal and a subsequent 'dorsalizing' signal (Smith & Slack, 1983; Dale & Slack, 1987). In this model, FGF might correspond to the initial mesodermalizing signal, and TGFβ provide an additional signal to enhance the formation of dorsal structures (e.g. muscle). Subsequently, however, Rosa *et al.* (1988) have shown TGFβ-2 alone to be sufficient for mesoderm induction, while Slack & Isaacs (1989) have found FGF alone at high doses to be sufficient to induce, albeit infrequently, notochord, the most dorsal mesodermal structure. It is therefore unclear whether the FGF and TGFβ families of inducers have separate roles in mesodermal patterning, or whether they each provide mesodermalizing signals which may, in some circumstances, be synergistic. Because much of the characterization of these factors has been done using markers for a single mesodermal tissue type (muscle) it is difficult to distinguish between quantitative and qualitative effects of doses or combinations of factors on mesoderm induction.

Since the initial demonstration that acidic and basic FGFs can induce mesoderm, several additional mesoderm-inducing heparin-binding growth factors (HBGFs) have been identified (Godsave *et al.*, 1988; Paterno *et al.*, 1989). More than one member of the TGFβ family may also be active as mesoderm inducers (Kimelman & Kirschner, 1987; Rosa *et al.*, 1988). Biochemical and immunological characterization of the inducing factor from *Xenopus* tissue-culture cell-conditioned medium (XTC-MIF) indicates that it may also be a member of the TGFβ family (Rosa *et al.*, 1988; Smith *et al.*, 1988). Whether different members of the same family of inducing PGFs utilize identical receptors of broad specificity or distinct, highly specific receptors remains unknown.

Growth factor-like molecules in the early embryo

The identification of PGFs with the ability to induce mesoderm raised the question of whether and where such factors might be expressed during embryogenesis. Transcription of zygotic genes in the *Xenopus* embryo does not begin until the mid-blastula transition (Newport & Kirschner, 1982), significantly after the process of mesoderm induction has begun (Jones & Woodland, 1987). Although later stages of mesoderm induction and patterning may depend on zygotic transcription of inducers, at least some of the endogenous mesoderm inducers, of the mRNAs encoding them, should be present as maternally derived determinants in the egg. Since mesoderm-inducing capacity is localized to blastomeres derived from the vegetal region of the egg, these maternally derived inducers might also be predicted to be localized to the vegetal pole. FGF mRNA and protein have been found to be present in both the oocyte and the egg (Kimelman *et al.*, 1988; Slack & Isaacs, 1989), but neither has been shown to be localized during early development. In addition, because embryonic FGF does not have a recognizable signal sequence and has not been shown to be secreted, it is not clear how it might be transmitted between cells during induction.

An mRNA localized during oogenesis to the cortical region of the vegetal pole of the oocyte has been identified and cloned (Rebagliati *et al.*, 1986; Weeks & Melton, 1987; Melton, 1987; Yisraeli & Melton, 1988). This mRNA, designated Vg-1, encodes a protein with a region of extensive sequence similarity to the TGFβ family (Weeks & Melton, 1987). The presence of a well defined signal sequence indicates that it may be a secreted protein. Tannahill & Melton (1989) and Dale *et al.* (1989) have made antibodies against this protein and found it to be a glycosylated protein of M_r 41 000 present in both oocytes and early embryos; during early cleavage stages it is localized to the vegetal hemisphere of the embryo. In an in-vitro translation system, the nascent protein appears to be efficiently translocated into dog kidney microsomes, but does not appear to be an integral membrane protein (Tannahill & Melton, 1989; Dale *et al.*, 1989). These results are consistent with the hypothesis that Vg-1 encodes a vegetally localized, secreted TGFβ-like factor. In spite of these suggestive observations, however, it has proved difficult to demonstrate that Vg-1 acts as a TGFβ-like inducer. Overexpression of Vg-1 protein in either the animal or vegetal region of the embryo by mRNA injection does not appear to alter normal development significantly (D. Tannahill, M. Whitman & D. A. Melton, unpublished results). Furthermore, unlike every other characterized member of the TGFβ family (Sporn *et al.*, 1986; Massague, 1987), Vg-1 does not appear to be detectably present as a hetero- or homo-dimer (M. Whitman, D. Tannahill & D. A. Melton, unpublished results). Although the possibility that a very small proportion of Vg-1 protein is present in dimeric form cannot be ruled out, this observation raises the possibility that, despite significant sequence similarity with the TGFβs, the structure of mature Vg-1 protein may be fundamentally different from those of previously characterized TGFβ-like factors.

In addition to Vg-1, mRNA encoding another TGFβ family member, TGFβ-5, has been found to be present in early oocytes and eggs (Kondaiah *et al.*, 1990), and also appears to be localized to the vegetal pole (H. P. O'Keefe & D. A. Melton, unpublished). Like Vg-1, however, the function of TGFβ-5 in the early embryo remains to be determined.

Although the function of these localized maternal RNAs remains unknown, they have provided a useful model system for studying the developmental localization of maternal mRNAs. Vegetal localization of endogenous or microinjected Vg-1 mRNA occurs during growth of early (stage III) oocytes *in vitro* (Yisraeli & Melton, 1988), and can be disrupted by pharmacological agents that affect oocyte cytoskeletal components (Yisraeli *et al.*, 1990). This in-vitro localization system allows the investigation of the *cis*-acting sequence(s) responsible for developmental localization. These sequences appear to reside in the 3′ untranslated region of the Vg-1 mRNA (K. Mowry, J. Yisraeli & D. A. Melton, unpublished). More precise localization of the sequences responsible for the developmental localization of Vg-1 is currently in progress.

A new-inducing factor: PIF

A new inducing factor has recently been identified in our laboratory with properties distinct from any of the factors described above. This factor was isolated from the conditioned medium of a macrophage cell line, P388D1 designated P388D1 cell-derived inducing factor (PIF). It, like FGF, TGFβ-2 and XTC-MIF, can induce several different mesoderm tissues, including mesenchyme, muscle and notochord (S. Sokol & D. A. Melton, unpublished). Like XTC-MIF, PIF can also induce significant quantities of neural tissue, perhaps as a seondary consequence of mesoderm induction. PIF appears to differ significantly from XTC-MIF and the other inducing factors, in that it can induce well-formed anterior mesoderm/neural structures, particularly eyes (S. Sokol & D. A. Melton, unpublished). Although we cannot rule out the possibility that another inducing factor or combination of factors might induce similar structures at a dose not yet achieved, it appears that PIF represents a new type of mesoderm-inducing activity. This activity does not appear to be a heparin-binding growth factor (S. Sokol & D. A. Melton, unpublished), and further biochemical characterization of this activity is in progress in our laboratory.

PGFs and pattern formation

The discovery that PGFs can respecify prospective ectoderm to form mesoderm has begun to shed some light on the molecular basis of induction, but the mechanism by which mesoderm is patterned into discrete structures organized along the dorso-ventral and antero-posterior axes remains unclear. Although neither XTC-MIF nor PIF has yet been shown to be present in the embryo, they have been useful in defining the capacity of responsive tissue to differentiate correctly patterned tissue in response to these inducing signals.

Cooke (1989) has shown that prospective ectodermal tissue exposed to XTC-MIF has dorsal organizing activity when transplanted to the ventral marginal zone of host embryos, while animal caps induced with FGF fail to show such activity. Similarly, Ruiz i Altaba & Melton (1989c) have shown that animal cap tissue induced with XTC-MIF and transplanted to the blastocoele induces secondary dorso-anterior structures, while animal cap tissue treated with FGF induces relatively ventro-posterior structures. The degree of recognizable axial patterning in these transplants is considerably better than that in treated tissue left to differentiate as an explant. Thus XTC-MIF, but not FGF, appears to be sufficient to provide dorso-anterior patterning, but only within the context of the whole embryo; the molecular nature of this context remains to be elucidated. In contrast, explanted tissue exposed to PIF appears to organize relatively well-formed dorso-anterior structures in explanted animal pole tissue, suggesting that explanted tissue has either a capacity for self-organization in response to a spatially homogeneous signal or some degree of spatial patterning already imposed before the time of explantation/induction. Dissociation/reassociation of explanted tissue before or after induction may help to distinguish between these possibilities.

Signal transduction and mesoderm induction

Membrane signals and induction

The observation that several PGFs can respecify early embryonic tissue raises the question of whether these factors modulate the same receptor/signal transduction pathways through which they regulate proliferation of cultured fibroblasts (reviewed by Whitman & Melton, 1989b). Virtually nothing is known about the membrane transduction of TGFβ family signals, making this question difficult to address for these factors. FGF, however, acts on cultured cells through a tyrosine kinase receptor (Lee *et al.*, 1989), and appears to activate a cellular signal transducing molecules similar to those activated by other tyrosine kinase receptors (Morrison *et al.*, 1988). We have examined whether activation of a signal transduction pathway for membrane tyrosine kinase is sufficient to respecify prospective ectoderm as mesoderm, using the viral oncogene polyoma middle T (Whitman & Melton, 1989b). When expressed in cells, polyoma middle T associates with and activates the cellular tyrosine kinase pp60c-src, and this complex in turn activates several other signal transduction pathways, including the c-raf serin kinase and a phosphatidylinositol-3-kinase (reviewed by Kaplan *et al.*, 1988; Whitman & Cantley, 1988). When polyoma middle T is expressed in embryonic blastomeres by mRNA microinjection, it associates with cellular pp60c-src and phosphatidylinositol-3-kinase, and respecifies prospective ectoderm to form mesoderm in animal pole explants (Whitman & Melton, 1989b). The polyoma middle T-induced mesoderm, like that induced by FGF, appears to be of a relatively ventro-posterior character (Ruiz i Altaba & Melton, 1989c). This result suggests that the same pathways responsible for transducing the proliferative signals of growth factors and oncogenes may be involved in mediating the signals specifying cell fates during early embryogenesis.

Early transcriptional responses to induction

Although the specification of mesoderm begins before the onset of embryonic gene transcription, changes in patterns of transcription are ultimately the means by which mesodermal determination is executed. The early transcriptional response to mesodermal induction is therefore likely to include expression of the genes responsible for regulation of mesodermal tissue differentiation and patterning. Two such early response genes, designated Mix.1 and Xhox-3, have been identified (Rosa, 1989; Ruiz i Altaba & Melton, 1989a, b).

Mix.1 is a homeobox-containing gene expressed at the mid-blastula transition in explanted animal pole tissue in response to treatment with XTC-MIF (Rosa, 1989). It is expressed in intact embryos primarily in prospective endoderm, raising the possibility that XTC-MIF acts in part by 'endodermalizing' prospective ectodermal tissue (Rosa, 1989). The function of the Mix.1 product, however, has not yet been determined. Xhox-3 is also a homeobox gene, and is expressed at the mid-blastula transition, both in isolated animal pole tissue treated with inducing factors and in mesodermal tissue in exogastrulated embryos (Ruiz i Altaba & Melton, 1989c). Soon after gastrulation, Xhox-3 transcripts appear to be localized in a gradient along the anterior–posterior axis, with the highest concentration of transcript at the posterior (Ruiz i Altaba & Melton, 1989a).

Overexpression of Xhox-3 in the anterior region of the embryo by microinjection prevents formation of normal anterior structures, strongly suggesting that the Xhox-3 gene may be involved in regulation of anterior–posterior mesodermal patterning (Ruiz i Altaba & Melton, 1989b). Xhox-3 therefore should prove useful, not only as an early marker of mesoderm induction, but also as a tool in the elucidation of the molecular basis of anterior–posterior patterning.

Concluding remarks

The identification of PGFs as inducing factors and of some of the early response genes of induction has begun to put the study of early embryonic specification on a firm molecular footing. Identification and localization of the endogenous inducing molecules should clarify the mechanisms of anterior–posterior and dorsal–ventral patterning of mesodermal structures. The development of molecular markers for distinct mesodermal tissues should allow the study of the biochemical coupling between an inductive stimulus and specific differentiation responses. With these molecular tools established, a more comprehensive understanding of early pattern formation should begin to emerge.

We thank Dr Charles Jennings for critical reading of the manuscript. M.W. was supported by a postdoctoral fellowship from the Jane Coffin Childs Memorial Fund. Research in this laboratory has been supported from grants from the National Institutes of Health.

References

Black, S.D. & Gerhart, J. (1985) Experimental control of the site of axis formation in Xenopus laevis embryos centrifuged before first cleavage. *Devl Biol.* **108**, 310–324.

Cooke, J. (1989) Mesoderm inducing factors and Spemann's organizer phenomenon in amphibian development. *Development* **107**, 229–241.

Dale, L. & Slack, J.M.W. (1987) Regional specification within the mesoderm of early embryos of *Xenopus laevis*. *Development* **100**, 279–295.

Dale, L., Matthews, G., Tabe, L. & Colman, A. (1989) Developmental expression of the protein product of Vg1, a localized maternal mRNA in the frog Xenopus laevis. *EMBO J.* **8**, 1057–1065.

Godsave, S.F., Isaacs, H.V. & Slack, J.M.W. (1988) Mesoderm inducing factors: a small class of molecules. *Development* **102**, 555–566.

Gurdon, J. (1987) Embryonic induction—molecular prospects. *Development* **99**, 285–306.

Jones, E.A. & Woodland, H.R. (1987) The development of animal cap cells in *Xenopus*: a measure of the start of animal cap competence to form mesoderm. *Development* **101**, 557–563.

Kaplan, D.R., Palla, D.C., Morgan, W., Schaffhausen, B. & Roberts, T. (1988) Mechanisms of transformation by polyoma virus middle T antigen. *Biochim. Biophys. Acta* **948**, 345–364.

Kimelman, D. & Kirschner, M. (1987) Synergistic induction of mesoderm by FGF and TGFβ and the identification of an mRNA coding for FGF in the early Xenopus embryo. *Cell* **51**, 869–877.

Kimelman, D., Abraham, J.A., Haaparanta, T., Palisi, T.M. & Kirschner, M.W. (1988) The presence of fibroblast growth factor in the frog egg: its role as a natural mesodermal inducer. *Science, NY* **242**, 1053–1056.

Kondaiah, P., Sands, M.J., Smith, J.M., Fields, A., Roberts, A.B., Sporn, M.B. & Melton, D.A. (1990) Identification of a novel transforming growth factor-β mRNA in *Xenopus laevis*. *J. biol. Chem.* **265**, 1089–1093.

Lee, P.A., Johnson, D.E., Cousens, L.S., Fried, V.A. & Williams, L.T. (1989) Purification and complementary DNA cloning of a receptor for basic fibroblast growth factor. *Science, NY* **242**, 57–61.

Massague, J. (1987) The TGF-β family of growth and differentiation factors. *Cell* **49**, 437–438.

Melton, D.A. (1987) Translocation of maternal mRNA to the vegetal pole of *Xenopus* oocytes. *Nature, Lond.* **328**, 80–82.

Mercola, M. & Stiles, C.D. (1988) Growth factor superfamilies and mammalian embryogenesis. *Development* **102**, 451–460.

Morrison, D., Kaplan, D.R., Rapp, U. & Roberts, T.M. (1988) Signal transduction from membrane to cytoplasm: growth factors and membrane-bound oncogene products increase raf-1 phosphorylation and associated protein kinase activity. *Proc. natn. Acad. Sci. USA* **85**, 8855–8859.

Newport, J. & Kirschner, M. (1982) A major developmental transition in early Xenopus embryos: I characterization and timing of cellular changes at the midblastula stage. *Cell* **30**, 675–686.

Nieuwkoop, P.D. (1969) The formation of mesoderm in urodelean amphibians. I Induction by the endoderm. *Wilhelm Roux's Arch. EntwMech.* **162**, 341–373.

Nieuwkoop, P.D., Johnen, A.G. & Albers, B. (1985) *The Epigenetic Nature of Early Chordate Development*. Cambridge University Press.

Paterno, G.D., Gillespie, L.L., Dixon, M.S., Slack, J.M.W. & Heath, J.K. (1989) Mesoderm inducing properties of INT-2 and kFGF: two oncogene encoded growth factors related to FGF. *Development* **106**, 79–83.

Rebagliati, M., Weeks, D.L., Harvey, R.P. & Melton, D.A. (1986) Identification and cloning of localized maternal RNAs from *Xenopus* eggs. *Cell* **42**, 769–777.

Rosa, F.M. (1989) Mix.1, a homeobox mRNA inducible by mesoderm inducers, is expressed mostly in the presumptive endodermal cells of *Xenopus* embryos. *Cell* **57**, 965–974.

Rosa, F., Roberts, A.B., Danielpour, D., Dart, L.L., Sporn, M.B. & Dawid, I.B. (1988) Mesoderm induction in amphibians: the role of TGFβ_2 like factors. *Science, NY* **239**, 783–785.

Ruiz i Altaba, A. & Melton, D.A. (1989a) Bimodal and graded expression of the *Xenopus* homeobox gene Xhox3 during embryonic development. *Development* **106**, 173–183.

Ruiz i Altaba, A. & Melton, D.A. (1989b) Involvement of the *Xenopus* homeobox gene Xhox3 in pattern formation along the anterior-posterior axis. *Cell* **57**, 317–326.

Ruiz i Altaba, A. & Melton, D.A. (1989c) Interaction between peptide growth factors and homeobox genes in the establishment of antero-posterior polarity in frog embryos. *Nature, Lond.* **341**, 33–38.

Slack, J.M.W. (1983) *From Egg to Embryo: Determinative Events in Early Development.* Cambridge University Press.

Slack, J.M.W. & Isaacs, H.V. (1989) Presence of fibroblast growth factor in the early *Xenopus* embryo. *Development* **105**, 147–154.

Slack, J.M.W., Darlington, B.G., Heath, J.K. & Godsave, S.F. (1987) Mesoderm induction in the early *Xenopus* embryos by heparin-binding growth factors. *Nature, Lond.* **326**, 197–200.

Smith, J.C. (1987) A mesoderm inducing factor is produced by a *Xenopus* cell line. *Development* **99**, 3–14.

Smith, J.C. (1989) Mesoderm induction and mesoderm-inducing factors in early amphibian development. *Development* **105**, 665–667.

Smith, J.C. & Slack, J.M.W. (1983) Dorsalization and neural induction: properties of the organizer in Xenopus laevis. *J. Embryol. exp. Morph.* **78**, 299–317.

Smith, J.C., Yaqoob, M. & Symes, K. (1988) Purification, partial characterization and biological effects of the XTC mesoderm-inducing factor. *Development* **103**, 591–600.

Sporn, M.B., Roberts, A.B., Wakefield, L.M. & Assoian, R.K. (1986) Transforming growth factor-β: biological function and chemical structure. *Science, NY* **233**, 532–534.

Tannahill, D. & Melton, D.A. (1989) Localized synthesis of the Vg1 protein during early *Xenopus* development. *Development* **106**, 775–786.

Weeks, D.L. & Melton, D.A. (1987) A maternal messenger RNA localized to the vegetal hemisphere in *Xenopus* eggs codes for a growth factor related to TGF-β. *Cell* **51**, 861–867.

Whitman, M. & Cantley, L.C. (1988) Phosphoinositide metabolism and the control of cell proliferation. *Biochim. Biophys. Acta* **948**, 327–344.

Whitman, M. & Melton, D.A. (1989a) Induction of mesoderm by a viral oncogene in early *Xenopus* embryos. *Science, NY* **244**, 803–806.

Whitman, M. & Melton, D.A. (1989b) Growth factors in early embryogenesis. *Annul Rev. Cell Biol.* **5**, 93–117.

Yisraeli, J. & Melton, D.A. (1988) The maternal mRNA Vg1 is correctly localized following injection into *Xenopus* oocytes. *Nature, Lond.* **336**, 592–595.

Yisraeli, J., Sokol, S. & Melton, D.A. (1990) A two step model for the localization of maternal mRNA in Xenopus oocytes: Involvement of microtubules and microfilaments in the translocation and anchoring of Vg1 mRNA. *Development* **108**, 289–298.

LIST OF AUTHORS CONTRIBUTING

INDEXES

LIST OF AUTHORS CITED

Entries in **bold type** indicate citations in the reference sections.

SUBJECTS